Welcome to

HOW IT WORKS

BOOK OF

Junior
Science

Science is a fascinating subject that helps us understand everything about the world we live in. Curious minds have led to fascinating discoveries, from gravity and atoms to ancient fossils and deadly animals.
If you're hungry for knowledge then the How It Works Book of Junior Science is packed with amazing facts and answers to some of life's biggest questions. With information displayed in an engaging and accessible way – supported by excellent illustrations and cutaways – you'll find everything you wanted to know about the human body, planet Earth, amazing animals and much more. On top of that, the Book of Junior Science is the perfect resource to help children get to grips with a range of scientific subjects. So whether you want to discover how electricity works, what blood is made up of, how volcanoes are formed or what the world's most venomous snake is, you'll find all the answers inside.

Enjoy the book

HOW IT WORKS
BOOK OF
Junior Science

Imagine Publishing Ltd
Richmond House
33 Richmond Hill
Bournemouth
Dorset BH2 6EZ
☎ +44 (0) 1202 586200
Website: www.imagine-publishing.co.uk
Twitter: @Books_Imagine
Facebook: www.facebook.com/ImagineBookazines

Editor in Chief
Dave Harfield

Production Editor
Jon White

Senior Art Editor
Danielle Dixon

Printed by
William Gibbons, 26 Planetary Road, Willenhall, West Midlands, WV13 3XT

Distributed in the UK & Eire by
Imagine Publishing Ltd, www.imagineshop.co.uk. Tel 01202 586200

Distributed in Australia by
Gordon & Gotch, Equinox Centre, 18 Rodborough Road, Frenchs Forest,
NSW 2086. Tel + 61 2 9972 8800

Distributed in the Rest of the World by
Marketforce, Blue Fin Building, 110 Southwark Street, London, SE1 0SU

Contents

Science in action

The human body

Planet Earth

Amazing animals

What causes
explosions?
p24

EXPLOSIVES

1

How do you
measure G-force?
p42

What are
batteries?
p23

Science in

What makes a
firework explode?
p28

MAGNETISM

What is the
sound barrier?
p39

© Ognjen Djokic

© Science Photo Library

action

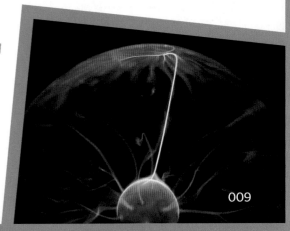

 Many people think of electricity as something you buy from the power companies, but as well as coming out of the wall socket, electricity is one of the many ingredients that make up the universe. Read on to find out why electricity occurs, how it behaves and how it reaches your home.

Everything in the universe is made of minuscule atoms and these atoms consist of a nucleus orbited by one or more electrons. These electrons carry a negative charge while the nucleus is positively charged.

We're all familiar with the effects of static electricity. We are not often aware of electricity around us as the positive and negative charges usually balance. When certain objects touch, however, electrons can jump between them. For instance, when you rub a balloon against your hair electrons will jump across to the balloon giving the balloon stationary negative charge or static electricity. Static electricity relies on electrons not being able to move around easily. Materials like wood, glass, ceramics and cotton all have electrons that like to stick with their atoms and because the electrons don't move the materials can't conduct electricity very well.

In most metals, electrons can move freely to form an electric current. When charges move, current electricity is formed and this is the power that drives much of the contemporary world. Current can be measured by the amount of charge passing a fixed point each second. ✿

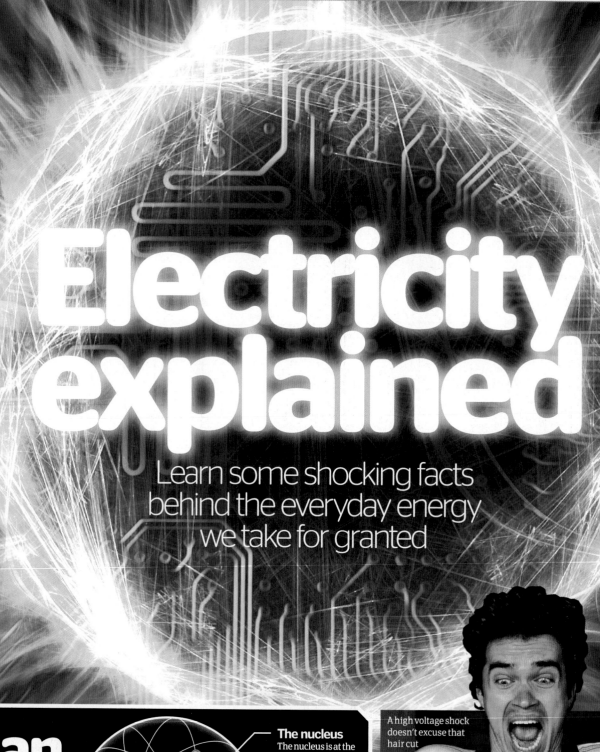

Electricity explained

Learn some shocking facts behind the everyday energy we take for granted

A high voltage shock doesn't excuse that hair cut

Inside an atom

Atoms are held together by electricity. The positive nucleus attracts the negative electron. The two cancel each other out so the atom has no electric charge

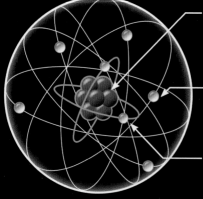

The nucleus
The nucleus is at the centre of the atom and is positively charged.

Negative charge
Each electron is negatively charged.

Electrons
Electrons orbit the nucleus.

Plasma balls – static incarnate

They went out of fashion in the Eighties but still demonstrate electricity really well

Full of gas
The glass ball is filled with a mixture of gases, usually helium and neon, at low pressure.

Touch the power
Placing your hand on the glass alters the electric field and causes a single beam to migrate from the inner ball to the point of contact, the glass does not block the electromagnetic field created by the current flowing through the gas.

Lights
Electricity moves across the gas filled globe from the electrode to the outer glass insulator.

Charged up
The metal ball at the centre is charged with electricity, serving as an electrode.

Conductors and insulators at work

Conductors and insulators are put to good use in a household cable

Rubber to be safe
The whole cable is encased in rubber or plastic to protect against electric shocks.

Plastic for protection
There is a further plastic insulator around each copper cable to stop current flowing between them.

Copper conductor
The copper wire provides an excellent conductor due to its low resistance.

Colour coded
Each wire is colour coded to ensure correct connection.

Conductors

Very simply, a conductor is a material that allows electric charge to pass along it as a current. As stated, metals make good conductors as the electrons of their atoms are loosely bound and free to move through the material. For instance, in copper the electrons are essentially free and strongly repel each other. Any external influence that moves one of them will be replicated through the material.

A superconductor is a material that has no resistance at all to the flow of current when kept below a certain temperature. For most superconducting materials, the critical temperature is below about 30K (30°C above absolute zero).

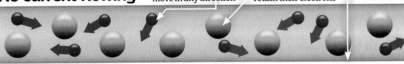

No current flowing
These free electrons can move in any direction | The copper atoms retain their electrons | Wire surface

Current flowing
The free electrons move towards the positive terminal | The copper atom remains in place

Insulators

Insulators are materials that have the exact opposite effect on the flow of electrons. Their atoms have tightly bound electrons which are not free to roam around. That said, insulators can still play an important role in the flow of electricity by protecting us from the dangerous effects of a current flowing through conductors. If the voltage is high enough an electric current can be made to flow through a material that is not a good conductor, like the human body. The function of our hearts can be affected by an electric shock and the heat generated by the current can cause burns.

The ceramic insulators on this pylon are there to prevent this worker becoming toast

An electric current passes through a thin filament, heating it so that it produces light

Vive la resistance

Resistance is a very important property, it's the factor behind many domestic appliances including old-school light bulbs, kettles, toasters, heaters and irons to name a few. All these rely on the creation of heat energy. Resistance is the ability of a substance to prevent or resist the flow of electrical current. Materials resist electric current because of a collision between electrons and atoms. This slows the electrons down and converts some of their energy to heat energy.

Circuits

Putting electricity to work all over the world

Now that we've explained where electricity comes from it's time to look at some of the work it can do for us. Electricity can't do a lot of work without circuits as these provide a path for the electricity to flow around. Circuits include devices such as resistors, which control the flow of voltage, or difference in electrical charge, and capacitors, which store electrical charge and come in one of two types, series and parallel.

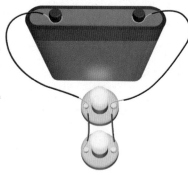

Parallel circuits

In a parallel circuit there is more than one pathway between its beginning and end. Since the electricity has more than one route to take, the circuit can still function should one component fail. This means that parallel circuits are much less prone to failure than the series variety. For this reason parallel circuits are the kind you will find in most everyday applications such as domestic appliances and household wiring.

Series circuits

A series circuit has more than one resistor and only has one path for the charges to move along. A resistor is anything that uses electricity to do work (in this case, light bulbs) and the electric charge must move in series from one resistor to the next. If one of the components in the circuit is broken then no charge can move through it. An example of a series circuit is old-style Christmas lights, if one bulb breaks the whole string goes out.

Laws of circuits

Ohm's triangle; not as exciting as the Bermuda triangle but more useful

There are many laws that apply to electrical circuits but Ohm's law is one of the most important. Ohm's law states that an electrical circuit's current is proportional to its voltage and inversely proportional to its resistance. So, if voltage increases, for example, the current will also increase, and if resistance increases, current decreases. The formula for Ohm's law is $V = I \times R$, where V = voltage in volts, I = current in amperes, and R = resistance in ohms.

Circuit control

The simplest electrical control is a switch. This simply breaks the circuit to stop the current flowing and this is most notably seen in domestic light switches. They may seem simple, but the most complex computers are made from millions of electronically controlled switches.

CIRCUIT JARGON

Voltage
The flow of an electric charge. Unit Volt, symbol V.

Current
Or electrical potential difference, the force that drives the current in one direction. Unit Ampere, symbol A.

Resistance
The opposition of an object to having current pass through it. Unit Ohm, symbol Ω.

How electricity reaches your home

It's taken for granted that the light will come on when you hit the switch, here's how the power gets to your house

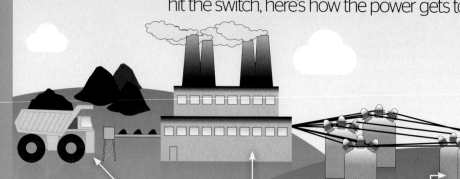

1. Coal or nuclear
To kick things off, coal is burnt at the electricity plant to generate steam. Nuclear power stations use a slightly different method to this, as do hydroelectric plants.

2. Generation X
Be it nuclear, coal-fired or hydro a turbine spins a huge magnet inside a copper wire. Heat energy converts to mechanical energy which then converts to electrical energy in the generator.

3. Danger! High voltage!
The electricity then flows though heavily insulated wires to a step-up transformer. This raises the pressure so it can travel long distances over the grid. It's raised as high as 756,000 volts.

4. Transform it
The electricity then runs along the power lines until it reaches a substation. This lowers the pressure to around 2,000-13,000 volts.

5. Pylon it up
The current continues along the lines to another transformer, either a pole transformer or an underground box, and pressure is lowered again to between 120 and 240 volts.

6. Service with a spark
The next stop is the service box at your home. Here your meter will measure how much power you use. Wires then take the electricity around your home powering your lights and everything else.

Electricity in your home

Once electricity reaches your home, how does it get around?

2. Electricity meter
Electricity meters are typically calibrated in billing units, the most common one being the kilowatt hour. Periodic readings of electric meters establishes billing cycles and energy used during a cycle.

3. Distribution box
This contains the main switch and fuses for each circuit.

4. Appliances of science
Domestic appliances are connected in parallel. In a parallel circuit even if there is a fault or short-circuiting in any one line, the corresponding fuse blows off, leaving the other circuits and appliances intact and prevents damage to the entire house.

1. Entry point
The electric power line enters our house through three wires – namely the live wire, the neutral wire and the Earth wire.

5. Current affairs
The more appliances you connect, the more current is drawn from the mains.

Why are British plugs so big?

It's all thanks to World War Two

Visitors to and natives of the British Isles get to use one of the weirdest plugs in the world; unlike many other plugs it has a fuse built in. After being bombed heavily by the Germans during WW2, much of the country had to be rebuilt. Building supplies were short so rather than wiring each socket to a fuseboard they were linked together on one wire and the fuses put in each plug, saving a great deal of copper in the process.

Ground to Earth
The Earth wire is there to prevent electric shock and is secured by a screw terminal.

Fused
The fuse is designed to blow and break the circuit if the appliance gets too much current.

All about AC/DC

Learn the differences

As we've seen, the word electricity is derived from the fact that current is electrons moving along a conductor that have been harnessed for energy. The difference between Alternating Current (AC) and Direct Current (DC) is related to the direction in which the electrons flow. In DC the electrons flow steadily in a single 'forward' direction. In AC electrons keep switching directions. The power supplied by electricity companies is AC because it's much easier to transport across long distances, it can easily be stepped up to a higher voltage with a transformer. It's also more efficient to send along power lines before being stepped down by another transformer at the customer's end.

Why do all countries have different plugs?

When using appliances abroad we have to use adapters

Even more than baggage handling and passport control, one of the biggest problems faced by the frequent traveller is the fact that every country in the world has different plugs. In the US, shortly after the AC/DC battle had been resolved (AC won) a man named Harvey Hubbell invented the two pin plug "so that electrical power in buildings may be utilised by persons having no electrical knowledge or skill" (his words). This was later developed into a three pin plug by Philip Labre in 1928 with the third pin for grounding. At the same time developments like this were occurring all around the world with absolutely no global-standardisation. There was some effort made by the International Electrotechnical Commission shortly before the Second World War occurred and spoilt it all!

Two pin or three pin? It depends where you are!

Atoms

Up and atom with our look at these particles inside all matter in the universe

At the centre of every atom is a nucleus containing protons and neutrons. Together, protons and neutrons are known as nucleons. Around this core of the atom, a certain number of electrons orbit in shells. The nucleus and electrons are referred to as subatomic particles. The electrons orbit around the centre of the atom, which is due to the charges present; protons have a positive charge, neutrons are neutral and electrons have a negative charge. It is the electromagnetic force that keeps the electrons in orbit due to these charges, one of the four fundamental forces of nature. It acts between charged objects – such as inside a battery – by the interaction of photons, which are the basic units of light.

An atom is about one tenth of a nanometre in diameter. 43 million iron atoms lined up side by side would produce a line only one millimetre in length. However, most of an atom is empty space. The nucleus of the atom accounts for only a 10,000th of the overall size of the atom, despite containing almost all of the atom's mass. Protons and neutrons have about 2,000 times more mass than an electron, making the electrons orbit the nucleus at a large distance.

An atom represents the smallest part of an element that can exist by itself. Each element's atoms have a different structure. The number of protons inside a specific element is unique. For example, carbon has six protons whereas gold has 79. However, some elements have more than one form. The other forms – known as isotopes – of an atom will have the same number of protons but a totally different number of neutrons. For example, hydrogen has three forms which all have one proton; tritium has two neutrons, deuterium has one neutron and hydrogen itself has none.

As different atoms have different numbers of protons and neutrons, they also have different masses, which determine the properties of an element. The larger the mass of an atom the smaller its size, as the electrons orbit more closely to the nucleus due to a stronger electromagnetic force. For example an atom of sulphur, which has 16 protons and 16 neutrons, has the same mass as 32 hydrogen atoms, which each have one proton and no neutrons. ✿

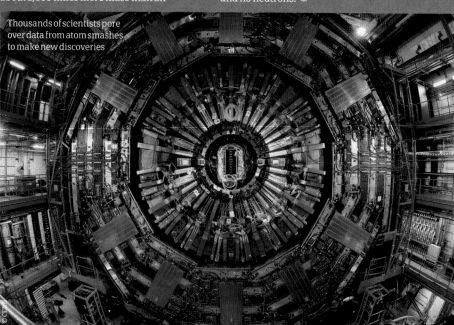

Thousands of scientists pore over data from atom smashes to make new discoveries

Inside the atom

Dissecting what makes up an atom

Shell
Each shell can hold a different number of electrons. The first can hold two, then eight, 18, 32 and so forth.

Protons
A stable elementary particle with a positive charge equal to the negative charge of an electron. A proton can exist without a neutron, but not vice versa.

Quantum jump
An electron releases or absorbs a certain amount of energy when it jumps from one shell to another, known as a quantum leap.

© Science photo library

Electron
An elementary particle (one of the basic particles of matter), an electron has almost no mass and a negative charge.

Nucleus
Held together by the strong nuclear force, the strongest force in nature, the nucleus is tightly bound and holds the protons and neutrons.

Neutrons
An elementary particle with a neutral charge and the same mass as a proton. The number of neutrons defines the other forms of an element.

Power of the atom

Atomic bombs are notorious around the world for their devastating power. By harnessing the energy in the nucleus of an atom, atomic bombs are one of the most powerful man-made weapons. In 1939, Albert Einstein and several other scientists told the USA of a process of purifying uranium, which could create a giant explosion known as an atomic bomb. This used a method known as atomic fission to 'split' atoms and release a huge amount of energy.

The only two bombs to ever be used in warfare were a uranium bomb on Hiroshima and a plutonium bomb on Nagasaki in 1945 at the end of World War II. The effects were frighteningly powerful, and since then no atomic bomb has ever been used as a weapon.

Early atomic bomb tests showed the raw power of the atom

Size of an atom

If the solar system were shrunk to the size of a gold atom, the distance from the Sun to Pluto would be half the distance from the nucleus of the gold atom to its furthest electron. One unit here is defined as the width of a gold atom.

Earth → Moon – 0.3 units away

Sun → Pluto – 5,000 units away

Gold atom → Furthest electron – 10,000 units away

Acids and bases

Learn the differences between acids and bases, and find out why they act the way they do

Acids and bases have many uses, but stronger ones can be harmful

It is widely known that lemons taste sour due to their acid content, soil needs the optimum pH level for plants to grow properly and acid rain can wipe out entire ecosystems. But what really makes one thing acidic and the other one basic (alkaline)? Why can they be so corrosive? And why does litmus paper turn different colours when dipped in acid or a base?

Acids and bases can be defined in terms of their concentration of hydrogen ions. Normally an atom of hydrogen consists of one proton and one electron giving it a balanced electrical charge – protons being positively charged and electrons being negatively charged. Take away the electron and you are left with an ion of hydrogen, or a single proton, or 'H+', as it is often written. The thing about ions is they are very reactive, as they no longer have a balanced charge. They are constantly seeking ions of the

opposite charge – an atom or molecule with an unequal number of electrons than protons, with which to react.

A strong acid has a high concentration of H+ ions and is defined by its ability to 'donate' hydrogen ions to a solution, whereas a base, also know as an alkali, has a much lower concentration of H+ ions and is defined by its ability to 'accept' hydrogen ions in a solution. Therefore, acids mixed with bases become less acidic and bases mixed with acids become less basic, or less alkaline.

Certain concentrated bases, like some concentrated acids, can attack living tissue and cause severe burns due to the ions reacting with the skin. However, the process of bases reacting with the skin, and other materials, is different to that of acids. That's why we call some concentrated acids 'corrosive', whereas reactive concentrated bases are 'caustic'. ✿

The power of hydrogen

The letters pH stand for 'power of hydrogen', as the scale refers to the concentration of hydrogen (H+) ions in the solution. It measures the acidity or basicity of a solution, with pH values ranging from 0-14, 0 being really acidic and 14 being really basic. A substance in the middle of the scale with a pH of 7 is classed as neutral, as it contains equal numbers of oppositely charged ions.

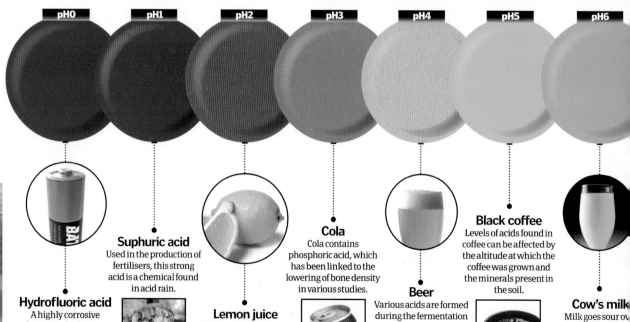

| pH0 | pH1 | pH2 | pH3 | pH4 | pH5 | pH6 |

Acid

A compound which 'donates' hydrogen ions when placed in an aqueous solution. The higher the concentration of hydrogen ions released, the stronger the acid.

Some natural boiling acid springs have a pH of about 1, similar to battery acid

© Allison Choppick

Suphuric acid
Used in the production of fertilisers, this strong acid is a chemical found in acid rain.

Hydrofluoric acid
A highly corrosive substance which as a gas is a severe poison and acts a catalyst in oil refining.

Lemon juice
Lemon juice is about 5% citric acid – a weak organic acid that gives lemons their sour taste.

Cola
Cola contains phosphoric acid, which has been linked to the lowering of bone density in various studies.

Beer
Various acids are formed during the fermentation process in beer production. The addition of CO_2 also causes the pH to lower slightly.

Black coffee
Levels of acids found in coffee can be affected by the altitude at which the coffee was grown and the minerals present in the soil.

Cow's milk
Milk goes sour over time due to the bacteria produci... lactic acid as part ... fermentation proc...

The litmus test

We can test the acidity or alkalinity of a substance using litmus paper. Litmus paper is that which has been treated with a mixture of 10-15 natural dyes obtained from lichens. The dyes work as indicators, whereby upon exposure to acids (a pH less than 7) the paper turns red and upon exposure to bases (a pH more than 7) the paper turns blue. When the pH is neutral (pH equal to 7), the dyes cause the paper to turn purple.

Red cabbage juice can also be used to distinguish between acids and bases, as it contains a natural pH indicator called 'flavin'. Upon exposure to acid, flavin turns a red colour, neutral solutions appear a purple colour and basic solutions result in a greenish-yellow colour.

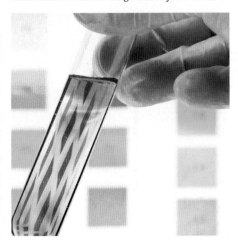

Neutralisation

A neutralisation reaction is the combination of an acid and base that results in a salt and, usually, water. In strong bases and acids, neutralisation is the result of the exchange of hydrogen and hydroxide ions, H+ and H- respectively, which produces water. With weak acids and bases, neutralisation is simply the transfer of protons from an acid to a base. The production of water, with a neutral pH of 7, indicates the neutralisation of the acid and base, while the resultant salt will often have a pH that is also neutral.

Neutralisation has a variety of practical uses. For example, as most plants grow best at neutral pH7,

Wasp stings are alkaline, so an acid-like vinegar will neutralise them

acidic or alkaline soil can be treated with chemicals to change its pH. In the case of acidic soil this is often calcium carbonate (chalk) or calcium oxide (quicklime). Another example is the human stomach, which contains hydrochloric acid. However, too much can lead to indigestion, so the acid can be neutralised with a base such as an indigestion tablet.

How do an acid and base react to produce salt, water and heat?

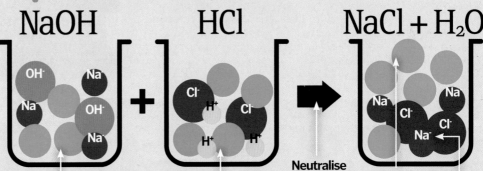

$$NaOH \quad HCl \quad NaCl + H_2O$$

Sodium hydroxide
This strong alkali (a base soluble in water) has a pH of 13 or 14.

Hydrochloric acid
With a pH of 1 or 2, the H+ ions of this strong acid are removed by the alkali.

Neutralise
By removing the H+ ions, the alkali neutralises the acid and turns the ions into water.

Water
Neutral water of pH7 is produced.

NaCl
Neutral sodium chloride, or table salt, is also produced.

| pH7 | pH8 | pH9 | pH10 | pH11 | pH12 | pH13 | pH14 |

Base

A compound which 'accepts' hydrogen ions in an aqueous solution. Contains ions of the opposite charge. For example, hydroxide (OH-) which is naturally found in water and is negatively charged.

Distilled water
Pure water is neutral as it contains the same amount of positive ions as negative ions, though most water isn't pure in this sense.

Baking soda
A slightly salty substance used as a base in foods to regulate the pH if something is too acidic.

Toothpaste
Acidic toothpaste can put enamel at risk of decay, so a weak base such as sodium hydroxide is added in order to regulate the pH.

Milk of magnesia
A weak base of magnesium hydroxide in water, used to ease stomach aches caused by too much acid.

Ammonia solution
When placed in water, ammonia removes protons from a small fraction of the water to form ammonium and hydroxide. It is used in many cleaning products for its basic properties.

Bleach
Can contain sodium hypochlorite at different strengths, making it a strong caustic base.

Caustic oven cleaner
Heavy-duty oven cleaners can be really caustic and corrosive, helping to break down fat and grease.

Caustic soda
Chemically known as sodium hydroxide, in its purest form it is a white solid and can cause severe burns due to its high alkalinity.

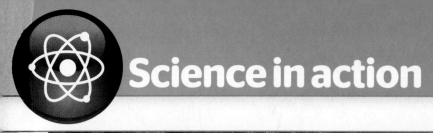

Fires can have
devastating effects

How does fire work?

What is fire and what are the chemical processes that underlie it?

 Fire is the result of the rapid oxidisation of a material undertaking the chemical process of combustion, a sequence of exothermic chemical reactions between fuel and an oxidant. This process releases heat, light and various by-products such as soot and ash. If the flame – the visible portion of the fire – reaches a temperature hot enough to ionise its gases, plasma may also be produced in the process.

To best understand the chemical processes that underlie fire, it is best to view the process as a tetrahedron. The fire tetrahedron, comprising of the four elements you need in order for fire – that being oxygen, heat, fuel and a chain reaction – helps visualise the processes involved.

All fires, if they are to be maintained, require the aforementioned four elements, starting with a combustible fuel (wood, for example) then adding an oxidiser to it (such as oxygen) before then exposing it to a source of heat greater than that of the fuel/oxidiser's flash point (the point where it will ignite in air), and ending with a chain reaction of continuous combustion. Take any one of these factors away and fire simply cannot exist and will choke and

be extinguished. A good example of this in practise can be seen in the retardant chemical Halon, which when exposed to a fire, slows the combustion's chemical reactions to the point where a chain reaction cannot be maintained and the fire ultimately ceases to burn.

Without this type of hindrance however, in a combustion reaction a compound (usually types of organic hydrocarbons) reacts with an oxidising element, such as hydrogen, before causing and propagating a chain reaction that, provided the input variables don't change, will stabilise itself and burn continuously emitting a flame.

The visible flame of any fire is the mixture of reacting gases and solids emitting both light and heat. This light is caused when excess energy is released through transient intermediate reactions in the burning process and it can lead to a variety of differing flame colours depending on its black body (an idealised object that absorbs and re-emits radiation in a characteristic pattern called a spectrum) radiation as well as its spectral band. The dominant colour of a flame changes with its temperature and – in general – the clearer the flame the hotter and more efficient its combustion and chemical processes are. ⚙

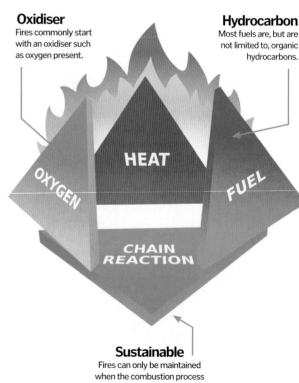

Oxidiser
Fires commonly start with an oxidiser such as oxygen present.

Hydrocarbon
Most fuels are, but are not limited to, organic hydrocarbons.

HEAT

OXYGEN

FUEL

CHAIN REACTION

Sustainable
Fires can only be maintained when the combustion process releases further heat energy.

Mercury

What makes this metal element so unique, and why do we normally see it as a liquid?

Also known as quicksilver, mercury is a heavy metal occurring naturally on Earth. It is the most common of five metals that are a liquid at room temperature. Compared to a number of other metals, mercury is a poor conductor of heat but a good carrier of electricity. It is most commonly found in rocks such as mercuric sulphide inside the ore cinnabar. Mercury is extracted by heating and compressing this ore.

Inside a mercury atom, the electrons are very tightly held together. For this reason the bonds between the atoms are very weak as they do not share electrons easily. The small amount of heat present at room temperature is enough to break the bonds between the atoms, which is why mercury is a liquid at such a low temperature. Other metals, such as gold, have much stronger bonds between their atoms and therefore require a lot more energy (or heat) to become a liquid. ⚙

Mercury bans
Mercury thermometers can be dangerous, but where have they been banned?

- ■ Banned
- ■ Considering ban
- ■ No ban
- ■ Not in discussion

ON THE MAP

Where is mercury mined?
1 Almaden, Ciudad Real, Spain
2 Idrija, former Yugoslavia
3 Santa Clara Co, California
4 China
5 Kyrgyzstan
6 Tuscany, Italy
7 Algeria

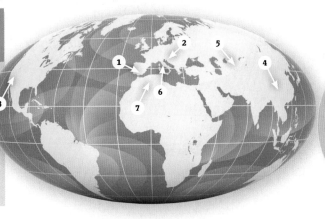

What we use mercury for today...

There have been calls to ban mercury, as it can be poisonous as a vapour. While it's slowly being phased out, it is still in use

Still in use

Barometer
The high density and surface tension of liquid mercury is perfect for measuring atmospheric pressure.

Mining
As mercury combines with other metals, it can be used to extract gold and silver from a mine.

Fillings
A mixture of liquid mercury and other materials can be used to fill in the holes in our teeth.

Batteries
Once used to prevent zinc corroding in regular batteries, liquid mercury is now only used in button batteries.

Being replaced

Thermometers
Liquid mercury expands and contracts evenly with a change in temperature, a useful feature for thermometers.

Mirrors
With excellent reflectively, mercury can be used as a compound with other products to make mirrors.

Mascara
Today mercury's rarely used in make-up. However, it was once an ingredient in mascara for its binding properties.

Paint
Before 1992, mercury was used in paint to prevent fungus growth, until it was discovered it could be poisonous.

No longer used

Hats
Mercury was used in the felting process to make hats in the mid-19th Century, coining the phrase "mad as a hatter".

(thermometer labels top to bottom: Barometer, Mining, Fillings, Batteries, Thermometers, Mirrors, Mascara, Paint, Hats)

What's inside a nuclear reactor?

Welcome to the world's largest plasma generator

The Joint European Torus (JET) is the world's largest tokamak magnetic confinement, nuclear fusion device. The system, which is located in Oxfordshire, England, is an experimental system designed to generate nuclear reactions that are considerably more efficient and clean than those that are possible in current nuclear reactors.

The system works by generating super-heated plasma (100 million Kelvin) and containing it within a toroidal (doughnut-shaped) container vessel. The plasma is then trapped within the device through magnetic confinement, with the charged plasma particles forced to spiral along the circling magnetic field lines running around the vessel and not onto the walls of the system. This allows the plasma to be contained as it is heated up to the level needed for nuclear fusion.

The fuel for the fusion is a gas mixture of the two heavy forms of hydrogen, deuterium and tritium. These elements are chosen as they produce the most efficient fusion reactions on Earth. The gas mix is pumped into the JET and heated in order to turn it into the aforementioned plasma where conditions force the two elements to fuse, releasing a large quantity of energy.

As of now, the JET system is being operated by a team of 350 international scientists to test the best methods of controlling the high-temperature plasma. Through this research, it is hoped that a new sustainable form of nuclear energy generation can be achieved to supply power for future generations, as well as reduce society's reliance on the rapidly diminishing fossil fuels. ☼

What is it? – This image shows the JET, the world's largest nuclear-fusion, magnetic confinement system in the world. Systems such as JET confine plasma within a hollow, doughnut-shaped vessel, before heating it to levels high enough to instigate nuclear fusion in order to generate useable energy.

Building dem

What it takes to turn solid cement and steel into a waterfall of cascading rubble

Modern building demolition is an exquisitely choreographed dance of destruction. Dynamite-triggered 'implosions' – where a building collapses in on itself just like a crumbling house of cards – are so violently beautiful that they have even become a spectator sport. Demolition junkies are known to camouflage themselves as shrubs just to get a close-up shot of the carnage.

Blowing up a building is easy, minimising damage to nearby structures is the tricky part. There are tumbling walls and flying debris to worry about, not to mention the earthquake-like vibrations produced by millions of tons of crashing cement and steel. The explosives alone can produce high-pressure shockwaves that shatter windows for miles.

Demolition experts are called blasters ('explosives engineer' lacks a certain punch). They know that the most powerful force on a demolition site isn't the thousands of pounds of dynamite, but the incredible potential energy of gravity. The key to minimising damage and softening the impact of 30 stories of rubble is to use the least amount of explosives possible and let gravity pull the building down in a progressive, 'liquid' collapse.

To trigger a progressive collapse, blasters divide the building into separate vertical columns. They drill thousands of holes in the weight-bearing supports under each column and stuff them with dynamite. The supports are wrapped tightly in chain-link fencing and thick plastic fabric to contain flying debris.

Each stick of dynamite is plugged with a blasting cap that controls the precise timing of the explosion. All of the explosives are connected back to a single detonator by miles of detonator cable. When the blaster yells "Fire in the hole!" he activates the detonator, initiating a series of sharp, popping explosions that obliterate the column supports section by section.

The result is breathtaking. Each column seems to melt to the Earth in a smooth, wave-like motion. The fluid collapse sequence minimises vibrations on the ground and the small, delayed explosions reduce the damaging effects of shockwaves. When the dust settles (which can take 15 to 30 minutes), all that is left is a two-storey pile of rubble, neatly contained within the footprint of the original structure. ✿

The swan song of the Stardust Hotel in Las Vegas before it comes crashing to the ground

© Andrew Ferguson 2007

© Torsten Bätge 2004

olition

1. Detonation
Following the explosion the building begins its breathtaking descent

2. Going, going...
Gone. All that is left is a pile of rubble and a cloud of dust

© Tannoy 2006

How implosions work
How the charges are placed within a building's structure in order to collapse it in on itself

Kit list
To demolish a ten-storey building you will need:

Conventional demolition equipment: Enough sledgehammers and shovels to gut the bottom floors of non-weight-bearing walls.

Two different kinds of explosives: Regular nitroglycerin-based dynamite for concrete supports and a high-velocity explosive called RDX for slicing through steel beams. In total, around 180kg of explosives.

Blasting caps: Thousands of small detonators attached to individual sticks of dynamite to precisely time the detonation.

Hundreds of metres of fencing: And geotextile fabrics to wrap around concrete supports stuffed with dynamite.

Detonating cord: Miles of cable to connect each stick of dynamite to a single detonator control.

Detonator control: Has two buttons, one to charge the electrical detonation and one to fire the explosives.

Years of experience: Blueprints only tell you so much. Expert blasters rely on a storehouse of hands-on knowledge.

EXPLOSIVES
1

How chemicals power batteries
There's a good reason why battery power is called 'juice'

Batteries are everywhere – in your car, your computer and even your cooker. While some are rechargeable and some disposable, they work on the same basic principle.

A battery has two poles labelled + and -. They provide more than a handy guide as to which way up the battery goes in your TV remote. Electrons are produced inside the battery and when it's inert they stay on the negative end. Connect the negative and positive ends with the heads inside a battery compartment and the electrons move to the positive end, producing electrical power.

But where do those electrons come from? The reaction of substances inside the battery produces them. Common elements used are nickel and cadmium, but zinc is also popular. The battery 'plates' are each made up of a different element and when connected they react with the electrolyte paste or 'juice' within the battery, producing electrons. Different substances are used depending on the battery life and power required. ☼

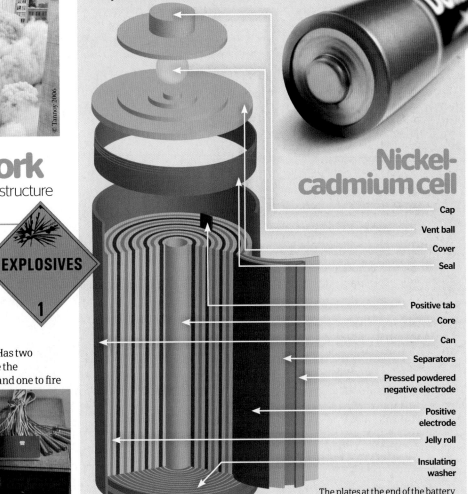

Nickel-cadmium cell

Cap
Vent ball
Cover
Seal
Positive tab
Core
Can
Separators
Pressed powdered negative electrode
Positive electrode
Jelly roll
Insulating washer

The plates at the end of the battery react with the substance inside

EXPLOSIVES

Man has created many different types of explosives over the past 1,000 years, deploying them in warfare, industry and society

Explosions are characterised by three factors: a rapid increase in volume, the generation of high temperatures and an extreme release of energy. In addition to this, every explosion generates a shock wave that varies depending on the explosive substance's detonation velocity.

The four main properties of explosions are force, velocity, heat and fragmentation. The force of any explosion is the physical impact it has on its immediate environment, something often increased through a warhead's shaped charge. An explosion's force when magnified in a shaped charge can gauge impact craters, tear through the armour of military vehicles and puncture buildings.

An explosive's detonation velocity is the rapidity of the expansion of its volume (gases mainly) post detonation. Typically, the greater the detonation velocity the higher up the relative effectiveness (RE) table the explosive is placed, with a direct correlation between velocity, pressure and generated heat. So, generally, the greater the velocity the greater the heat and damage produced.

Heat, generated by and also the cause of an explosion's high-pressures, is its ability to liberate its exothermic material's elements at a certain temperature. Coal, for example, is very good at liberating its material's elements at a high temperature in an exothermic reaction, albeit at such a slow rate that it cannot be used as an explosive (why

we use it for fires). Nitroglycerin (the chemical base of explosives such as dynamite) produces five times less heat as coal but has the necessary rapidity in liberation for an explosion to be caused.

Finally, almost all explosions are subject to fragmentation – the accumulation and projection of particles as a result of its detonation. Fragmentation is proportional to the explosion's generated shock waves and detonation velocity, with supersonic shock waves (those travelling faster then the speed of sound) producing considerably more fragmentation than subsonic varieties. Fragmentation increases an explosion's potency ten-fold as low-angle high-velocity shards can shred human tissue, render vehicle armour and level structures. ✿

The history of explosives

Chart the rise of man-made explosives over the centuries

800AD
Ancient Chinese: The ancient Chinese are credited with the creation of early explosives – which were crude black powders – used in rockets and fireworks.

1300AD
European gunpowder: By the 1300s, the knowledge of the East had reached Europe and a new era of explosive warfare ensued, relegating suits of medieval armour to museums.

1846AD
Nitroglycerine: More powerful than black powder, nitroglycerine paved the way for the creation of dynamite and other explosives.

This Schlieren photograph shows a reconstruction of a bomb exploding beneath the passenger seat of an aircraft. Notice how the blast generates circular shock waves of heat and light energy that radiate vertically within the cabin

© Science Photo Library

A Schlieren photograph of a firecracker explosion detailing the cloud of gas, particles and blast wave that are generated

© Science Photo Library

Why are explosions deadly?

Capable of breaking the physical threshold of human tissue, explosions claim many lives

Explosions are deadly for a variety of reasons. The basis of any explosion is the rapid burning and decomposition of a material, a process that creates a large amount of heat, pressure and gas in a short amount of time. All these factors can have an effect on humans, as their physical thresholds to withstand the various forces and chemicals in play is easily broken. For example, the heat generated by an explosion of HMX reaches thousands of degrees Celsius in a matter of seconds, something that the skin of a human – which would be subjected to third-degree burns – could not withstand, with the skin tissues and structures being destroyed.

The force and velocity of the detonation is equally as deadly. The shock wave created by an explosion carries tremendous amounts of energy and can easily project objects of such light weight hundreds of feet. Fragmentation – the shattering of explosive casing and material in an explosion's immediate vicinity – too, in supersonic explosions, can cause severing and puncturing to human tissue. In addition, the force of any explosion is often increased if it is a consequence of the detonation of an explosive device. This is because many warheads, mortars, rockets, shells and bombs have shaped charges, as demonstrated in the example of C-4, a type of plastic explosive based on cyclotrimethylene-trinitramine (RDX). C-4 is deadly as it can be moulded into various shapes to increase its destructive potential.

Gunpowder

Since its invention by the ancient Chinese, gunpowder has been one of the most used explosives on Earth

Gunpowder, unlike other modern explosives, is classified as a low explosive – an explosive that undertakes subsonic combustion – as it deflagrates slowly. For this reason, despite its creation over 1,000 years ago, it was still used as the explosive mechanism in guns all over the world up until the 20th Century, providing enough energy to propel a bullet out of a muzzle, but not enough to break the weapon and injure the user (of course, backfires and jams lead to bad injuries).

Modern rifle cartridges – the combination of a bullet, case, powder and primer – such as the one fired in the accompanying image, use smokeless powders (they are not actually smokeless, however, just considerably less so than conventional black powder), as their combustion efficiency is greatly increased, allowing rounds to be fired with less explosive. Further, smokeless powder does not leave heavy fouling (unwanted residue materials) within the weapon, allowing for semi and full automatic rifles to operate cleanly and efficiently.

This image shows the shock waves from the passage of the supersonic bullet and the muzzle blast, as well as a white cloud of propellant gas

© Science Photo Library

1863AD

Trinitrotoluene: Trinitrotoluene or TNT for short, was created by German chemist Joseph Wilbrand in 1863. It is now used as the modern benchmark for all other explosives.

1950AD

C-4: A common type of plastic explosive due to its easy handling, C-4 is based on the explosive RDX and provides massive, yet refined, damage.

2000AD

Octanitrocubane: With performance roughly 25 per cent greater than HMX, this is currently considered the most powerful non-nuclear explosive on the planet.

What are the most powerful explosives?

Trinitrotoluene

The first real breakthrough for explosives post gunpowder, trinitrotoluene is one of the most commonly used explosives on Earth. It was formed in 1863 and has an RE factor of 1.00.

Molecular formula:

$C_6H_2(NO_2)_3CH_3$

Dynamite

Based on nitroglycerin, dynamite has 60 per cent greater energy density than TNT. It was created in 1867 by renowned German chemist Alfred Nobel and has an RE factor of 1.50.

Molecular formula:

$C_3H_5N_3O_9$

C-4

Based on the explosive RDX, C-4 is the most famous plastic explosive used today. It is easily moulded into any shape (excellent for shaped charges) and has a high detonation velocity. It has an RE factor of 1.34.

Molecular formula:

$C_3H_6N_6O_6$

Semtex

Another brand of plastic explosives used mainly in commercial and industrial applications, Semtex is a mix of RDX and PETN. It is brick-orange in colour and has an RE factor of 1.66.

Molecular formula:

$C_5H_8N_4O_{12}$

1.5/5
Small explosion. Detonation velocity of 6,900m/s.

2/5
Modest explosion. Detonation velocity of 7,700m/s.

2.5/5
Large explosion. Detonation velocity of 8,040m/s.

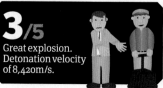

3/5
Great explosion. Detonation velocity of 8,420m/s.

A visual guide to the six most powerful non-nuclear explosives on the planet

HMX

Related to RDX but much more explosive, HMX is a nitroamine high explosive. Difficult to manufacture, it is only used for specialist military purposes, such as a nuclear bomb detonator. It has an RE factor of 1.70.

Molecular formula:

$C_4H_8N_8O_8$

Octanitrocubane

The most explosive chemical structure on Earth, Octanitrocubane has 25 per cent greater performance than HMX. It was synthesised at the University of Chicago in 1999 and has an RE factor of 2.70.

Molecular formula:

$C_8(NO_2)_8$

4/5
Massive explosion. Detonation velocity of 9,100 m/s.

5/5
Epic explosion. Detonation velocity of 10,100 m/s.

Explosions in nature

Explosions are not always man-made, with many natural examples visible over the Earth and in space

Organic – Many explosions are caused by plants and trees when subjected to hot and volatile conditions. For example, the Eucalyptus tree – which is predominantly found in Australia, New Guinea and Indonesia – is often prone to spontaneous combustion in periods of sustained heat and dry conditions. This is caused by the tree's high oil content (ie Eucalyptus oil) that rises above the bush as vapour when heated sufficiently creating a characteristic haze in dense forested areas. This oil, in both liquid and vapour forms, is incredibly flammable and if environmental pressure and heat reach critical levels, is prone to combust suddenly. This factor is severely exacerbated when a forest fire passes into Eucalyptus-heavy areas, as the resulting explosions and general flammability of the tree's bark carries and generates fire quickly.

Volcanic – Maybe the most obvious example of a natural explosion, volcanoes cause explosions when magma, which has risen to the Earth's surface, releases large amounts of accumulated dissolved gases into the atmosphere. This reduction in pressure above ground causes the gas to be separated from the magma and rapidly increase in volume, sending massive clouds of volcanic dust and particles spiralling into the atmosphere. Further, if a volcano's resulting magma flow reaches a water source, such as the ocean, then further steam-based explosions may be caused when the high-temperature flow meets the cold water, rupturing sections of coastline.

Stellar – The largest natural explosion currently known in the universe is that of a supernova, the resulting explosion that follows a dying star. Supernova explosions are ridiculously powerful and send the remnants of the star's material screaming out through space at a velocity up to 30,000km/s – that is ten per cent the speed of light – in a vast shock wave. Supernovas can be caused in a variety of different ways, however the most common is when the core of an aging star ceases to generate nuclear fusion, collapsing in on itself under the effects of gravity and expelling its outer layers as it releases its gravitational potential energy. During its short explosion (due to its size this would last several weeks or months) the amount of radiation of a supernova can total the entire amount it has ever radiated over its whole life span.

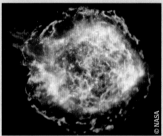

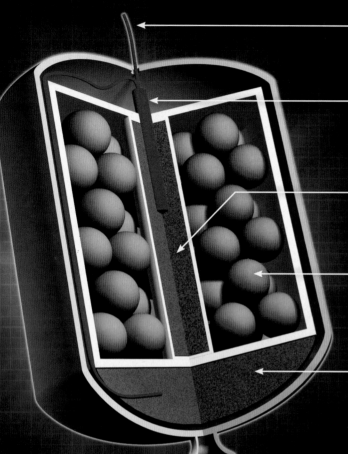

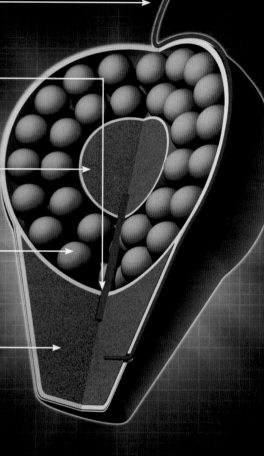

1. Fuse
The first fuse sets everything in motion. After the shell is in the mortar, the fuse is lit and the flame makes its way to the lifting charge.

3. Time-delayed fuse
While the shell soars up into the air, the time-delayed fuse continues to burn, buying enough time to get the shell at its highest point before reaching the bursting charge.

4. Bursting charge
The bursting charge is more black powder, stored higher up the shell. Once the time-delayed fuse reaches the bursting charge, the combustion sets off the stars.

5. Stars
The stars begin their heat-induced chemical reactions. The shell can no longer contain the power of the combustion, and the stars are sent flying, creating the traditional fireworks shapes.

2. Lifting charge
Black powder (also called gunpowder) is ignited by the fuse, and the explosion can send a shell up to 1,000 feet into the air.

Italian-style shell
Creates more elaborate bursts

Oriental-style shell
Produces spherical bursts

Inside fireworks
What makes the firework explode

How fireworks explode

These chemistry experiments have been delighting people for hundreds of years

Despite all their different colours, shapes, and sounds, all fireworks have the same basic components. Aerial fireworks consist of a shell made of heavy paper that holds the 'lift charge', the 'bursting charge', and the 'stars'. All of these glittery spectacles come from good old-fashioned combustion. Combustion is a chemical reaction between two substances (a fuel and an oxidant) that produces light and heat. The heat causes gasses to expand rapidly, building pressure. The shells are tightly wrapped cylinders, which provide good resistance to this pressure, giving it a short time to build in intensity. Then, when the reaction overpowers the shell, you get the explosive firework effect.

It all starts when the shell is placed into a mortar (a cylinder the same size as the shell, which holds the firework in place while the fuse burns). The lift charge, at the bottom of the shell, is basically concentrated black powder (charcoal, sulphur, and potassium nitrate). When lit by the dangling fuse, the lift charge sends the shell into the air. Basic firecrackers are just paper-covered black powder: you light the fuse and listen to the popping sound.

The bursting charge is another round of black powder with its own time-delayed fuse higher up in

What makes the colours?

Colours are a matter of delicate balance. The wrong combination can mean a wrong colour, or worse

Colours involve different measurements and combinations of oxygen producers, fuels, binders, and colour producers. You can make colour through incandescence – light created through heat (orange, red, white), or luminescence – light created from a chemical reaction without extreme heat (blue, green). It's all about temperature control and balance.

Red – Strontium and lithium
Orange – Calcium
Gold – Incandescence of iron, charcoal or lampblack
Yellow – Sodium
Electric white – Magnesium or aluminium
Green – Barium plus a chlorine producer
Blue – Copper plus a chlorine producer
Purple – Strontium plus copper
Silver – Aluminium, titanium or magnesium powder or flakes

The time-delay fuse continues to burn, reaching the next cluster of stars as the first explosion fades.

Each set of stars is in its own cardboard compartment, allowing for separate explosions. The first bursting charge sets off the first cluster of stars.

The shell rises into the air as the time-delay fuse burns.

The fuse is lit, setting off the lift charge.

The short life of a firework

A lot of careful planning has to go into a multi-break firework. All for about three seconds' worth of entertainment...

the shell. The bursting charge creates the heat to activate the stars that surround it and explode them outward from the shell. The stars are where the magic happens.

Stars are balls made up of fuels, oxidisers, colour-creating combinations of different kinds of metals, and a binder to hold everything together. The stars can be arranged within the firework shell to create shapes. The shapes can be things like hearts, stars,

and circles. Hundreds of stars can be used in a single firework shell.

More complex fireworks – for example, ones that produce a shape like a smiley face, have multiple phases of different colours, or make extra sounds like whistles – have shells with a more intricate infrastructure. In these types of fireworks, there are more time-delayed fuses linked to various bursting charges with their own surrounding stars. Each of

these may sit in its own individual interior shell. These are called 'multi-break shells'.

While a sight to behold, fireworks are individually wrapped chemistry experiments. Tapping one too hard or creating a static electricity shock with your synthetic-material clothing could be deadly and one exploding near to your face could result in horrific burns and even blindness. They don't have the word 'fire' in them for nothing. ✿

How do party poppers pop?

Explore the science behind these party pieces to see what makes them explode

Party poppers are basically tiny sticks of dynamite inside a plastic seal. Of course, the explosion generated is nowhere near as dangerous as any proper explosives, but the bang can still be a surprise for some.

Inside the popper is an assortment of confetti, in addition to a small stick containing the gunpowder and two disks, made of plastic or cardboard. The stick consists of paper or plastic wrapped around a tiny amount of gunpowder, typically much less than 1mg (federal law in the US allows for up to 50mg in fireworks). A string runs a few centimetres into the handle of the popper and comes out the other side for someone to pull.

When the string is pulled it creates friction within the stick as it rubs against the sides. This creates heat and ignites the gunpowder, producing a small explosion and the trademark party popper 'bang'. The explosion moves outwards through the confined space, pushing the first disk into about a dozen rolls of colourful confetti. This forward motion continues into the second disk enclosing the popper, allowing the rolls of confetti to be flung into the air and unravelled. ✿

Inside the explosion
What happens when a party popper explodes?

Boom
The rapid expansion of pressure within the popper and the explosion itself produces an audible bang.

Pressure
The pressure inside the enclosed compartment pushes the containing disk of plastic outwards, freeing the contents from the popper.

Shape
The bell shape of a party popper is imperative to its success, allowing the pressure to build uniformly away from the tiny explosion.

Party
The wave of pressure carries with it the entire contents of the popper, sending confetti streaming across the room.

Blast
The explosion inside produces heat energy and smoke as the paper holding the gunpowder burns slightly.

© Science Photo Library

Inside a party popper

How does the construction of these tiny explosive charges produce an attractive party decoration?

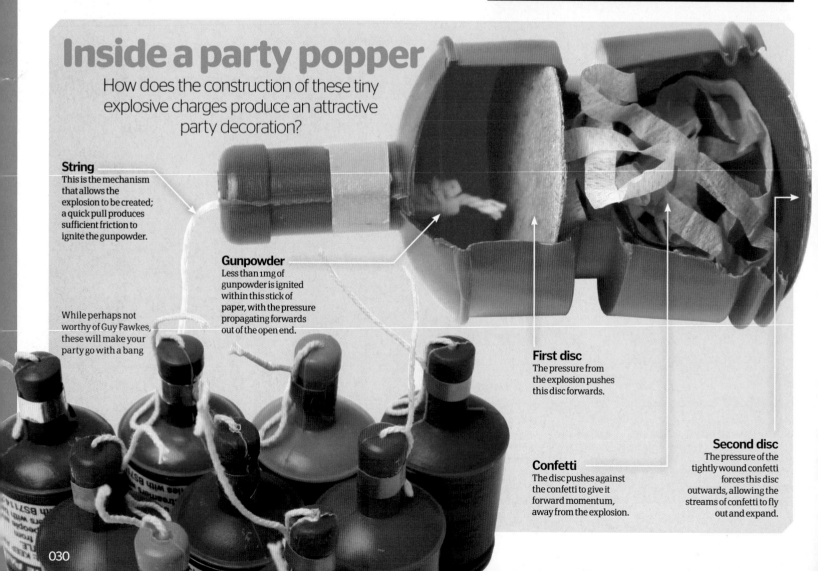

String
This is the mechanism that allows the explosion to be created; a quick pull produces sufficient friction to ignite the gunpowder.

Gunpowder
Less than 1mg of gunpowder is ignited within this stick of paper, with the pressure propagating forwards out of the open end.

While perhaps not worthy of Guy Fawkes, these will make your party go with a bang

First disc
The pressure from the explosion pushes this disc forwards.

Confetti
The disc pushes against the confetti to give it forward momentum, away from the explosion.

Second disc
The pressure of the tightly wound confetti forces this disc outwards, allowing the streams of confetti to fly out and expand.

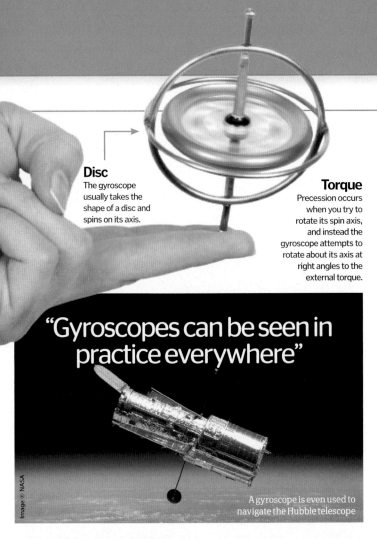

Disc
The gyroscope usually takes the shape of a disc and spins on its axis.

Torque
Precession occurs when you try to rotate its spin axis, and instead the gyroscope attempts to rotate about its axis at right angles to the external torque.

Gyroscopes

How does a gyroscope defy gravity?

Gyroscopes have their place in a wide variety of realms and have been utilised for a plethora of purposes from fascinating office toys to adrenaline-infused fairground rides to navigational equipment in space shuttles – gyroscopes can be seen in practice everywhere.

A gyroscope measures and maintains orientation based on the principles of angular momentum and appear to defy gravity – an effect know as precession. Precession occurs when you try to rotate its spin axis, and instead the gyroscope attempts to rotate about its axis at right angles to the external torque. Essentially this means the device is a spinning wheel with an axle that is free to take any orientation. When the gyroscope is spinning what happens to these parts follows

Newton's first law of motion; ie a body in motion continues to move at constant speed along a straight line unless acted upon by an unbalanced force. Therefore the top point of the gyroscope is acted on by the force applied to the axle and begins to move. Precession causes the different sections of the gyroscope to receive forces at one point but then rotate to new positions, always remaining perpendicular to the 'spin axis'. The forces acting on the top and bottom of the wheel act against each other and force the wheel to spin, creating a gravity-defying illusion.

Gyroscopes are used in a huge variety of applications, including navigation when magnetic compasses do not work, such as those found in the Hubble telescope, or aviation where they are an integral part of any jet-powered aeroplane. ✿

"Gyroscopes can be seen in practice everywhere"

Image © NASA

A gyroscope is even used to navigate the Hubble telescope

Why do glow sticks glow?

What's going on inside these popular light sticks?

Inside a glow stick is a very thin glass vial containing chemicals. When you bend the stick you're breaking this vial open, releasing the chemicals into the rest of the glow stick, where other chemicals react with them and release light.

Some chemical reactions produce light, known as 'chemiluminescence'. Usually the vial contains a solution phenyl oxalate ester and a fluorescent dye – which will determine the colour of the glow stick – while the surrounding tube contains a solution of hydrogen peroxide. Mixing these compounds causes the electrons to rise to a higher energy level and return to their normal state, releasing energy as light as they do. ✿

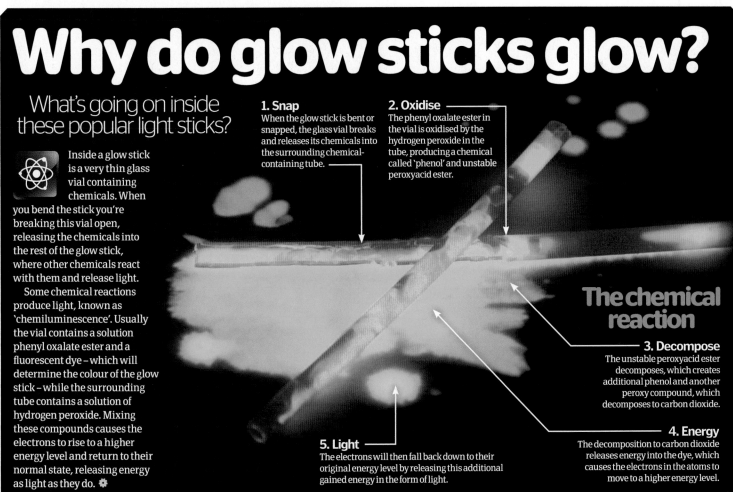

1. Snap
When the glow stick is bent or snapped, the glass vial breaks and releases its chemicals into the surrounding chemical-containing tube.

2. Oxidise
The phenyl oxalate ester in the vial is oxidised by the hydrogen peroxide in the tube, producing a chemical called 'phenol' and unstable peroxyacid ester.

The chemical reaction

3. Decompose
The unstable peroxyacid ester decomposes, which creates additional phenol and another peroxy compound, which decomposes to carbon dioxide.

4. Energy
The decomposition to carbon dioxide releases energy into the dye, which causes the electrons in the atoms to move to a higher energy level.

5. Light
The electrons will then fall back down to their original energy level by releasing this additional gained energy in the form of light.

Light in a prism

Discover how light is dispersed into a rainbow

Before we can tackle what happens to light in a prism, we need to look at the nature of light itself. Visible light is a form of electromagnetic radiation that forms part of the electromagnetic spectrum. It occupies a specific wavelength on the spectrum, from violet at 380 nanometres to red at 740 nanometres.

Light travels at varying speeds in different materials, and it is for this reason that it will disperse within a prism. Every material has a specific refractive index, which is a ratio of how the speed of light differs within that material to when it is in a vacuum (where the speed of light is c, roughly 3×10^8 metres per second). The refractive index of a material is not constant, however; it varies depending upon the wavelength of the incoming light. This will determine the amount of refraction – the change of speed that alters its direction – the light undergoes.

As the colour red has a higher wavelength than violet, it refracts less as it enters and then exits the prism. The amount of refraction determines the path each colour will take, so the light splits up into its constituent colours. ✿

The spectrum

Visible light occupies only a small part of the electromagnetic spectrum. The wavelength of each individual colour ultimately determines how much it will refract (bend) as it passes through a prism, creating a rainbow when all the colours undergo different levels of refraction. Perfect white light contains equal amounts of all colours.

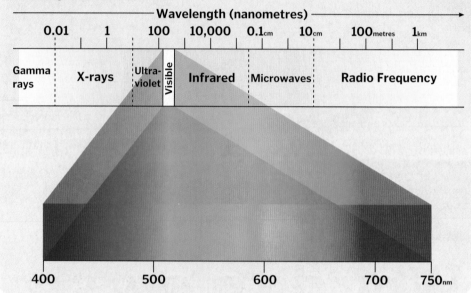

				Wavelength (nanometres)					
0.01	1		100	10,000	0.1cm	10cm	100metres	1km	
Gamma rays	X-rays		Ultra-violet	Visible	Infrared	Microwaves		Radio Frequency	

400	500	600	700	750nm

I can see a rainbow

Light refracts as it enters and exits the prism, creating a rainbow effect as the colours separate – but what's going on inside?

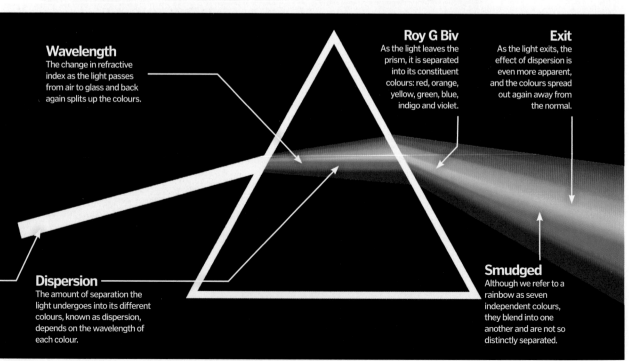

Wavelength
The change in refractive index as the light passes from air to glass and back again splits up the colours.

Roy G Biv
As the light leaves the prism, it is separated into its constituent colours: red, orange, yellow, green, blue, indigo and violet.

Exit
As the light exits, the effect of dispersion is even more apparent, and the colours spread out again away from the normal.

Towards normal
As light enters the glass prism, it naturally moves towards the normal, a line perpendicular to the edge.

Dispersion
The amount of separation the light undergoes into its different colours, known as dispersion, depends on the wavelength of each colour.

Smudged
Although we refer to a rainbow as seven independent colours, they blend into one another and are not so distinctly separated.

How do marker pens work?

Permanent or non-permanent, that is the question

Permanent marker pens were invented by American inventor Sidney Rosenthal in 1953 and work by binding their contained ink to a variety of surfaces. Water resistant, the marker's liquid ink is mixed with solvents such as xylene and toluene to ensure water-insolubility. This means that once applied to a surface, the ink binds via evaporation and can only be removed by dedicated paint-thinning solvents such as acetone, which break down the ink's binding. Permanent markers can be hazardous to human health if tampered with, as they radiate volatile organic compounds like in spray paint.

In contrast, non-permanent markers use erasable ink. This ink adheres to surfaces without binding or being absorbed by it, as it does not contain the toxic binding compounds of that in permanent markers. This means that their ink is water-soluble and can be easily removed by wiping the applied surface with a damp cloth. Recently, these markers have been superseded by wet erase markers.

The ink in these markers contains water, resin and titanium dioxide, and using a paste instead of alcohol as a base, makes them both non-permanent and – if left for an elongated period of time – permanent. ✿

© Ognjen Djokic

What is a mirage?

How does this optical illusion bring invisible distant objects into view?

Commonly seen in the desert or at sea, a mirage is an optical phenomenon associated with light refraction. As light rays pass from a distant object through one material and into another, their refractive index changes, which alters the speed at which the rays travel. This is known as 'refraction' and it causes the light rays to bend and change direction. So when light passes from a layer of denser cool air through to a layer of less-dense warm air, refraction occurs. Due to the curvature of the Earth, the bent light rays can bring otherwise obscured objects beyond the horizon into view above it, in line with the viewer.

The 'vision in the desert'-type mirage is known as an 'inferior' mirage. These mirages make objects appear much closer than they are, and light coming from objects on the horizon will appear as images down on the ground. They occur when the ground is so hot that it warms the air just above the surface. Light rays passing from the overlying cool air through to this warmer air near the surface will bring a distant object into view at a closer range. Where the light would normally go to the ground, it goes up to meet the viewer's eyes.

Conversely, 'superior' mirages can make an image of an object appear unfeasibly high off the ground. This occurs when a layer of cool air sits beneath a layer of warm air (ie, over an area of ice or very cold water, such as the poles). Because the cold air near the ground is denser than the air higher up, light is refracted downwards, bending the light rays towards the viewer's eyes. ✿

How a mirage is formed

Superior mirage
A superior mirage appears high in the sky, making the object beyond the horizon visible to the viewer.

Seeing the invisible
Due to of the curvature of the Earth, this village, which is situated beyond the horizon line, is concealed from the viewer.

Bending the light
Because the cold air near the surface is denser than the warmer air overlying it, light rays passing from the object through the air are refracted.

© Science Photo Library

What is condensation?

Anyone who's had a cold drink on a hot day has seen condensation in action

Air contains water vapour in various quantities depending on where it is in the atmosphere. The amount of water vapour air can hold is dependent on its temperature – with the amount decreasing as the air itself begins to cool. The lower the air temperature, the less water the air is capable of holding. This increases the overall humidity of the air until – if the temperature drops low enough – the air hits what is known as the 'dew point'.

This is the point at which the excess water vapour literally condenses out of the air and forms water.

What's genuinely fascinating is how this process differs depending on the location of the air. Warm air that's cooled to the dew point due to expanding and rising forms clouds. The cooling of a large amount of air near the ground, however, will cause mist or fog to form. Air in contact with the ground will become dew if its dew point is above 0°C or frost if it's below.

Condensation
This forms when the air hits its 'dew point'.

Warm moist air
As the air cools, the amount of water vapour the air can hold decreases.

Cold glass
Water droplets will form on the outside of the glass.

Boiling water

Steam
As the vapour cools and condenses, it produces visible steam.

Vapour pressure
Evaporation occurs when the vapour pressure reaches that of the surrounding air.

Boil
When water boils at 100°C (212°F), vapour pressure increases.

© Science Photo Library

Evaporation and steam

How do these processes work, and is there a difference between them?

The change of state from a solid or a liquid to a vapour is known as 'evaporation'. This change of state occurs from the amount of energy the molecules have. Apart from at absolute zero (-273.15 °C), when molecules are said to have zero energy, molecules are in constant motion and, as temperature increases, they gain more and more energy.

This in turn increases their movement and, the faster they move, the more likely they are to collide with one another. When these collisions occur, a molecule can gain enough energy – and

subsequently heat – to rise up into the atmosphere.

However, there is a difference between evaporation of vapour and steam. While vapour can be said to be any substance in a gaseous state at the same temperature as its environment, steam is specifically vapour from water that is hotter than the surrounding environment, commonly seen when boiling. There is no difference in chemical composition of the two. The steam we actually observe is the vapour cooling and condensing as it leaves the hot water and enters the cooler surrounding air.

Yo-yos

How the laws of physics make these toys so much fun

When a yo-yo is held in your palm, it has potential energy from its height above the ground and the winding of the string. As the yo-yo is released this potential energy becomes kinetic energy, with the yo-yo travelling towards the ground and also spinning, gaining linear and rotational momentum respectively.

When the yo-yo reaches the end of its string, it can fall no further. In old designs, the angular (rotational) momentum would mean that the yo-yo immediately rose again to almost the same height as momentum and energy are conserved, although both lose out slightly to friction. Modern yo-yos, however, employ technologies in a special spool (axle) that allows the yo-yo to use its momentum to continue spinning at the end of its tether. To get the yo-yo to rise, a tug on the string will increase the friction between the string and the spool so the yo-yo rewinds. ✿

© Science Photo Library

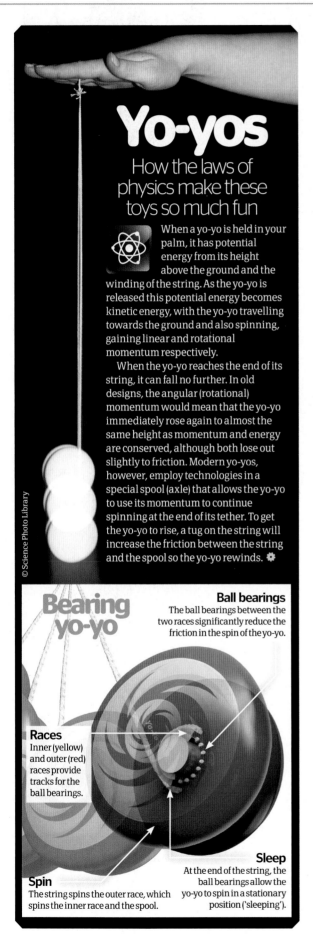

Bearing yo-yo

Ball bearings
The ball bearings between the two races significantly reduce the friction in the spin of the yo-yo.

Races
Inner (yellow) and outer (red) races provide tracks for the ball bearings.

Spin
The string spins the outer race, which spins the inner race and the spool.

Sleep
At the end of the string, the ball bearings allow the yo-yo to spin in a stationary position ('sleeping').

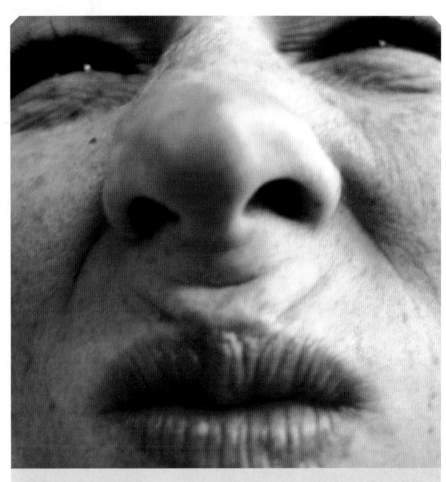

BAD

1. Rotten eggs
When the protein in an egg breaks down, it creates an awful smell.

WORSE

Tom Freidel

2. Skunk
Skunk scent glands can release a smell described as a combination of eggs, garlic and burnt rubber.

WORST

3. Titan arum
When the 'corpse flower' blooms it smells like rotting meat to attract prey.

Scratch and sniff

Our sense of smell has one of the strongest connections to our memory

At the heart of this technology is the link between smell and memory. Scratch and sniff cards and stickers have been used to sell everything from perfume to Smell-o-Vision since the Seventies. In each case the scratch and sniff product is sprayed with a fragrance and then covered with a layer of micro capsules. These micro capsules provide an air-tight seal to lock the fragrance in place. When ruptured by scratching, the capsules break, which releases the fragrance.

When scratch and sniff was in its infancy, the level of acidity in the card and sticker sheets could damage the fragrance. However, when the level of acidity was reduced in the Eighties, this problem was solved. In addition to this, one advantage to the process is that the same seal can be used to cover multiple fragrances on one card. ✿

Hot-air ballo

How do these gasbags get off the ground and return to Earth safely?

A hot-air balloon consists of three basic parts: an envelope big enough to displace a large amount of air, burners beneath the envelope to heat the air inside, and a basket in which to sit back and enjoy the ride. The scientific principle that enables this lift is convection, or heat transfer.

Heating the air inside the envelope causes it to expand, forcing some of the air out of the envelope. The weight of air inside then decreases, making the balloon lighter and giving it lift. Once the burner is shut off, however, the air inside cools and contracts, causing cold air to rush in from below, weighing the envelope down and causing the balloon to descend. If the burner is powered up intermittently, the balloon can maintain a pretty much constant altitude. Hot-air balloons have an upper limit because at particularly high altitudes the air is so thin that the lift is not actually strong enough to raise the balloon.

Because hot-air balloons have no real means of changing direction other than upwards and downwards, the vehicle will drift along with the wind. However, a skilled balloonist can manoeuvre horizontally by altering their altitude. You see, wind is known to blow in different directions at different heights and so the pilot can ascend or descend until they find the appropriate wind to send them in the direction they wish to travel. ✱

Envelope
Reinforced ripstop nylon fabric (also used for kites, sails and sleeping bags) is the principle material used for hot-air balloon envelopes. This lightweight fabric can also be coated with silicone to make it more hard-wearing.

An alternative to queuing at the airport...

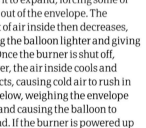

The envelope is made from ripstop nylon

1. Inflation
A balloon crew inflate the envelope using a powerful fan to blow air in from the base of the envelope for several minutes.

2. Erection
To get the inflated envelope off the ground, the propane-fuelled burner beneath the envelope is placed at the entrance to the envelope and blasted.

4. Air expands and rises
Warm air expands and rises, causing about a quarter of the air to exit through the bottom of the envelope.

3. Burner on
The burner heats the air inside the envelope to a temperature of about 100°C. This causes the air particles to gain energy and move about faster and farther apart.

5. Ascent
The balloon ascends because the air inside the envelope is lighter and less dense than cold air outside.

ons

Parachute vent
If the balloon needs to descend quickly, some colder air can enter via a parachute valve or vent in the top of the envelope controlled by a cord pulled by the pilot.

Gores
To create the balloon shape from a flat piece of material, it must be cut into long panels (from the crown to the base) called gores. These gores are then stitched together to create the shape.

Turning up the heat gets you airborne...

7. Air contracts
The cooler air contracts leaving space inside the envelope to suck in more cold air from below.

8. Descent
The increased weight of the cooler air inside the balloon exceeds the upthrust and so the balloon will start to sink.

6. Burner off
Shutting off the burner causes the air to cool down.

Propane tanks
Compressed liquid propane is stored in lightweight tanks in the basket.

Skirt
The flame-resistant material at the base of the envelope is called the skirt. This stops the rest of the envelope from catching fire.

9. Landing
By gently controlling the burner and descent, the balloon will normally come in to land bouncing along the ground before stopping.

10. Landing site
Given the relatively uncontrollable nature of directing a hot-air balloon, the landing site cannot always be predicted and so the pilot must select a large enough area free from pylons and bodies of water where they can lay out the envelope.

Burner
Liquid propane flows from the tanks through steel pipes coiled around the burner. When the balloonist triggers the burner, liquid propane flows out and is ignited by a pilot light. In the meantime this flame heats the metal pipes, turning the liquid propane into a gas that is more powerful and fuel-efficient than the liquid when it's cold.

Basket
Traditionally a hot-air balloon's basket is made of wicker because it's durable, flexible and lightweight. Today hot-air balloons can come with double-decker baskets that seat 50 people if necessary. Enclosed gondolas are also available for serious, long-distance ballooning.

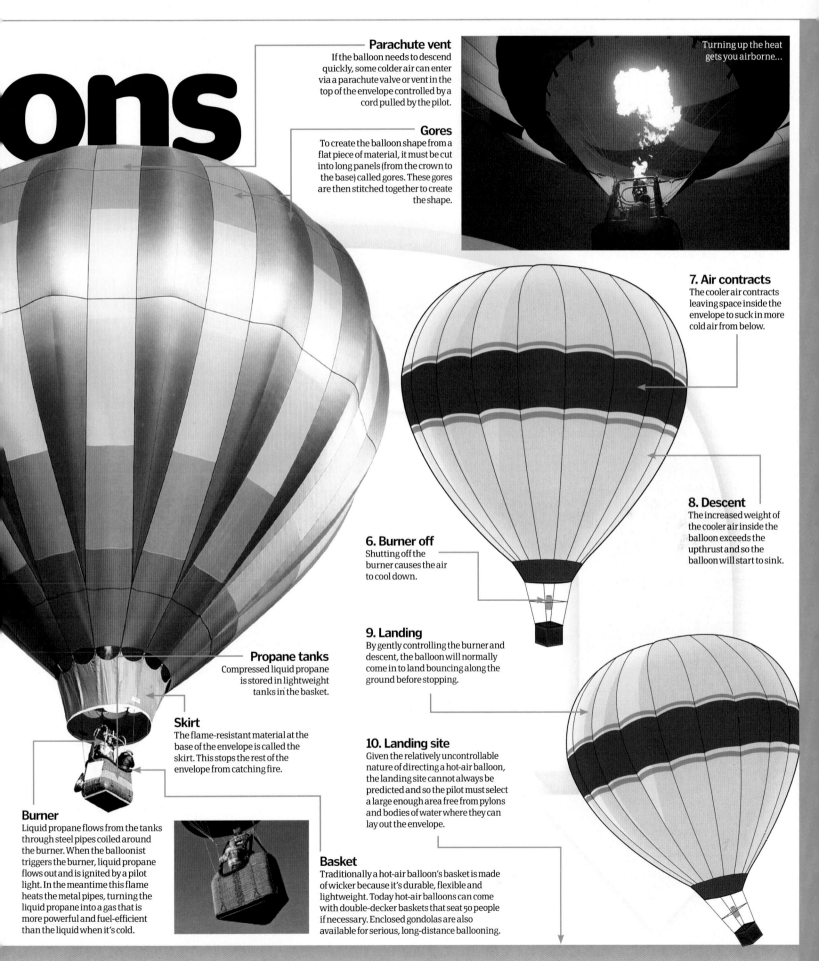

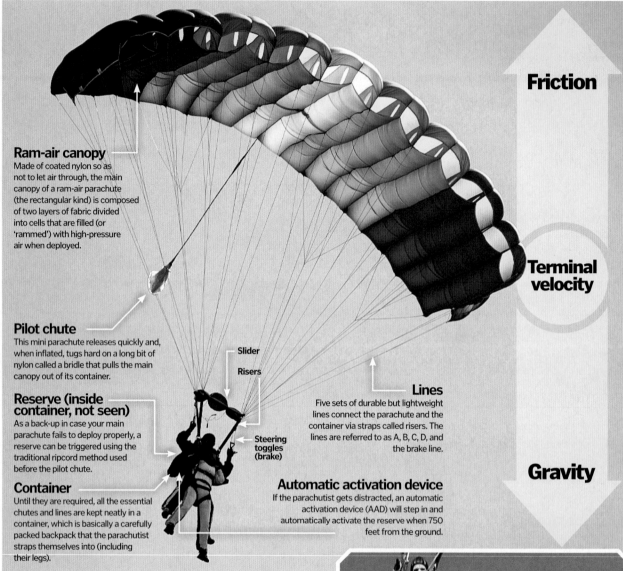

Getting down
The steps to land safely

Jump
With the need for additional oxygen, the typical altitude you would choose for your jump is 13,000 feet.

Freefall
'Freefall' begins the second you step off the plane and will last about a minute. 2,500 feet from the ground is a good time to deploy the parachute.

Landing
The ground exerts an upward force on you, stopping motion and bringing you down to Earth with a bump.

Ram-air canopy
Made of coated nylon so as not to let air through, the main canopy of a ram-air parachute (the rectangular kind) is composed of two layers of fabric divided into cells that are filled (or 'rammed') with high-pressure air when deployed.

Pilot chute
This mini parachute releases quickly and, when inflated, tugs hard on a long bit of nylon called a bridle that pulls the main canopy out of its container.

Reserve (inside container, not seen)
As a back-up in case your main parachute fails to deploy properly, a reserve can be triggered using the traditional ripcord method used before the pilot chute.

Container
Until they are required, all the essential chutes and lines are kept neatly in a container, which is basically a carefully packed backpack that the parachutist straps themselves into (including their legs).

Slider

Risers

Steering toggles (brake)

Lines
Five sets of durable but lightweight lines connect the parachute and the container via straps called risers. The lines are referred to as A, B, C, D, and the brake line.

Automatic activation device
If the parachutist gets distracted, an automatic activation device (AAD) will step in and automatically activate the reserve when 750 feet from the ground.

Friction

Terminal velocity

Gravity

The science of parachutes
Friction versus gravity in a battle to the ground

When you jump out of a plane, two major forces are competing for attention: friction (or drag) between you and the air whizzing past, and gravity pulling you down. When freefalling, you will experience acceleration because the force of friction is initially much weaker than the force of gravity. Eventually, the downward force of gravity will equal the upward force of drag and you will stop accelerating and fall at a constant speed – usually around 120mph. This is known as terminal velocity: the point at which no force is acting upon your body.

While gravity is a constant force, the force of friction changes with velocity and surface area. For example, stick your hand out the window of a stationary vehicle and you'll not experience friction. However, stick your hand out the window of a moving vehicle and you'll experience a large force of friction. Upon opening the parachute, the frictional force is greater than the force of gravity because the canopy has increased your cross-sectional area – this is what slows you down. As your acceleration drops, so too does the force of friction until it is equal to the force of gravity and again you descend at a constant rate.

Precise control
Steering a parachute is remarkably easy with the use of two handheld toggles to control the lines. The parachute canopy behaves like a wing due to the airfoil shape created by the air-filled cells. To turn left, you should pull on the left-hand toggle because this lowers the back-left section of the parachute, which also slows down that side of the 'wing'. The same goes for turning right, except that you tug on the right-hand toggle instead of the left. Pulling on both at the same time has a braking effect and will slow the whole parachute down.

What is the sound barrier?

Breaking the sound barrier means exceeding the speed of sound at 40,000 feet, that's about 660 miles per hour

When Chuck Yeager broke the sound barrier with the Bell X-1 rocket plane in 1947, his mum wasn't mad. This was one case where breaking something was a good thing. The sound barrier is simply the point an object exceeds the speed of sound – a speed many scientists once considered impossible.

Sound is a travelling wave of pressure. A moving object pushes nearby air molecules, which push the molecules next to them, and so on. As a plane approaches the speed of sound, its pressure waves 'stack up' ahead of it to form a massive area of pressurised air, called a shock wave. Shock waves would shake old planes violently, creating an apparent 'barrier' to higher speeds.

You can hear shock waves as sonic booms. Sometimes they're even visible: the high pressure area can cause water vapour to condensate into liquid droplets, briefly forming a cloud around the plane. ✿

Falling force

Legend has it that Galileo famously disproved Aristotle by dropping two cannonballs of different mass from the top of the Tower of Pisa and showing that they land simultaneously. In 1971, astronaut Dave Scott dropped a feather and a hammer on the moon, proving that all objects fall at the same rate in a vacuum.

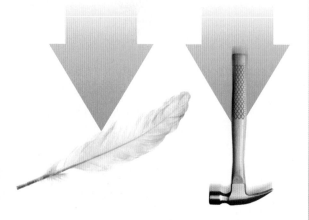

What is

Surprisingly weak yet mysteriously powerful, gravity is the super glue of the universe

 Everything in the universe is made of matter – the cosmic 'stuff' of creation. Mass is a measurement of the amount of matter contained in any object, from planets to protons. The Earth, for example, has a mass of 5.9742×10^{24} kilograms, while the mass of a single proton is $1.67262158 \times 10\text{-}27$ kilograms.

When we think of gravity, we usually think of the gravitational force exerted by massive (literally) celestial bodies like the Earth, the Moon or the Sun. But the truth is that any object of any mass – even a sub-atomic particle – exerts a gravitational pull on nearby objects.

Sir Isaac Newton proved that objects of greater mass exert a stronger gravitational force. That's why we typically talk about gravity in reference to planets and not protons. But the shocking truth about gravity is that even a colossal hunk of rock like the Earth exerts an exceptionally puny pull. An infant, in fact, can defeat the combined gravitational pull of every single atom on the planet by lifting a wooden block off the floor.

That's what makes Newton's discoveries so amazing, even today. Gravity – this wimp of a force – is somehow powerful enough to pull the moon into orbit and keep the Earth cruising in a perfect elliptical path around the Sun. Without the constant tug of gravity, planets would crumble into dust and stars would collapse.

Gravity is also responsible for giving objects weight. But don't confuse weight with mass. While mass is a measurement of the amount of matter in an object, weight is the downward force exerted by all of that matter in a gravitational field. In the zero-gravity vacuum of space, objects are weightless, but they still have mass.

On the surface of the Earth, where the force of gravity is essentially constant, we consider mass and weight to be equal. But that same object – with the same mass – will weigh 17 per cent less on the Moon, where the gravitational pull is weaker. On Jupiter – not the best place to start a diet – that same object will weigh 213 per cent more. ✿

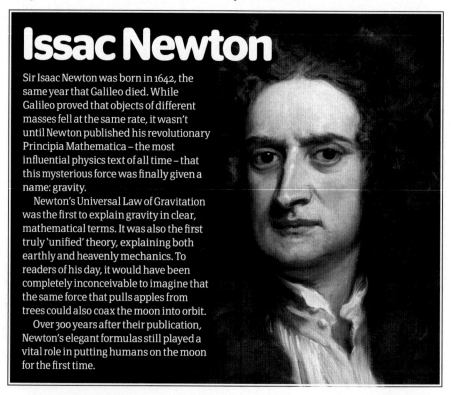

Issac Newton

Sir Isaac Newton was born in 1642, the same year that Galileo died. While Galileo proved that objects of different masses fell at the same rate, it wasn't until Newton published his revolutionary Principia Mathematica – the most influential physics text of all time – that this mysterious force was finally given a name: gravity.

Newton's Universal Law of Gravitation was the first to explain gravity in clear, mathematical terms. It was also the first truly 'unified' theory, explaining both earthly and heavenly mechanics. To readers of his day, it would have been completely inconceivable to imagine that the same force that pulls apples from trees could also coax the moon into orbit.

Over 300 years after their publication, Newton's elegant formulas still played a vital role in putting humans on the moon for the first time.

gravity?

1. Short-range
If a cannonball is fired from a mountain peak above the Earth's atmosphere, gravity will pull it down in the direction of the centre of the Earth.

8. Escape velocity
With enough velocity, the cannonball will escape the Earth's gravitational pull entirely. The Earth's escape velocity, as calculated by Newton, is 11.2 kilometres/second (7 miles/second).

2. Mid-range
With a higher muzzle velocity, the cannonball travels a longer horizontal distance, while falling at the same rate of acceleration (gravity).

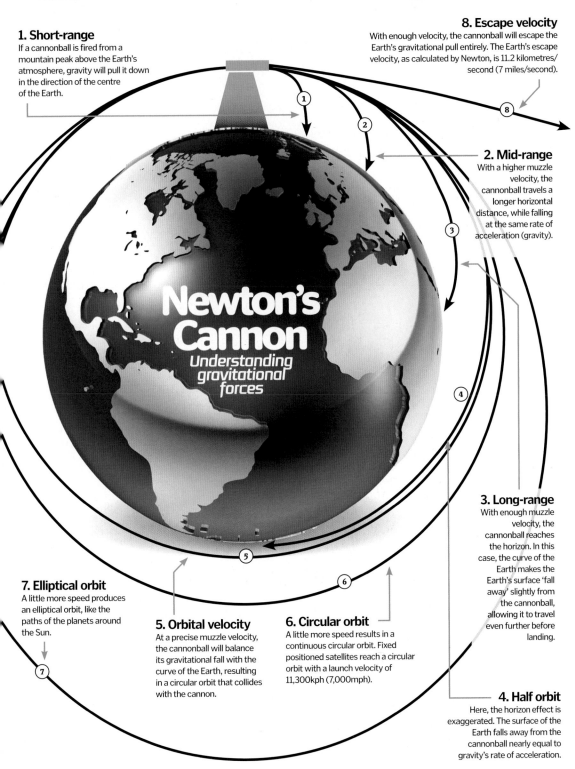

Newton's Cannon
Understanding gravitational forces

3. Long-range
With enough muzzle velocity, the cannonball reaches the horizon. In this case, the curve of the Earth makes the Earth's surface 'fall away' slightly from the cannonball, allowing it to travel even further before landing.

7. Elliptical orbit
A little more speed produces an elliptical orbit, like the paths of the planets around the Sun.

5. Orbital velocity
At a precise muzzle velocity, the cannonball will balance its gravitational fall with the curve of the Earth, resulting in a circular orbit that collides with the cannon.

6. Circular orbit
A little more speed results in a continuous circular orbit. Fixed positioned satellites reach a circular orbit with a launch velocity of 11,300kph (7,000mph).

4. Half orbit
Here, the horizon effect is exaggerated. The surface of the Earth falls away from the cannonball nearly equal to gravity's rate of acceleration.

Albert Einstein

While Newton was able to mathematically prove the existence of gravity, he had no idea where it came from or how it actually worked. In the Newtonian world view, gravity was a constant, independent force that acted instantaneously. If the Sun were to disappear, Newton argued, then the planets would immediately spin off into the void.

In 1905, a young and unknown Albert Einstein postulated that light travelled at a discrete speed limit through the vacuum of space. Since nothing can travel faster than light, the force of gravity cannot act instantaneously. If the Sun disappeared, it would take over eight minutes for the loss of gravity to be felt by Earth.

But Einstein's most mind-boggling gravitational insight came in 1916 with the General Theory of Relativity. In his radical view of the universe, the three dimensions of space are merged with a fourth dimension of time and represented as a flexible, two-dimensional 'space-time' fabric.

According to Einstein, objects of great mass act like bowling balls on a trampoline, bending and warping the space-time fabric. If a smaller object rolls too close one of these bowling balls, it will be drawn toward it. Gravity is not some mysterious independent force, but the result of the collective wrinkles in the fabric of the universe.

He's smiling now, but wait until he realises he left his parachute in the plane...

G-forces can be felt on fairground rides

Not a good time to have a blackout...

G-force explained

Intense acceleration in fast cars, fighter planes, rockets and roller coasters

When you're hurtling down the steel track of a roller coaster, it might seem that your stomach is climbing into your throat, and your eyes are squishing deep into your skull. Several forces are at play when you feel that way. Earth is constantly pulling down on every one of us. It has a great deal of mass, and that gives it a large gravitational field. And when we take a sharp turn on a fast ride, blast off in a rocket, or slam on the brakes, we're thrown around by forces far stronger than Earth's gravity. But why?

Engineers rate those experiences with numbers called g-forces, to explain how strong they are. One g is the amount of force that Earth's gravitational field exerts on your body when you are standing still on the ground. Every particle that makes up our planet is tugging on you simultaneously. Each one of those pulls is quite weak, but combined they are strong enough to keep your feet on the ground. Five g acceleration, something that race car drivers regularly experience, is five times as intense. Any time that an object changes its velocity faster than gravity can change it, the forces will be greater than one g. At zero g, you would feel weightless. And past 100g, you're almost certainly dead. Forces that intense can crush bones and squash organs.

Gravity is not the only source of g-forces. They take hold whenever a vehicle, like a car or a plane, suddenly changes its velocity. Speed up, slow down, or make a turn, and your velocity will change. The faster it happens, the more force you will experience. ⚙

What a knockout

If you are riding in a jet while it is making sharp turns, the blood in your head may rush out into your lower body. As the plane turns, all of the fluids in your body will act as if they were in a centrifuge, moving toward your feet, or whatever part of your body is on the outer edge of the turn. When that happens, your eyes will not get enough oxygen and you may experience a greyout, a sudden loss of colour vision, or a full blackout, temporary blindness. Accelerate harder and you will lose consciousness as blood retreats from your brain, depriving it of oxygen. Some people will experience these effects below 5g, but seasoned fighter pilots can take a bit more because they are very physically fit. They train themselves to resist the forces, and wear special suits that squeeze blood up into their heads.

Understanding g-forces

To find out how many gs you experienced during an intense acceleration, take your maximum speed, divide it by the time it took to hit that rate, and then divide by $9.81 m/s^2$. The resulting number is how many gs you experienced.

Example: Put the pedal to the metal in a Bugatti Veyron and you will go from 0-100kph in 2.3 seconds.

100kph is 28m/s, $28 / 2.3 = 12 m/s^2$, $12 / 9.8 = 1.2g$

© Bugatti

Acceleration

The relationship between acceleration and velocity is more complex than it first appears

Rollercoaster acceleration is typically measured against gravity, symbolised by the Roman unit g

Acceleration is the rate of change of velocity over time, with velocity being the rate of change of position. However, their relationship is not constricted, as is commonly understood, to merely increased mono-directional movement. This is because velocity is a vector physical quantity, requiring both speed and direction to define it. So absolutely any change in speed – including a decrease – is classed as acceleration, as is any change of directional motion, regardless of a speed increase or decrease. Therefore, it is not only a supercar that accelerates from 0-60, but also a spinning globe, dropped ball and rotating compass.

To attain an object's acceleration its velocity should be divided by time, or in unit terms, by dividing metres per second by seconds. So if a ball is thrown across a room at a velocity of six metres per second into a container, and the whole action takes three seconds, then the ball's acceleration would be six divided by three and therefore two metres per second.

However, as acceleration is a vector quantity (measured against both the rate of change in speed and direction), this figure is then squared to achieve the full measurement of 2m/s2. It is important to note, however, that acceleration can be measured as both average acceleration and instantaneous acceleration, the former being velocity divided by time, while the latter acceleration at any given point in time.

Acceleration can also be measured against gravity, symbolised by the unit g, that in some situations is a convenient benchmark where variations can be juxtaposed against it. For example, Earth's gravity is 1g, roughly 9.8m/s2, and if you drop an apple from your hand to the floor it accelerates at that speed.

Rollercoasters increase and vary g from the natural 1g we are used to. This is why when riding a rollercoaster you can feel increased and decreased pressure on your body and also why, despite travelling often at no greater speed than 30mph, rides feel dangerous and fast. ❖

The science of skateboarding

Kick, twist and grab your way through the physics of half pipes

In a halfpipe a skateboarder will typically start at one end (deck), then roll down into the flat of the halfpipe. They carry enough speed and momentum to shoot up the other side, gaining 'air' to perform tricks before landing again in the bowl of the halfpipe. ❖

1. Potential energy
At the deck of the halfpipe, before the skateboarder jumps into the halfpipe, they have a certain amount of potential energy, the result of gravity pulling them down.

7. Pumping
The skateboarder crouches on entry to the flat and rises as they go upwards, tightening their radius of travel in the 'circle' and increasing their linear momentum.

2. Potential to kinetic
As a skateboarder travels down the slope of one side, the potential energy becomes kinetic energy, giving them forward momentum.

5. All potential
When in the air, all the energy is now potential energy again. If the skateboarder makes the landing, he can use that energy to reach the other side again.

4. Kinetic to potential
As the rider travels up the opposite slope, kinetic energy turns back to potential as they move against the force of gravity, slowing them down.

3. All kinetic
At the flat bottom of the halfpipe, all of the rider's energy is kinetic energy, so they are at their maximum speed.

6. Work
If a skateboarder wants to go higher at one end, they need to do some work as they travel through the pipe.

Energy in a halfpipe

Wind tunnels

Allowing engineers to test aircraft designs in the lab, wind tunnels are invaluable to scientific research

A wind tunnel simulates in a laboratory the flow of air around, for example, an aeroplane or a building. This allows designers to work out the impact this airflow will have on the finished product and make cars and planes more aerodynamic and structures more wind resistant.

Wind tunnels are large circular tubes through which air is blown in one direction by giant fans: the test object – usually a scale model of the actual design – is mounted in the centre. In the case of an aircraft or a plane, in reality the object will be moving while the air stays still, but this doesn't matter as long as the relative velocity between the air and the object is the same. An enclosed cylinder is needed to allow for uniform airflow in one direction (known as laminar flow), simulating the airflow past a plane moving in a straight line or the wind hitting a skyscraper. ❖

Testing in the supersonic wind tunnel at NASA's Lewis Flight Propulsion Laboratory

Anatomy of a wind tunnel
The role of each section explained

Closed loop
Most – but not all – wind tunnels save energy by feeding the moving air from the exhaust back to the input

Fans
Most wind tunnels use fans or banks of fans, although the very fastest use explosive expansion of compressed air

Lighting
Illumination is usually provided by shining light in through windows – lighting would heat up air and produce turbulence

Observation windows
Kept level with the inside of wind tunnel and usually curved to keep inside as smooth as possible and prevent introduction of turbulence.

Test object
As some drag from walls is inevitable, the object is mounted in the centre of a wind tunnel where air stream is most stable.

Internal casing
Kept as smooth as possible to minimise friction between the wind tunnel and air, which would introduce turbulence to airflow.

Settling chamber
Air produced by fans is highly turbulent. Metal grating with a series of holes filters air current to create stable, unidirectional flow.

Water slides

Explaining the science behind these adrenaline-inducing attractions

Water slides work by exploiting the power of the Earth's gravity, the lubricating properties of water and the smooth friction-reducing surface of artificial plastic and fibreglass composites, in order to generate necessary force and momentum to propel riders through their systems. Slide construction tends to be highly eccentric – tuned to maximise g-forces experienced – with riders funnelled down twisting fibreglass tubes or gullies from an elevated position typically between 10-40 degrees.

There are three main types of water slide: body slides, tube/raft slides and mechanical hydro slides. The former is the simplest design and relies merely on the relationship between the rider's mass and the effect of gravity to propel them, with their changing position aided by the plastic, fluid properties of water, which helps to restrict the amount of friction. Tube/raft slides operate along the same principle of body slides but introduce an intermediary layer between the rider and the carrier – such as a rubber ring or foam sled – allowing for a greater speed and angle of attack when riding the attraction.

Mechanical hydro slides, while bearing a resemblance to and exploiting similar force-generating methods of both aforementioned slide types, are more complex constructions. Here, riders are propelled both downwards and upwards by a series of magnets and/or conveyor belts, which run exterior to or underneath the slide's water flow. These hydro-magnetic water slides utilise linear induction motors to propel the rider's inner tube (a necessity for this slide type) up inclines that would not be possible if just exposed to natural forces. ✿

Terminate
Water slides terminate the rider's gathered momentum and speed by depositing them into a large body of water, which absorbs and disperses their kinetic energy.

Velocity
Aided by the plastic, lubricating properties of water, the rider's potential energy is converted into kinetic energy as they travel down the slide, increasing their velocity.

Potential
At the top of the water slide the rider has a large amount of potential energy due to their height relative to the ground.

G-force
Due to the eccentric design of the slide and increased acceleration, riders experience increased g-forces in bends and loops.

Whirlpools

The often deadly vortex explained

Whirlpools are formed by the rising and falling of fast-flowing water through ocean channels on the seabed. Due to this, tsunamis – as seen in Japan – are major whirlpool creators, with their massive waves receding quickly away from the shoreline. If this massive quantity of water is funnelled into narrow channels, a whirlpool can form, with a powerful vortex sweeping water towards its centre in a downdraught. While whirlpools can be dangerous, with rare cases of people drowning in them, there have been no reported cases of boats actually being sunk in their vortices. ✿

Rise and fall
Whirlpools are caused by the rising and falling of fast-flowing water through ocean channels

Naruto whirlpools, located in the Naruto Strait channel

Vortex
Water is swept towards the whirlpool's centre in a downdraught. Smaller examples of whirlpools can be seen in your bath at home and even in small ponds.

The power of MAGNETISM

This invisible force allows the production of super-powerful electromagnets and everyday items such as credit cards, but what does it mean to be magnetised?

Magnetism is the force of nature responsible not only for our ability to live on a rock floating through space, but also for major technological achievements that have advanced the human race like never before. Our computers rely on them, our livelihood on Earth depends on their principles and our greatest science experiments use the most powerful magnets ever created by man. Were it not for magnetism we simply would not exist, and indeed without discovering the power of this fundamental force of nature, our life on Earth would bear no resemblance to what it is today.

Scientists over the years have employed magnetism in new and innovative ways, delving into realms of particle physics otherwise unexplored, but let's take a look at how basic magnets are made. It's fairly common knowledge that objects can be magnetised, making them stick to other magnetic objects, and we know that things such as a fridge or horseshoe magnet always have magnetism. To make permanent magnets like these, substances such as magnetite or neodymium are melted into an alloy and grounded into a powder. This powder can be moulded into any shape by compressing it with hundreds of pounds of pressure. A huge surge of electricity is then passed through it for a brief period of time to permanently magnetise it. Typically, a permanent magnet will lose about one per cent of its magnetism every ten years unless it is subjected to a strong magnetic or electric force, or heated to a high temperature.

Now let's take a look at the magnets themselves, and what's in and around them. Surrounding every magnet is a magnetised area known as a magnetic field that will exert a force, be it positive or negative, on an object placed within its influence. Every magnet also has two poles, a north and south. Two of the same poles will repel, while opposite poles attract. Inside and outside a magnet there are closed loops known as magnetic field lines, which travel through and around the magnet from the north to south pole. The closer together the field lines of this magnetic field are, the stronger it will be. This is why unlike poles attract – the magnetic forces are moving in the same direction, so the field lines leaving the south of one magnet have an easy route into the north of another, creating one larger magnet.

Conversely, like poles repel as the forces are moving in opposite directions, hitting one another and pushing away. It's the same effect as other forces. If you push a revolving door while someone pushes from the other side, the door stays still and your forces repel. If you push in the same direction,

Magnetic atom

So what's the difference between the atoms of magnetic and non-magnetic elements? Well, the main difference is the appearance of unpaired electrons. Atoms that have all their electrons in pairs can't be magnetised, as the magnetic fields cancel each other out. However, atoms that can be magnetised have several unpaired electrons. All electrons are essentially tiny magnets, so when they are unpaired they can exert their own force – known as a magnetic moment – on the atom. When they combine with electrons in the other atoms, the element as a whole gains a north and south pole and becomes magnetised.

Nucleus
Electrons of an atom orbit around the nucleus in the same way planets orbit the Sun, but this is due to the electromagnetic force and not gravity.

Paired electrons
Moving electrons create magnetism due to their electric charge, but in most atoms electrons are paired and there's no resultant magnetic force.

Unpaired electrons
Some atoms contain unpaired electrons, free to exert a magnetic moment (force) on the atom with a north and south pole.

Shells
Electrons travel round the nucleus in shells, moving in cloud-like orbits rather the common description of them as rigid circles.

Inside a magnet

An object that can become magnetic is full of magnetic domains, chunks of about one quadrillion atoms. When the object is magnetised, the domains line up to and point in the direction of the magnetic field now present. This is why a magnetic object is sometimes stroked with a magnet to magnetise it. It aligns the domains in one direction, so that a magnetic field can flow around the material.

Unmagnetised
With no magnetism, the object does not have a north and south pole, so there is no magnetic field present to align the domains.

Scattered
When a substance that can be magnetic is unmagnetised its domains go in random directions, cancelling each other out.

Magnetised
Introducing a magnet or electric current to the substance makes the domains all point in the same direction, with a magnetic field running from the north to south poles.

Aligned
When the domains are lined up, the substance as a whole becomes a magnet, with one end of it acting as a north pole and the other a south.

however, the door swings round and you eventually end up back at your starting point.

The defining feature of magnetic poles is that they always occur in pairs. Cut a bar magnet in half and a new north and south pole will instantly be created on each of the two new magnets. This is because each atom has its own north and south pole, which we will talk about later. However, the obvious question is why the poles are there in the first place. Why do magnets have to have these field lines moving from north to south? The answer involves magnetic domains. It is best to picture a magnet as smaller magnet chunks put together. Each chunk (or domain) has its own north and south pole and again, as explained before, magnetic field lines travel from north to south. This means that all the domains stick together, with their forces

concentrated in the same direction. They combine to make a larger magnet, exactly the same effect as when two magnets are stuck together. Each domain has about 1,000,000,000,000,000 (one quadrillion) atoms, while 6,000 domains are approximately equivalent to the size of a pinhead. Domains within a magnet are always aligned, but elements such as iron that can become

magnetic initially have their domains pointing in random directions when the iron is unmagnetised. They cancel each other out until a magnetic field or current is introduced, making them point in the same direction and magnetising the iron, which creates its own new magnetic field.

To really understand magnets, though, we need to get into exactly what is happening inside these ▶

An electronic motor relies on magnets

Ferromagnetism
The strongest magnet in this list, a ferromagnet will retain its magnetism unless heated to a temperature known as the Curie point. Cooling it again will return its ferromagnetic properties. Every atom in a ferromagnetic material aligns when a magnetic field is applied. Horseshoe magnets are ferromagnets.

© Gregory F. Maxwell

Ferrimagnetism
Ferrimagnets have a constant amount of magnetisation regardless of any applied magnetic field. Natural magnets like lodestones (magnetite) are ferrimagnets, containing iron and oxygen ions. Ferrimagnetism is caused by some of the atoms in a mineral aligning in parallel. It is different from ferromagnetism in that not every atom aligns.

© Ryan Somma

Antiferromagnetism
At low temps, the atoms in an antiferromagnet align in antiparallel. Applying a magnetic field to an antiferromagnet such as chromium will not magnetise it, as the atoms remain opposed. Heating to Néel temp (when paramagnetism can occur) will allow weak magnetism, but further heating will reverse this.

Paramagnetism
Paramagnets, such as magnesium and lithium, have a weak attraction to a magnetic field but don't retain any magnetism after. It's caused by at least one unpaired electron in the atoms of a material.

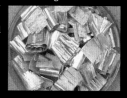

Diamagnetism
Gold, silver and many other elements in the periodic table are diamagnets. Their magnetic loops around the atoms oppose applied fields, so they repel magnets. All materials have some magnetism, but only those with a form of positive magnetism can cancel the negative effects caused by diamagnetism.

© Jeff Belmonte

domains. For that, we need to get right down into the atom. Let's take an iron atom, for example. Electrons circle the nucleus of an atom in cloud-like orbitals, commonly described as rigid shells (although in actuality, their motion is much more random). Each atom has a particular number of shells depending on how many protons and neutrons it has, while within each shell electrons orbit in pairs. Electrons are just like tiny magnets, each one having its own north and south pole. In their pairs, the electrons cancel out with one another so there is no overall magnetic force. In an atom such as that of iron, however, this is not the case. There are four electrons that are unpaired, which exert a magnetic force on the atom. When all the atoms are combined together and aligned, as we explained when talking about domains, the iron itself becomes magnetised and attracts other magnetic objects.

So we've snapped our magnet, broken it into chunks and subsequently examined the atoms of those tiny chunks. But is there a way that we can we go even deeper? The answer to that is yes and no, as we delve into the unknown areas of quantum physics. The underlying principle of magnetism is that in the universe there are four fundamental forces of nature; these consist of gravity, electromagnetism, the weak force and the strong force. Even smaller than atoms and electrons are fundamental particles known as quarks and leptons, which are responsible for these forces. Any force – such as gravity, magnetism, nuclear decay or friction – results from these fundamental life forces. A force such as magnetism at this level is 'thrown' between particles on what are known as force carrier particles, pushing or pulling the other particles around accordingly.

Unfortunately, at this level magnetism goes into the realm of theoretical physics, entering areas of quantum physics that have not been explored in as much detail as particle physics – at least for the time being. For now, this standard model of physics explains magnetism to a level that can only be furthered when we advance our understanding of quantum physics some time in the future.

Earth's magnetic field

It's best to imagine the Earth as a bar magnet 12,400 miles (20,000km) long. The magnetic fields move around us like they would in a fridge magnet, but they also protect us from the universe. Compass needles always point to a magnet's south pole, so the Earth's geographical north pole is actually magnetically south.

Alaska
Siberia
Canada
1200
1300 A.D.
1100
2000
1400
Russia
1900
1000
500
1800
400
800
300
Greenland

Key: ——▶ wandering path of the magnetic north
⊕ rotational north pole

Magnetic movement
The North Magnetic Pole moves up to 1mm a second because of changes in the core. In 2005 it was pinpointed just off Ellesmere Island in Canada, but is now moving towards Russia.

Iron filings

Filings
By scattering tiny iron filings around a magnet on paper, it is possible to visibly see the magnetic field in action.

Field
By tapping the paper, the magnetic filings will align along the magnetic field lines of the magnet that run from its north to south pole.

Effect
Charged particles from the Sun are deflected by the Earth's magnetic field, with some trapped in bands of radiation.

Tilt
The central 'bar magnet' of the Earth's magnetic field, the dipole, is tilted approximately 11° off the Earth's axis.

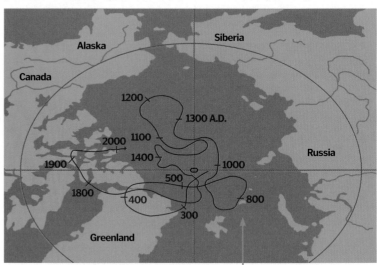

North Magnetic Pole

N

South Magnetic Pole

S

Cause
The magnetic field of any planet, including Earth, is the result of the circulation of electrically conducting material in the core, in our case molten iron.

South is north
Magnetic fields always run from north to south, so when a compass points to the North Pole it is actually indicating southern magnetic polarity.

Off-centred
The magnetic north and south poles do not draw a straight line through the centre of the Earth. In fact, they miss by several hundred miles.

Electromagnets

One of the four fundamental forces in the universe, electromagnetism results from the interaction of electrically charged particles. Physicist Michael Faraday deduced that a changing magnetic field produces an electric field, while James Maxwell discovered that the reverse is also true: a changing electric field produces a magnetic field. This is the basis of how an electromagnet works.

Electric fields
A wire wrapped around a magnetic core, such as iron, produces electric fields when a current runs through it, in turn creating a magnetic field.

Coil
The number of coils will increase the strength of the electromagnet because there is more current flowing in one direction, magnifying the force proportionally.

Core
As discussed on the previous page, the domains within the core are unaligned until a magnetic field is introduced, created by a moving current in the coil.

Magnetic field
The wire's magnetic field combines with the field of the core to produce a stronger field, with a larger current aligning more domains and increasing its strength.

Magnets in your home

You'll be surprised at the number of magnets that are under your roof...

Doorbell
For a buzzer-style doorbell, pressing the button moves and releases a contact from an electromagnet to break and complete a circuit. A chiming doorbell, meanwhile, moves an iron core through an electromagnet coil and back when the button is pressed, hitting two chime bars in sequence.

Microwave
Inside a microwave oven is a magnetron, which contains magnets. Strong permanent magnets are mounted inside this tube. When electricity passes through the magnetron, the resultant electric and magnetic fields produce electromagnetic energy in the form of microwaves.

Vacuum cleaner
Electromagnetism is used here to produce the desired effect. A magnetically conducting material is inside the motor of the vacuum cleaner. When an electric current is introduced to a coil around the material, repulsive forces make the motor spin. The material loses its magnetism when the vacuum is turned off.

Computer
Like credit cards, the storage disks inside computers are coated with bits of iron. By changing the magnetic orientation of the iron, a pattern can be created to store a particular set of data. This pattern can be read by the computer and replicate the data on screen. The monitor itself uses magnets in the same way as an old cathode ray tube TV (see television).

Speakers
Using electromagnetism, most speakers contain a stationary magnet and a wire coil inside a semi-rigid membrane. When a current runs through the coil, the membrane rotates in and out because of the force between coil and magnet, creating vibrations that produce sound. Phone speakers use this same mechanism, only smaller.

Television
Most modern LCD or plasma TVs don't use magnets. However, older models use a cathode ray tube to fire electrons against the back of the screen. Coated in phosphor, parts of the screen glow when struck by the beam. Coils produce magnetic fields that move the beams horizontally and vertically to produce the desired picture.

Credit card
All credit cards have a black strip on them, known as a magnetic stripe. Inside, minuscule bits of iron are held in a plastic film. These can be magnetised in a north or south direction to store important data. When you swipe the card through a machine, the line of tiny magnets is read and information is obtained.

EMP
An Electromagnetic Pulse (EMP) works by overwhelming electric circuits with an intense electromagnetic field. A non-nuclear EMP explodes a metal cylinder full of explosives inside a coil of wire, pushing out magnetic and electric fields that fry electric circuits. A nuclear EMP would explode a nuclear bomb in the atmosphere. The resultant gamma radiation would take in positive air molecules but push out negative electrons, sending a large electromagnetic field in all directions. A 10-megaton device detonated 200 miles (320km) above the centre of the United States would destroy every electronic device in the country but leave structures and life intact.

Buildings would survive; electronics wouldn't

Solar blackout 2013?

Could the geomagnetic storm of 1859 be repeated?

In 1859, a great geomagnetic storm wiped out transmission cables and set fire to telegraph offices when the Sun went through a period of intense activity. Scientists at NASA have warned that a similar storm could occur in May 2013, when many more modern electrical components could be affected. The Sun's magnetic cycle peaks every 22 years, while every 11 years the number of solar flares hits a maximum. In May 2013 these events could combine and produce huge levels of radiation, potentially wiping out electric power on Earth for hours – or days.

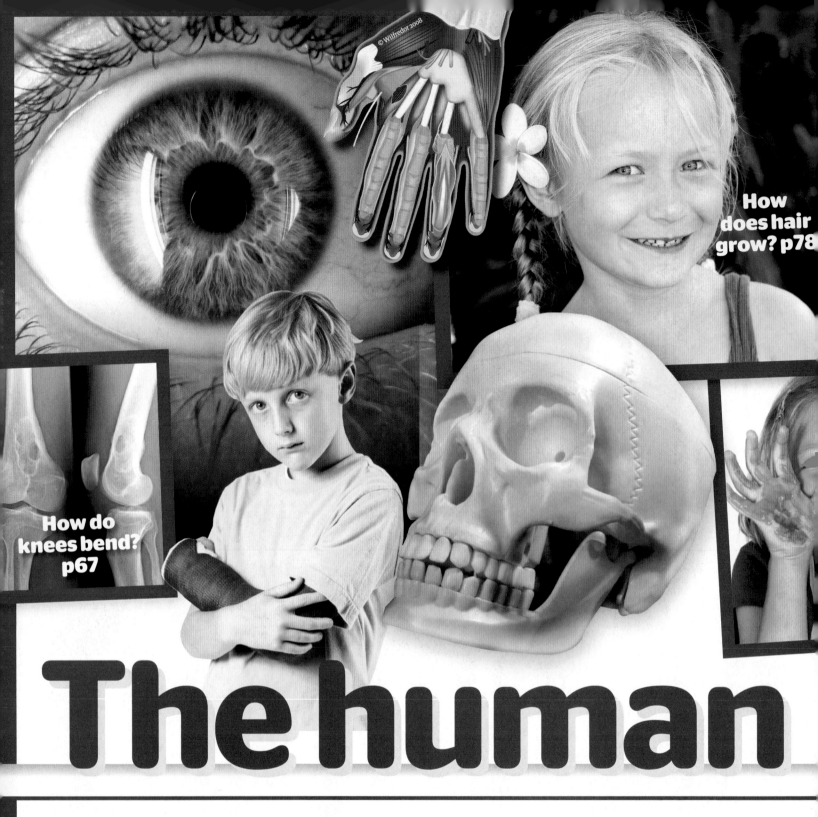

How does hair grow? p78

How do knees bend? p67

The human

050

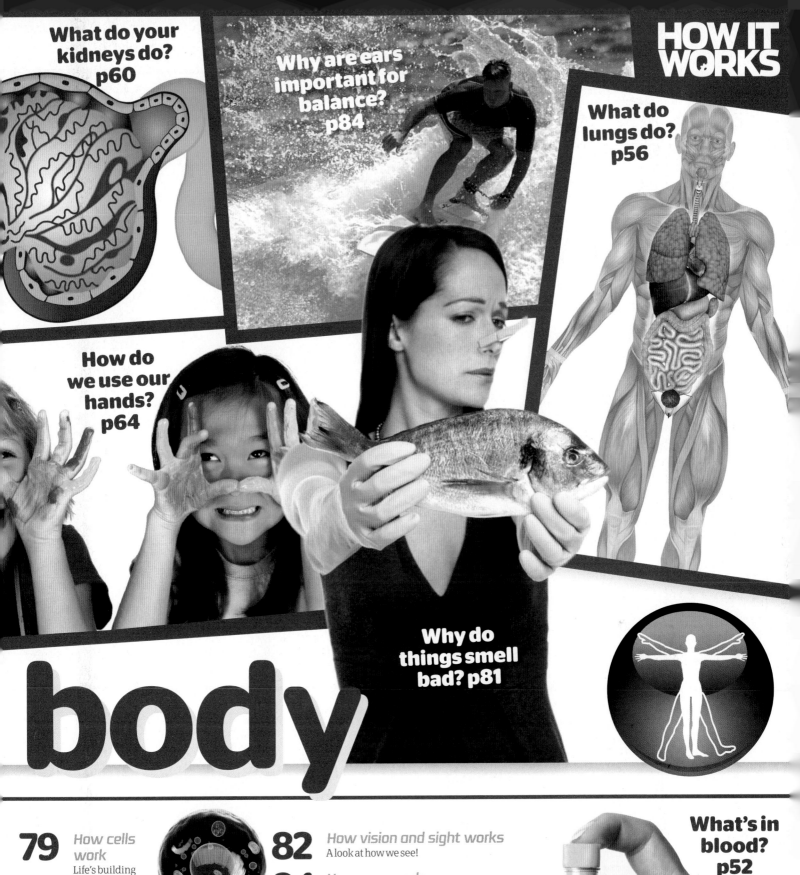

What do your kidneys do? p60

Why are ears important for balance? p84

What do lungs do? p56

How do we use our hands? p64

Why do things smell bad? p81

body

What's in blood? p52

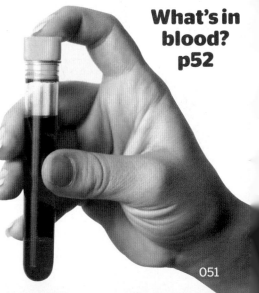

How your blood works

The science behind the miraculous fluid that feeds, heals and fights for your life

White blood cells
White blood cells, or leukocytes, are the immune system's best weapon, searching out and destroying bacteria and producing antibodies against viruses. There are five different types of white blood cells, all with distinct functions.

Platelet
When activated, these sticky cell fragments are essential to the clotting process. Platelets adhere to a wound opening to stem the flow of blood, then they team with a protein called fibrinogen to weave tiny threads that trap blood cells.

Red blood cell
Known as erythrocytes, red blood cells are the body's delivery service, shuttling oxygen from the lungs to living cells throughout the body and returning carbon dioxide as waste.

Blood vessel wall
Arteries and veins are composed of three tissue layers, a combination of elastic tissue, connective tissue and smooth muscle fibres that contract under signals from the sympathetic nervous system.

Granulocyte
The most numerous type of white blood cell, granulocytes patrol the bloodstream destroying invading bacteria by engulfing and digesting them, often dying in the process.

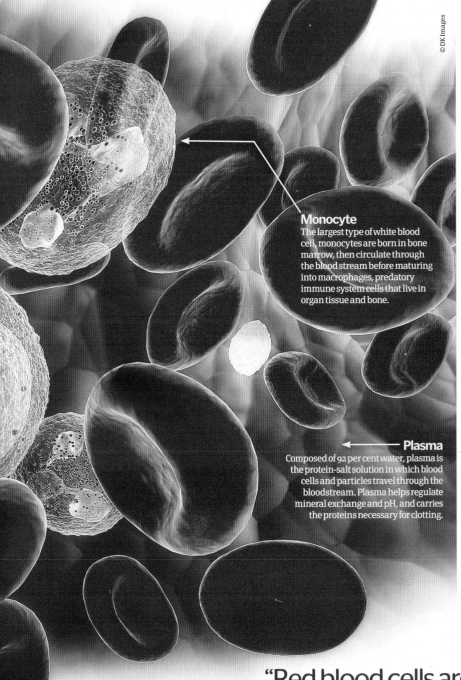

© DK Images

Monocyte
The largest type of white blood cell, monocytes are born in bone marrow, then circulate through the blood stream before maturing into macrophages, predatory immune system cells that live in organ tissue and bone.

Plasma
Composed of 92 per cent water, plasma is the protein-salt solution in which blood cells and particles travel through the bloodstream. Plasma helps regulate mineral exchange and pH, and carries the proteins necessary for clotting.

Components of blood

Blood is a mix of solids and liquids, a blend of highly specialised cells and particles suspended in a protein-rich fluid called plasma. Red blood cells dominate the mix, carrying oxygen to living tissue and returning carbon dioxide to the lungs. For every 600 red blood cells, there is a single white blood cell, of which there are five different kinds. Cell fragments called platelets use their irregular surface to cling to vessel walls and initiate the clotting process.

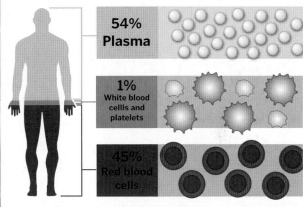

54% Plasma

1% White blood cells and platelets

45% Red blood cells

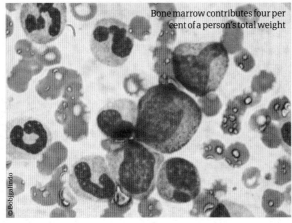

Bone marrow contributes four per cent of a person's total weight

© Bobjgalindo

"Red blood cells are so numerous because they perform the most essential function of blood"

Blood is the river of life. It feeds oxygen and essential nutrients to living cells and carries away waste. It transports the foot soldiers of the immune system, white blood cells, which seek out and destroy invading bacteria and parasites. And it speeds platelets to the site of injury or tissue damage, triggering the body's miraculous process of self-repair.

Blood looks like a thick, homogenous fluid, but it's more like a watery current of plasma – a straw-coloured, protein-rich fluid – carrying billions of microscopic solids consisting of red blood cells, white blood cells and cell fragments called platelets. The distribution is far from equal. Over half of blood is plasma, 45 per cent is red blood cells and a tiny fragment, less than one per cent, is composed of white blood cells and platelets.

Red blood cells are so numerous because they perform the most essential function of blood, which is to deliver oxygen to every cell in the body and carry away carbon dioxide. As an adult, all of your red blood cells are produced in red bone marrow, the spongy tissue in the bulbous ends of long bones and at the centre of flat bones like hips and ribs. In the marrow, red blood cells start out as undifferentiated stem cells called hemocytoblasts. If the body detects a minuscule drop in oxygen carrying capacity, a hormone is released from the kidneys that triggers the stem cells to become red blood cells. Because red blood cells only live 120 days, the supply must be continuously replenished; roughly 2 million red blood cells are born every second.

A mature red blood cell has no nucleus. The nucleus is spit out during the final stages of the cell's two-day development before taking on the shape of a concave, doughnut-like disc. Like all cells, red blood cells are mostly water, but 97 per cent of their solid matter is haemoglobin, a complex protein that carries four atoms of iron. Those iron atoms have ▶

Life cycle of red blood cells

Every second, roughly 2 million red blood cells decay and die. The body is keenly sensitive to blood hypoxia – reduced oxygen carrying capacity – and triggers the kidney to release a hormone called erythropoietin. The hormone stimulates the production of more red blood cells in bone marrow. Red blood cells enter the bloodstream and circulate for 120 days before they begin to degenerate and are swallowed up by roving macrophages in the liver, spleen and lymph nodes. The macrophages extract iron from the haemoglobin in the red blood cells and release it back into the bloodstream, where it binds to a protein that carries it back to the bone marrow, ready to be recycled in fresh red blood cells.

1. Born in the bones
When the body detects a low oxygen carrying capacity, hormones released from the kidney trigger the production of new red blood cells inside red bone marrow.

2. One life to live
Mature red blood cells, also known as erythrocytes, are stripped of their nucleus in the final stages of development, meaning they can't divide to replicate.

6. Reuse and recycle
As for the globin and other cellular membranes, everything is converted back into basic amino acids, some of which will be used to create more red blood cells.

Waste product of blood cell

Waste excreted from body

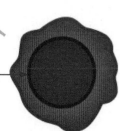

5. Iron ions
In the belly of Kupffer cells, haemoglobin molecules are split into heme and globin. Heme is broken down further into bile and iron ions, some of which are carried back and stored in bone marrow.

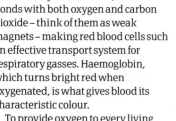

4. Ingestion
Specialised white blood cells in the liver and spleen called Kupffer cells prey on dying red blood cells, ingesting them whole and breaking them down into reusable components.

3. In circulation
Red blood cells pass from the bone marrow into the bloodstream, where they circulate for around 120 days.

▶ the ability to form loose, reversible bonds with both oxygen and carbon dioxide – think of them as weak magnets – making red blood cells such an effective transport system for respiratory gasses. Haemoglobin, which turns bright red when oxygenated, is what gives blood its characteristic colour.

To provide oxygen to every living cell, red blood cells must be pumped through the body's circulatory system. The right side of the heart pumps CO_2-heavy blood into the lungs, where it releases its waste gasses and picks up oxygen. The left side of the heart then pumps the freshly oxygenated blood out into the body through a system of arteries and capillaries, some as narrow as a single cell. As the red blood

cells release their oxygen, they pick up carbon dioxide molecules, then course through the veins back toward the heart, where they are pumped back into the lungs to 'exhale' the excess CO_2 and collect some more precious O_2.

White blood cells are greatly outnumbered by red blood cells, but they are critical to the function of the immune system. Most white blood cells are also produced in red bone marrow, but white blood cells – unlike red blood cells – come in five different varieties, each with its own specialised immune function. The first three varieties, collectively called granulocytes, engulf and digest bacteria and parasites, and play a role in allergic reactions. Lymphocytes, another type of white blood cell, produce anti-bodies that

build up our immunity to repeat intruders. And monocytes, the largest of the white blood cells, enter organ tissue and become macrophages, microbes that ingest bad bacteria and help break down dead red blood cells into reusable parts.

Platelets aren't cells at all, but fragments of much larger stem cells found in bone marrow. In their resting state, they look like smooth oval plates, but when activated to form a clot they take on an irregular form with many protruding arms called pseudopods. This shape helps them stick to blood vessel walls and to each other, forming a physical barrier around wound sites. With the help of proteins and clotting factors found in plasma, platelets weave a mesh of fibrin that stems blood

loss and triggers the formation of new collagen and skin cells.

But even these three functions of blood – oxygen supplier, immune system defender and wound healer – only begin to scratch the surface of the critical role of blood in each and every bodily process. When blood circulates through the small intestine, it absorbs sugars from digested food, which are transported to the liver to be stored as energy. When blood passes through the kidneys, it is scrubbed of excess urea and salts, waste that will leave the body as urine. The proteins in plasma transport vitamins, hormones, enzymes, sugar and electrolytes. Pause for a second to listen to your pumping heart and be thankful for the river of life coursing through your veins. ❀

Haemophilia

This rare genetic blood disorder severely inhibits the clotting mechanism of blood, causing excessive bleeding, internal bruising and joint problems. Platelets are essential to the clotting and healing process, producing threads of fibrin with help from proteins in the bloodstream called clotting factors. People who suffer from haemophilia – almost exclusively males – are missing one of those clotting factors, making it difficult to seal off blood vessels after even minor injuries.

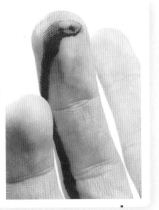

Thalassemia

Another rare blood disorder affecting 100,000 newborns worldwide each year, thalassemia inhibits the production of haemoglobin, leading to severe anaemia. People who are born with the most serious form of the disease, also called Cooley's anaemia, suffer from enlarged hearts, livers and spleens, and brittle bones. The most effective treatment is frequent blood transfusions, although a few lucky patients have been cured through bone marrow transplants from perfectly matching donors.

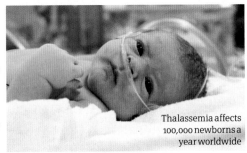

Thalassemia affects 100,000 newborns a year worldwide

Sickle cell anaemia

Anaemia is the name for any blood disorder that results in a dangerously low red blood cell count. In sickle cell anaemia, which afflicts one out of every 625 children of African descent, red blood cells elongate into a sickle shape after releasing their oxygen. The sickle-shaped cells die prematurely, leading to anaemia, or sometimes lodge in blood vessels, causing terrible pain and even organ damage. Interestingly, people who carry only one gene for sickle cell anaemia are immune to malaria.

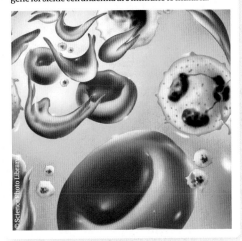

©Science Photo Library

Blood disorders

Blood is a delicate balancing act, with the body constantly regulating oxygen flow, iron content and clotting ability. Unfortunately, there are several genetic conditions and chronic illnesses that can disturb the balance, sometimes with deadly consequences.

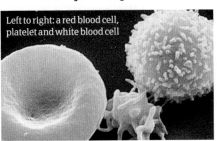

Left to right: a red blood cell, platelet and white blood cell

Hemochromatosis

One of the most common genetic blood disorders, hemochromatosis is the medical term for "iron overload," in which your body absorbs and stores too much iron from food. Severity varies wildly, and many people experience few symptoms, but others suffer serious liver damage or scarring (cirrhosis), irregular heartbeat, diabetes and even heart failure. Symptoms can be aggravated by taking too much vitamin C.

Deep vein thrombosis

Thrombosis is the medical term for any blood clot that is large enough to block a blood vessel. When a blood clot forms in the large, deep veins of the upper thigh, it's called deep vein thrombosis. If such a clot breaks free, it can circulate through the bloodstream, pass through the heart and become lodged in arteries in the lung, causing a pulmonary embolism. Such a blockage can severely damage portions of the lungs, and multiple embolisms can even be fatal.

Blood and healing

More than a one-trick pony, your blood is a vital cog in the healing process

Think of blood as the body's emergency response team to an injury. Platelets emit signals that encourage blood vessels to contract, stemming blood loss. The platelets then collect around the wound, reacting with a protein in plasma to form fibrin, a tissue that weaves into a mesh. Blood flow returns and white blood cells begin their hunt for bacteria. Fibroblasts create beds of fresh collagen and capillaries to fuel skin cell growth. The scab begins to contract, pulling the growing skin cells closer together until damaged tissue is replaced.

STAGE 1

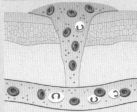

INJURY
When the skin surface is cut, torn or scraped deeply enough, blood seeps from broken blood vessels to fill the wound. To stem the flow of bleeding, the blood vessels around the wound constrict.

STAGE 2

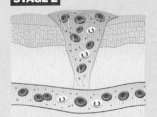

HAEMOSTASIS
Activated platelets aggregate around the surface of the wound, stimulating vasoconstriction. Platelets react with a protein in plasma to form fibrin, a web-like mesh of stringy tissue.

STAGE 3

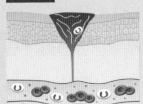

INFLAMMATORY STAGE
Once the wound is capped with a drying clot, blood vessels open up again, releasing plasma and white blood cells into the damaged tissue. Macrophages digest harmful bacteria and dead cells.

STAGE 4

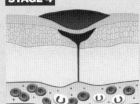

PROLIFERATIVE STAGE
Fibroblasts lay fresh layers of collagen inside the wound and capillaries begin to supply blood for the forming of new skin cells. Fibrin strands and collagen pull the sides of the wound together.

Human respiration

Respiration is crucial to an organism's survival. The process of respiration is the transportation of oxygen from the air that surrounds us into the tissue cells of our body so that energy can be broken down

The primary organs used for respiration in humans are the lungs. Humans have two lungs, with the left lung being divided into two lobes and the right into three. The lungs have between 300–500 million alveoli, which is where gas exchange occurs.

Respiration of oxygen breaks into four main stages: ventilation, pulmonary gas exchange, gas transportation and peripheral gas exchange. Each stage is crucial in getting oxygen to the body's tissue, and removing carbon dioxide. Ventilation and gas transportation need energy to occur, as the diaphragm and the heart are used to facilitate these actions whereas gas exchanging is passive. As air is drawn into the lungs at a rate of between 10-20 breaths per minute while resting, through either your mouth or nose by diaphragm contraction, and travels through the pharynx, then the larynx, down the trachea, and into one of the two main bronchial tubes. Mucus and cilia keep the lungs clean by catching dirt particles and sweeping them up the trachea.

When air reaches the lungs, oxygen is diffused into the bloodstream through the alveoli and carbon dioxide is diffused from the blood into the lungs to be exhaled. Diffusion of gases occurs because of differing pressures in the lungs and blood. This is also the same when oxygen diffuses into tissue around the body. When blood has been oxygenated by the lungs, it is transferred around the body to where it is most needed in the bloodstream. If the body is exercising, breathing rate increases and consequently so does heart rate

to ensure that oxygen reaches tissues that need it. Oxygen is then used to break down glucose to provide energy for the body. This happens in the mitochondria of cells. Carbon dioxide is one of the waste products of this, which is why we get a build up of this gas in our body that needs to be transported back into the lungs to be exhaled.

The body can also respire anaerobically, but this produces far less energy and instead of producing CO_2 as a byproduct, lactic acid is produced. The body then takes a time to break this down after exertion has finished as the body has a so-called oxygen debt. ✿

How our lungs work

Lungs are the major respiratory organ in humans

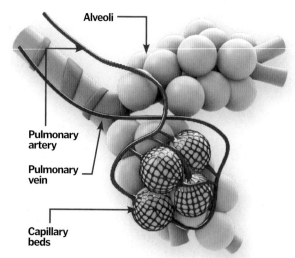

Alveoli

Pulmonary artery

Pulmonary vein

Capillary beds

Nasal passage/oral cavity
These areas are where air enters into the body so that oxygen can be transported into and around the body to where it's needed. Carbon dioxide also exits through these areas.

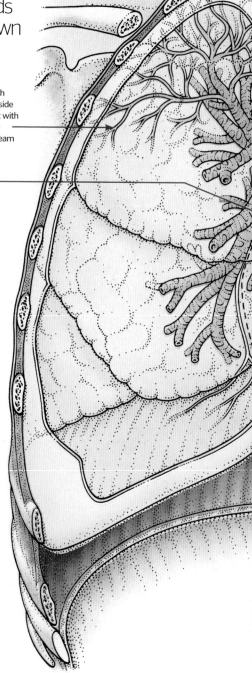

Alveoli
The alveoli are tiny little sacs which are situated at the end of tubes inside the lungs and are in direct contact with blood. Oxygen and carbon dioxide transfer to and from the blood stream through the alveoli.

Bronchial tubes
These tubes lead to either the left or the right lung. Air passes through these tubes into the lungs, where they pass through progressively smaller and smaller tubes until they reach the alveoli.

How do we breathe?

The intake of oxygen into the body is complex

Breathing is not something that we have to think about, and indeed is controlled by muscle contractions in our body. Breathing is controlled by the diaphragm, which contracts and expands on a regular, constant basis. When it contracts, the diaphragm pulls air into the lungs by a vacuum-like effect. The lungs expand to fill the enlarged chest cavity and air is pulled right through the maze of tubes that make up the lungs to the alveoli at the ends, which are the final branching. The chest will be seen to rise because of this lung expansion. Alveoli are surrounded by blood vessels, and oxygen and carbon dioxide are then interchanged at this point between the lungs and the blood. Carbon dioxide removed from the blood stream and air that was breathed in but not used is then expelled from the lungs by diaphragm expansion. Lungs deflate back to a reduced size when breathing out.

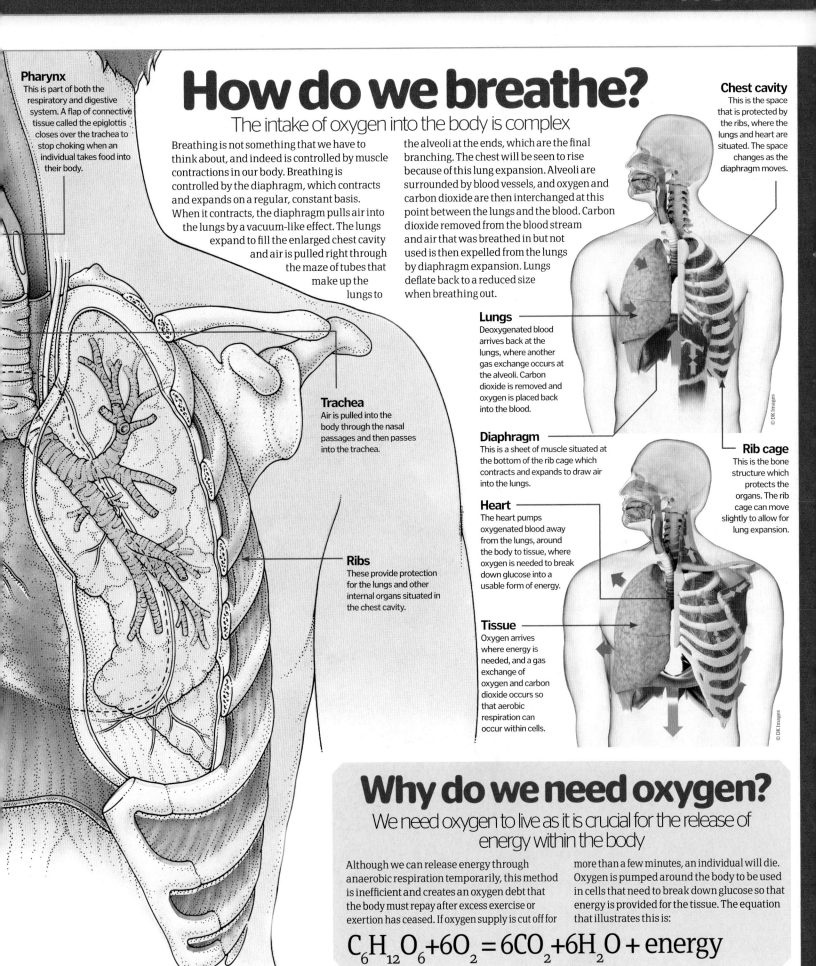

Pharynx
This is part of both the respiratory and digestive system. A flap of connective tissue called the epiglottis closes over the trachea to stop choking when an individual takes food into their body.

Trachea
Air is pulled into the body through the nasal passages and then passes into the trachea.

Ribs
These provide protection for the lungs and other internal organs situated in the chest cavity.

Chest cavity
This is the space that is protected by the ribs, where the lungs and heart are situated. The space changes as the diaphragm moves.

Lungs
Deoxygenated blood arrives back at the lungs, where another gas exchange occurs at the alveoli. Carbon dioxide is removed and oxygen is placed back into the blood.

Diaphragm
This is a sheet of muscle situated at the bottom of the rib cage which contracts and expands to draw air into the lungs.

Heart
The heart pumps oxygenated blood away from the lungs, around the body to tissue, where oxygen is needed to break down glucose into a usable form of energy.

Tissue
Oxygen arrives where energy is needed, and a gas exchange of oxygen and carbon dioxide occurs so that aerobic respiration can occur within cells.

Rib cage
This is the bone structure which protects the organs. The rib cage can move slightly to allow for lung expansion.

© DK Images

© DK Images

Why do we need oxygen?

We need oxygen to live as it is crucial for the release of energy within the body

Although we can release energy through anaerobic respiration temporarily, this method is inefficient and creates an oxygen debt that the body must repay after excess exercise or exertion has ceased. If oxygen supply is cut off for more than a few minutes, an individual will die. Oxygen is pumped around the body to be used in cells that need to break down glucose so that energy is provided for the tissue. The equation that illustrates this is:

$$C_6H_{12}O_6 + 6O_2 = 6CO_2 + 6H_2O + energy$$

A look inside your heart

Your heart is a turbocharged double-pumping muscle that beats more than 40 million times every year

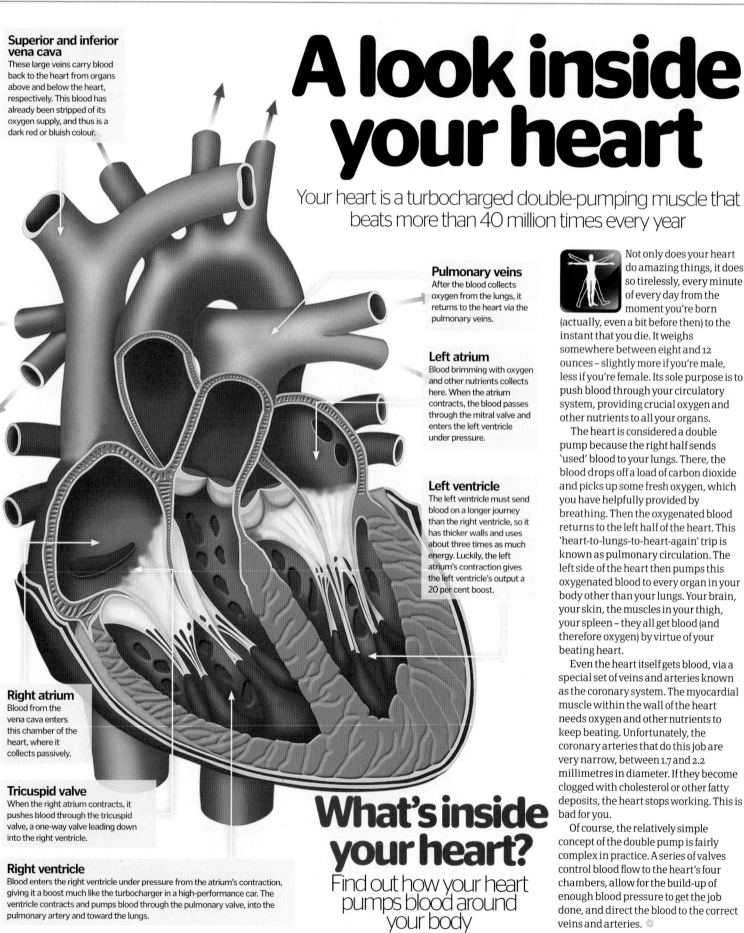

Superior and inferior vena cava
These large veins carry blood back to the heart from organs above and below the heart, respectively. This blood has already been stripped of its oxygen supply, and thus is a dark red or bluish colour.

Pulmonary veins
After the blood collects oxygen from the lungs, it returns to the heart via the pulmonary veins.

Left atrium
Blood brimming with oxygen and other nutrients collects here. When the atrium contracts, the blood passes through the mitral valve and enters the left ventricle under pressure.

Left ventricle
The left ventricle must send blood on a longer journey than the right ventricle, so it has thicker walls and uses about three times as much energy. Luckily, the left atrium's contraction gives the left ventricle's output a 20 per cent boost.

Right atrium
Blood from the vena cava enters this chamber of the heart, where it collects passively.

Tricuspid valve
When the right atrium contracts, it pushes blood through the tricuspid valve, a one-way valve leading down into the right ventricle.

Right ventricle
Blood enters the right ventricle under pressure from the atrium's contraction, giving it a boost much like the turbocharger in a high-performance car. The ventricle contracts and pumps blood through the pulmonary valve, into the pulmonary artery and toward the lungs.

What's inside your heart?
Find out how your heart pumps blood around your body

Not only does your heart do amazing things, it does so tirelessly, every minute of every day from the moment you're born (actually, even a bit before then) to the instant that you die. It weighs somewhere between eight and 12 ounces – slightly more if you're male, less if you're female. Its sole purpose is to push blood through your circulatory system, providing crucial oxygen and other nutrients to all your organs.

The heart is considered a double pump because the right half sends 'used' blood to your lungs. There, the blood drops off a load of carbon dioxide and picks up some fresh oxygen, which you have helpfully provided by breathing. Then the oxygenated blood returns to the left half of the heart. This 'heart-to-lungs-to-heart-again' trip is known as pulmonary circulation. The left side of the heart then pumps this oxygenated blood to every organ in your body other than your lungs. Your brain, your skin, the muscles in your thigh, your spleen – they all get blood (and therefore oxygen) by virtue of your beating heart.

Even the heart itself gets blood, via a special set of veins and arteries known as the coronary system. The myocardial muscle within the wall of the heart needs oxygen and other nutrients to keep beating. Unfortunately, the coronary arteries that do this job are very narrow, between 1.7 and 2.2 millimetres in diameter. If they become clogged with cholesterol or other fatty deposits, the heart stops working. This is bad for you.

Of course, the relatively simple concept of the double pump is fairly complex in practice. A series of valves control blood flow to the heart's four chambers, allow for the build-up of enough blood pressure to get the job done, and direct the blood to the correct veins and arteries. ✿

How do allergies affect us?

Hay fever is seen to be becoming more common, but how and why do allergens cause our bodies to react?

Allergic reactions occur in response to specific environmental stimuli (called allergens), such as pollen, dust, bee stings and food, and the reaction displayed in individuals is normally due to an immune system disorder. Most allergies are mild, but some can be severe and even fatal depending on the reaction and treatment received following exposure to the allergen.

Allergies are actually caused by the immune system being hypersensitive to elements within the environment, rather than – as many people suppose – it being under active. Large numbers of antibodies are produced in response to the allergen, which then cause an over-reaction in the immune system when the individual next comes into contact with the allergen – so creating the allergic reaction. ⚙

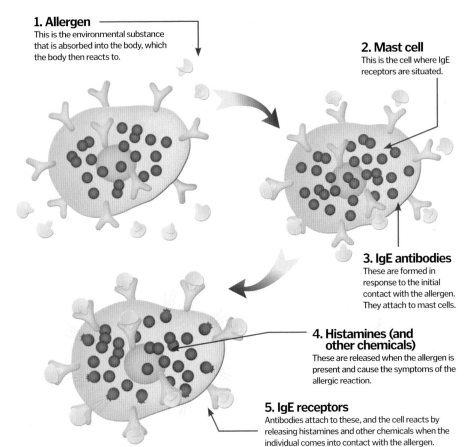

1. Allergen
This is the environmental substance that is absorbed into the body, which the body then reacts to.

2. Mast cell
This is the cell where IgE receptors are situated.

3. IgE antibodies
These are formed in response to the initial contact with the allergen. They attach to mast cells.

4. Histamines (and other chemicals)
These are released when the allergen is present and cause the symptoms of the allergic reaction.

5. IgE receptors
Antibodies attach to these, and the cell reacts by releasing histamines and other chemicals when the individual comes into contact with the allergen.

Asthma attacks

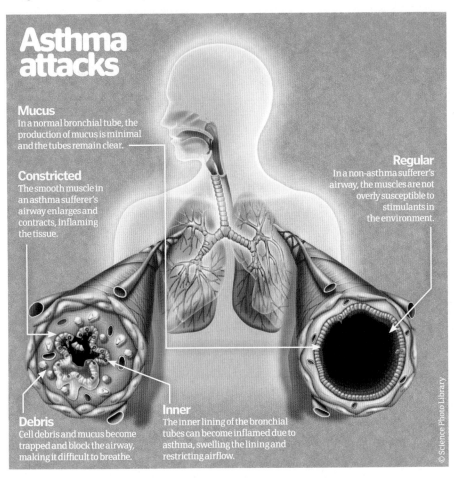

Mucus
In a normal bronchial tube, the production of mucus is minimal and the tubes remain clear.

Constricted
The smooth muscle in an asthma sufferer's airway enlarges and contracts, inflaming the tissue.

Regular
In a non-asthma sufferer's airway, the muscles are not overly susceptible to stimulants in the environment.

Debris
Cell debris and mucus become trapped and block the airway, making it difficult to breathe.

Inner
The inner lining of the bronchial tubes can become inflamed due to asthma, swelling the lining and restricting airflow.

© Science Photo Library

Asthma

Why does this disease make it difficult for sufferers to breathe?

Asthma is caused by the sudden contraction of smooth muscles in the airways of the body. This is normally due to unusually viscous mucus being produced in abundance in the bronchial mucous glands. One of the primary causes of asthma is the narrowing of bronchial tubes because of inflammation. Asthmatics are overly sensitive (hyperreactive) to stimulants in the environment that can cause the bronchial muscles and tubes to contract. Tubes become irritated and swollen, in turn producing excess mucus and blocking the flow of air. While asthma is often hereditary, it can also be acquired through prolonged exposure to substances such as solder and sulphite.

In severe asthma attacks, the accumulation of additional mucus from the bronchial tree can also inhibit airflow within the airways, making it more difficult for an asthma sufferer to breathe. There are several things that can trigger an asthma attack, including exercising and traffic fumes. To overcome an attack, an asthma inhaler can be used to relax the muscles and widen the bronchial tubes so that normal breathing can be resumed. ⚙

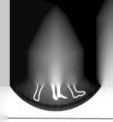

Kidney function

How do your kidneys filter waste from the blood to keep you alive?

Kidneys are bean-shaped organs situated halfway down the back just under the ribcage, one on each side of the body, and weigh between 115 and 170 grams each, dependent on the individual's sex and size. The left kidney is commonly a little larger than the right and due to the effectiveness of these organs, individuals born with only one kidney can survive with little or no adverse health problems. Indeed, the body can operate normally with a 30-40 per cent decline in kidney function. This decline in function would rarely even be noticeable and shows just how effective the kidneys are at filtering out waste products as well as maintaining mineral levels and blood pressure throughout the body. The kidneys manage to control all of this by working with other organs and glands across the body such as the hypothalamus, which helps the kidneys determine and control water levels in the body.

Each day the kidneys will filter between 150 and 180 litres of blood, but only pass around two litres of waste down the ureters to the bladder for excretion. This waste product is primarily urea – a byproduct of protein being broken down for energy – and water, and it's more commonly known as 'urine'. The kidneys filter the blood by passing it through a small filtering unit called a nephron. Each kidney has around a million of these, which are made up of a number of small blood capillaries, called glomerulus, and a urine-collecting tube called the renal tubule. The glomerulus sift the normal cells and proteins from the blood and then move the waste products into the renal tubule, which transports urine down into the bladder through the ureters.

Alongside this filtering process, the kidneys also release three crucial hormones (known as erythropoietin, renin and calcitriol) which encourage red blood cell production, aid regulation of blood pressure and aid bone development and mineral balance respectively.

Inside your kidney

As blood enters the kidneys, it is passed through a nephron, a tiny unit made up of blood capillaries and a waste-transporting tube. These work together to filter the blood, returning clean blood to the heart and lungs for re-oxygenation and recirculation and removing waste to the bladder for excretion.

Renal cortex
This is one of two broad internal sections of the kidney, the other being the renal medulla. The renal tubules are situated here in the protrusions that sit between the pyramids and secure the cortex and medulla together.

Renal artery
This artery supplies the kidney with blood that is to be filtered.

Renal vein
After waste has been removed, the clean blood is passed out of the kidney via the renal vein.

© DK Images

Ureter
The tube that transports the waste products (urine) to the bladder following blood filtration.

Renal pelvis
This funnel-like structure is how urine travels out of the kidney and forms the top part of the ureter, which takes urine down to the bladder.

Renal medulla
The kidney's inner section, where blood is filtered after passing through numerous arterioles. It's split into sections called pyramids and each human kidney will normally have seven of these.

Renal capsule
The kidney's fibrous outer edge, which provides protection for the kidney's internal fibres.

Nephrons – the filtration units of the kidney

Nephrons are the units which filter all blood that passes through the kidneys. There are around a million in each kidney, situated in the renal medulla's pyramid structures. As well as filtering waste, nephrons regulate water and mineral salt by recirculating what is needed and excreting the rest.

Proximal tubule
Links Bowman's capsule and the loop of Henle, and will selectively reabsorb minerals from the filtrate produced by Bowman's capsule.

Collecting duct system
Although not technically part of the nephron, this collects all waste product filtered by the nephrons and facilitates its removal from the kidneys.

Glomerulus
High pressure in the glomerulus, caused by it draining into an arteriole instead of a venule, forces fluids and soluble materials out of the capillary and into Bowman's capsule.

Bowman's capsule
Also known as the glomerular capsule, this filters the fluid that has been expelled from the glomerulus. Resulting filtrate is passed along the nephron and will eventually make up urine.

Distal convoluted tubule
Partly responsible for the regulation of minerals in the blood, linking to the collecting duct system. Unwanted minerals are excreted from the nephron.

Renal artery
This artery supplies the kidney with blood. The blood travels through this, into arterioles as you travel into the kidney, until the blood reaches the glomerulus.

Renal vein
This removes blood that has been filtered from the kidney.

Loop of Henle
The loop of Henle controls the mineral and water concentration levels within the kidney to aid filtration of fluids as necessary. It also controls urine concentration.

Renal tubule
Made up of three parts, the proximal tubule, the loop of Henle and the distal convoluted tubule. They remove waste and reabsorb minerals from the filtrate passed on from Bowman's capsule.

The glomerulus

This group of capillaries is the first step of filtration and a crucial aspect of a nephron. As blood enters the kidneys via the renal artery, it is passed down through a series of arterioles which eventually lead to the glomerulus. This is unusual, as instead of draining into a venule (which would lead back to a vein) it drains back into an arteriole, which creates much higher pressure than normally seen in capillaries, which in turn forces soluble materials and fluids out of the capillaries. This process is known as ultrafiltration and is the first step in filtration of the blood. These then pass through the Bowman's capsule (also know as the glomerular capsule) for further filtration.

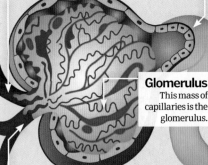

Afferent arteriole
This arteriole supplies the blood to the glomerulus for filtration.

Proximal tubule
Where reabsorption of minerals from the filtrate from Bowman's capsule will occur.

Glomerulus
This mass of capillaries is the glomerulus.

Efferent arteriole
This arteriole is how blood leaves the glomerulus following ultrafiltration.

Bowman's capsule
This is the surrounding capsule that will filter the filtrate produced by the glomerulus.

What is urine and what is it made of?

Urine is made up of a range of organic compounds such as proteins and hormones, inorganic salts and numerous metabolites. These by-products are often rich in nitrogen and need to be removed from the blood stream through urination. The pH-level of urine is typically around neutral (pH7) but varies depending on diet, hydration levels and physical fitness. The colour of urine is also determined by these factors, with dark-yellow urine indicating dehydration and greenish urine being indicative of excessive asparagus consumption.

94% water

6% other organic compounds

How the liver w

The human liver is the ultimate multitasker – it performs many different functions all at the same time without you even asking

 The liver is the largest internal organ in the human body and amazingly has over 500 different functions. In fact, it is the second most complex organ after the brain and is intrinsically involved in almost every aspect of the body's metabolic processes. The liver's main functions are energy production, removal of harmful substances and the production of crucial proteins. These tasks are carried out within liver cells, called hepatocytes, which sit in complex arrangements to maximise efficiency.

The liver is the body's main powerhouse, producing and storing glucose as a key energy source. It is also responsible for breaking down complex fat molecules and building them up into cholesterol and triglycerides, which the body needs but in excess are bad. The liver makes many complex proteins, including clotting factors which are vital in arresting bleeding. Bile, which helps digest fat in the intestines, is produced in the liver and stored in the adjacent gallbladder.

The liver also plays a key role in detoxifying the blood. Waste products, toxins and drugs are processed here into

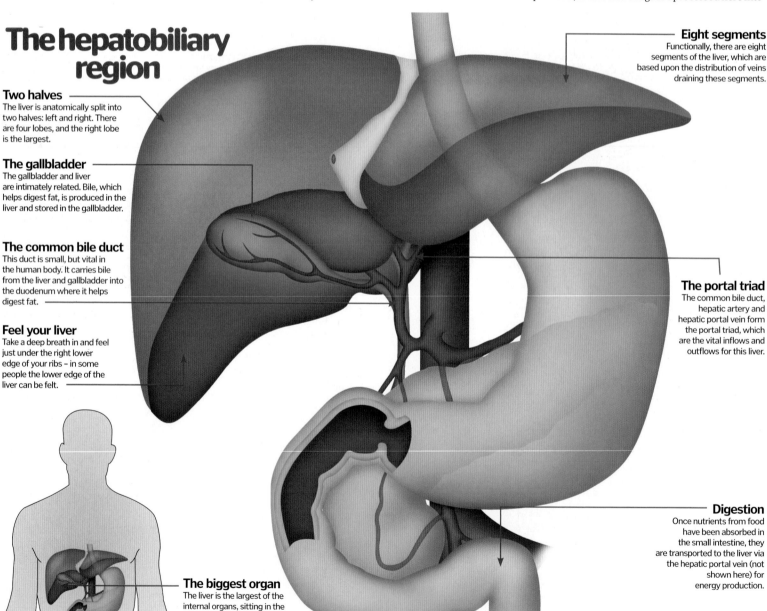

The hepatobiliary region

Two halves
The liver is anatomically split into two halves: left and right. There are four lobes, and the right lobe is the largest.

The gallbladder
The gallbladder and liver are intimately related. Bile, which helps digest fat, is produced in the liver and stored in the gallbladder.

The common bile duct
This duct is small, but vital in the human body. It carries bile from the liver and gallbladder into the duodenum where it helps digest fat.

Feel your liver
Take a deep breath in and feel just under the right lower edge of your ribs – in some people the lower edge of the liver can be felt.

Eight segments
Functionally, there are eight segments of the liver, which are based upon the distribution of veins draining these segments.

The portal triad
The common bile duct, hepatic artery and hepatic portal vein form the portal triad, which are the vital inflows and outflows for this liver.

Digestion
Once nutrients from food have been absorbed in the small intestine, they are transported to the liver via the hepatic portal vein (not shown here) for energy production.

The biggest organ
The liver is the largest of the internal organs, sitting in the right upper quadrant of the abdomen, just under the rib cage and attached to the underside of the diaphragm.

orks

forms which are easier for the rest of the body to use or excrete. The liver also breaks down old bloods cells, produces antibodies to fight infection and recycles hormones such as adrenaline. Numerous essential vitamins and minerals are stored in the liver: vitamins A, D, E and K, iron and copper.

Such a complex organ is also unfortunately prone to diseases. Cancers (most often metastatic from other sources), infections (hepatitis) and cirrhosis (a form of fibrosis often caused by excess alcohol consumption) are just some of those which can affect the liver. ⚙

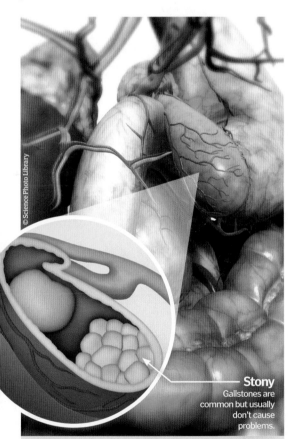

© Science Photo Library

Stony
Gallstones are common but usually don't cause problems.

The gallbladder

Bile, a dark green slimy liquid, is produced in the hepatocytes and helps to digest fat. It is stored in a reservoir which sits on the under-surface of the liver, to be used when needed. This reservoir is called the gallbladder. Stones can form in the gallbladder (gallstones) and are very common, although most don't cause problems. In 2009, just under 60,000 gallbladders were removed from patients within the NHS making it one of the most common operations performed; over 90 per cent of these are removed via keyhole surgery. Most patients do very well without their gallbladder and don't notice any changes at all.

A high demand organ

The liver deals with a massive amount of blood. It is unique because it has two blood supplies. 75 per cent of this comes directly from the intestines (via the hepatic portal vein) which carries nutrients from digestion, which the liver processes and turns into energy. The rest comes from the heart, via the hepatic artery (which branches from the aorta), carrying oxygen which the liver needs to produce this energy. The blood flows in tiny passages inbetween the liver cells where the many metabolic functions occur. The blood then leaves the liver via the hepatic veins to flow into the biggest vein in the body – the inferior vena cava.

Blood vessels
Blood vessels infiltrate liver tissue, supplying lobules with blood.

3. Sinusoids
These blood filled channels are lined by hepatocytes and provide the site of transfer of molecules between blood and liver cells.

4. Kupffer cells
These specialised cells sit within the sinusoids and destroy any bacteria which are contaminating blood.

9. Central vein
Blood from sinusoids, now containing all of its new molecules, flows into central veins which then flow into larger hepatic veins. These drain into the heart via the inferior vena cava.

1. The lobule
This arrangement of blood vessels, bile ducts and hepatocytes form the functional unit of the liver.

2. The hepatocyte
These highly active cells perform all of the liver's key metabolic tasks.

Liver lobules
The functional unit which performs the liver's tasks

The liver is considered a 'chemical factory,' as it forms large complex molecules from smaller ones brought to it from the gut via the blood stream. The functional unit of the liver is the lobule – these are hexagonal-shaped structures comprising of blood vessels and sinusoids. Sinusoids are the specialised areas where blood comes into contact with the hepatocytes, where the liver's biological processes take place.

5. Hepatic artery branch
Blood from here supplies oxygen to hepatocytes and carries metabolic waste which the liver extracts.

6. Bile duct
Bile, which helps digest fat, is made in hepatocytes and secreted into bile ducts. It then flows into the gallbladder for storage before being secreted into the duodenum.

7. Portal vein
This vein carries nutrient-rich blood directly from the intestines, which flows into sinusoids for conversion into energy within hepatocytes.

8. The portal triad
The hepatic artery, portal vein and bile duct are known as the portal triad. These sit at the edges of the liver lobule and are the main entry and exit routes for the liver.

The human hand is an important feature of the human body, which allows individuals to manipulate their surroundings and also to gather large amounts of data from the environment that the individual is situated within. A hand is generally defined as the terminal aspect of the human arm, which consists of prehensile digits, an opposable thumb, and a wrist and palm. Although many other animals have similar structures, only primates and a limited number of other vertebrates can be said to have a 'hand' due to the need for an opposable thumb to be present and the degree of extra articulation that the human hand can achieve. Due to this extra articulation, humans have developed fine motor skills allowing for much increased control in this limb. Consequently we see improved ability to grasp and grip items and development of skills such as writing.

A hand is made up of five digits, the palm and wrist. It consists of 27 bones, tendons, muscles and nerves, with each fingertip of each digit containing numerous nerve endings making the hand a crucial area for gathering information from the environment using one of man's most crucial five senses: touch. Muscles interact together with tendons to allow fingers to bend, straighten, point and, in the case of the thumb, rotate. However, the hand is an area that sees many injuries due to the number of ways we use it, one in ten injuries in A&E being hand related, and there are also several disorders that can affect the hand development in the womb, such as polydactyly, where an individual is born with extra digits, which are often in perfect working order. ✿

The human hand

We take our hands for granted, but they are actually quite complex and have been crucial in our evolution

Bones in the hand

The human hand contains 27 bones, and these divide up into three distinct groups: the carpals, metacarpals and phalanges. These also then further break down into three: the proximal phalanges, intermediate phalanges and distal phalanges. Eight bones are situated in the wrist and these are collectively called the carpals. The metacarpals, which are situated in the palm of the hand account for a further five out of the 27, and each finger has three phalanges, the thumb has two. Intrinsic muscles and tendons interact to control movement of the digits and hand, and attach to extrinsic muscles that extend further up into the arm, which flex the digits.

Distal phalanges
A distal phalange (fingertip) is situated at the end of each finger. Deep flexors attach to this bone to allow for maximum movement.

Intermediate phalanges
This is where the superficial flexors attach via tendons to allow the digit to bend.

Proximal phalanges
Each finger has three phalanges, and this phalange joins the intermediate to its respective metacarpal.

Metacarpals
These five bones make up the palm, and each one aligns with one of the hand's digits.

Carpals
The carpals (scaphoid, triquetral, trapezium, trapezoid, lunate, hamate, capitate and pisiform) sit between the ulna and radius and the metacarpals.

Muscles and other structures

The movements and articulations of the hand and by the digits are controlled by tendons and two muscle groups situated within the hand and wrist. These are the extrinsic and intrinsic muscle groups, so named as the extrinsics are attached to muscles which extend into the forearm, whereas the intrinsics are situated within the hand and wrist. The flexors and extensors, which make up the extrinsic muscles, use either exclusively tendons to attach to digits they control (flexors) or a more complex mix of tendons and intrinsic muscles to operate (extensors). These muscles will contract in order to cause digit movement, and flexors and extensors work in a pair to complement each to straighten and bend digits. The intrinsic muscles are responsible for aiding extrinsic muscle action and other movements in the digits and have three distinct groups; the thenar and hypothenar (referring to the thumb and little finger respectively), the interossei and the lumbrical.

Opposable thumbs

Increased articulation of the thumb has been heralded as a key factor in human evolution. It allowed for increased grip and control, and for tool use to develop among human ancestors as well as other primates. This has later also facilitated major cultural advances, such as writing. Alongside the four other flexible digits, the opposable thumb makes the human hand one of the most dexterous in the world. A thumb can only be classified as opposable when it can be brought opposite to the other digits.

Left handed or right handed?

The most common theory for why some individuals are left handed is that of the 'disappearing twin'. This supposes that the left-handed individual was actually one of a set of twins, but that in the early stages of development the other, right handed, twin died. However, it's been found that dominance of one hand is directly linked with hemisphere dominance in the brain, as in many other paired organs.

Individuals who somehow damage their dominant hand for extended periods of time can actually change to use the other hand, proving the impact and importance of environment and extent to which humans can adapt.

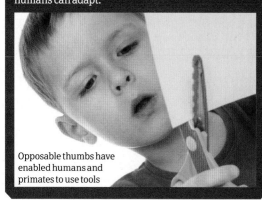

Opposable thumbs have enabled humans and primates to use tools

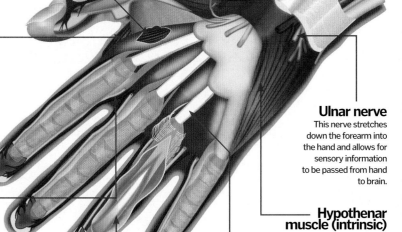

© Wilfredor 2008

Thenar space
Thenar refers to the thumb, and this space is situated between the first digit and thumb. One of the deep flexors (extrinsic muscle) is located in here.

Interossei muscle (intrinsic)
This interossei muscle sits between metacarpal bones and will unite with tendons to allow extension using extrinsic muscles.

Arteries, veins and nerves
These supply fresh oxygenated blood (and take away deoxygenated blood) to hand muscles.

Ulnar nerve
This nerve stretches down the forearm into the hand and allows for sensory information to be passed from hand to brain.

Hypothenar muscle (intrinsic)
Hypothenar refers to the little finger and this muscle group is one of the intrinsic muscles.

Insertion of flexor tendon
This is where the tendon attaches the flexor muscle to the finger bones to allow articulation.

Mid palmar space
Tendons and intrinsic muscles primarily inhabit this space within the hand.

Forearm muscles

Extrinsic muscles are so called because they are primarily situated outside the hand, the body of the muscles situated along the underside or front of the forearm. This body of muscles actually breaks down into two quite distinct groups: the flexors and the extensors. The flexors run alongside the underside of the arm and allow for the bending of the digits, whereas the extensor muscles' main purpose is the reverse this action, to straighten the digits. There are both deep and superficial flexors and extensors, and which are used at any one time depends on the digit to be moved.

© Science photo library

Tendons and intrinsics
These attach the flexor muscles to the phalanges, and facilitate bending. Tendons also interact with the intrinsics and extensors in the wrist, palm and forearm to straighten the digits.

Thenars
The intrinsic group of muscles is used to flex the thumb and control its sideways movement.

Superficial flexors
The other flexor that acts on the digits is the superior flexor, which attaches to the intermediate phalanges.

Deep flexors
The digits have two extrinsic flexors that allow them to bend, the deep flexor and the superficial. The deep flexor attaches to the distal phalanges.

Extensors
Extensors on the back of the forearm straighten the digits. Divided into six sections, their connection to the digits is complex.

How fingernails grow

You can paint them and cut them, but how do fingernails grow?

If you look at your fingernails, you will see a white semi-circle where the nail meets the skin. This is called the 'lunula' and it is the visible part of what is called the nail 'matrix', or the root of the nail. The matrix produces cells which are converted into keratin, a hardened protein. Keratin is the key structural component of nails, as well as hair.

As new cells are produced, older ones are pushed out and they become part of the hard, nail plate at the end of our fingers. These cells are flattened and become compressed, leading to transparency, hence why nails are pinkish in colour (because of the colour of the nail bed beneath). The more cells that are produced, the thicker the nail will become. In some cases, fingernails can become detached through injury or infection, and can take a while to grow back. ✿

Look after your fingernails, you use them more than you think!

Scratching the surface

Nail matrix
The matrix produces the cells, which convert to keratin and form the nail plate.

Nail root
The base of the nail embedded underneath the skin.

Cuticle
The strip of dead skin cells at the base of the fingernail.

Lunula
This crescent-shaped white area is the visible part of the nail matrix.

Nail plate
The nail itself is made of keratin protein and consists of several layers of dead, flattened cells.

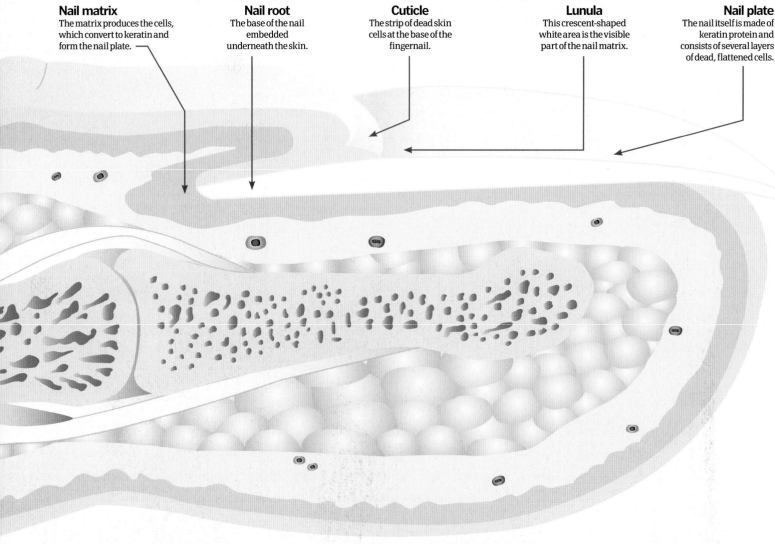

Inside the knee

How do our knee joints allow us to walk and run?

The knee is the largest and also one of the most complex joints in the body, allowing us bipedal humans to move around and get from point A to point B. Three different bones meet at the knee joint and work together to allow for movement and protection. At the top of the knee is the lower part of the thighbone (femur). This rotates on top of the shinbone (tibia) and the kneecap (patella), the latter of which moves in a groove between the femur and tibia. Cartilage within the knee cushions it from shock caused by motion, while ligaments prevent damage occurring to the joint in case of unusual or erratic motion. Muscles running from the hip down to the knee joint are responsible for working the knee joint and allowing our legs to bend, stretch, and ultimately allowing us to walk, run and skip. ✿

Quadriceps
The quadriceps, made up of four muscles, are on the front of the thigh and help to straighten the leg.

Hamstrings
Hamstring muscles running from the thigh to the knee joint are responsible for bending the leg at the knee.

Femur
This bone runs from the hip to the knee joint. It is the thickest and the longest bone in the human body.

©Science Photo Library

The knee structure

How does everything work in tandem to allow for movement?

Cartilage
The point at which the three bones meet is covered in tough, elastic articular cartilage, allowing smooth movement of the joint and absorbing shock.

Patella
This bone slides at the front of the femur and tibia as the knee moves, protecting the knee and giving the muscles leverage.

Menisci
The three bones are separated with two discs of connective tissue called 'menisci', also acting as shock absorbers and enhancing stability.

Tendons
These tough cords of tissue attach muscle to bone, so that the muscles can bend and straighten the leg as required.

Tibia
This bone connects the knee to the ankle, running parallel to the thinner fibula bone.

Synovial membrane
The soft tissue at the centre of the knee joint contains synovial fluid, providing lubrication for the moving knee.

Ligaments
These elastic bands of tissue connect the bones together and provide stability and strength to the knee joint.

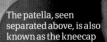

The patella, seen separated above, is also known as the kneecap

How do your feet work?

Feet are immensely complex structures, yet we put huge amounts of pressure on them every day. How do they cope?

The human foot and ankle is crucial for locomotion and is one of the most complex structures of the human body. This intricate structure is made up of no less than 26 bones, 20 muscles, 33 joints – although only 20 are articulated – as well as numerous tendons and ligaments. Tendons connect the muscles to the bones and facilitate movement of the foot, while ligaments hold the tendons in place and help the foot move up and down to initiate walking. Arches in the foot are formed by ligaments, muscles and foot bones and help to distribute weight, as well as making it easier for the foot to operate efficiently when walking and running. It is due to the unique structure of the foot and the way it distributes pressure throughout all aspects that it can withstand constant pressure throughout the day.

One of the other crucial functions of the foot is to aid balance, and toes are a crucial aspect of this. The big toe in particular helps in this area, as we can grip the ground with it if we feel we are losing balance.

The skin, nerves and blood vessels make up the rest of the foot, helping to hold the shape and also supplying it with all the necessary minerals, oxygen and energy to help keep it moving easily and constantly. ✿

What happens when you sprain your ankle?

A sprained ankle is the most common type of soft tissue injury. The severity of the sprain can depend on how you sprained the ankle, and a minor sprain will generally consist of a stretched or only partially torn ligament. However, more severe sprains can cause the ligament to tear completely, or even force a piece of bone to break off.

Generally a sprain happens when you lose balance or slip, and the foot bends inwards towards the other leg. This then overstretches the ligaments and causes the damage. Over a quarter of all sporting injuries are sprains of the ankle.

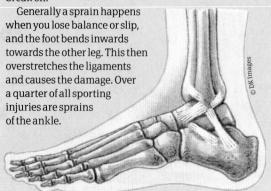

© DK Images

Toes
Terminal aspects of the foot that aid balance by grasping onto the ground. They are the equivalent of fingers in the foot structure.

Muscles – including the extensor digitorum brevis muscle
Muscles within the foot help the foot lift and articulate as necessary. The extensor digitorum brevis muscle sits on the top of the foot, and helps flex digits two-four on the foot.

Blood vessels
These supply blood to the foot, facilitating muscle operation by supplying energy and oxygen and removing deoxygenated blood.

Ligaments
Ligaments support the tendons and help to form the arches of the foot, spreading weight across it.

Tendons (extensor digitorum longus, among others)
Fibrous bands of tissue which connect muscles to bones. They can withstand a lot of tension and link various aspects of the foot, facilitating movement.

Tibia
The larger and stronger of the lower leg bones, this links the knee and the ankle bones of the foot.

Fibula
This bone sits alongside the tibia, also linking the knee and the ankle.

The structure of the foot and how the elements work together

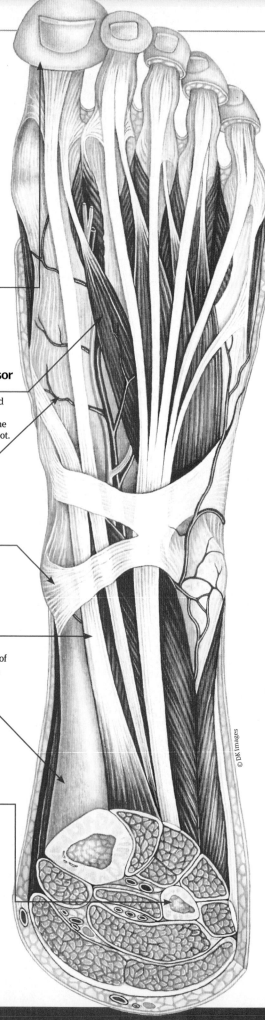

© DK Images

How do we walk?

'Human gait' is the term to describe how we walk. This gait will vary between each person, but the basics are the same

2. Weight transfer
The weight will transfer fully to the foot still in contact with the ground, normally with a slight leaning movement of the body.

3. Foot lift
After weight has transferred and the individual feels balanced, the ball of the first foot will then lift off the ground, raising the thigh.

5. Heel placement
The heel will normally be the part of the foot that's placed first, and weight will start to transfer back onto this foot as it hits the ground.

4. Leg swing
The lower leg will then swing at the knee, under the body, to be placed in front of the stationary, weight-bearing foot.

1. Heel lift
The first step of walking is for the foot to be lifted off the ground. The knee will raise and the calf muscle and Achilles tendon, situated on the back of the leg, will contract to allow the heel to lift off the ground.

6. Repeat process
The process is then repeated with the other foot. During normal walking or running, one foot will start to lift as the other starts to come into contact with the ground.

Bones of the foot

Distal phalanges
The bones which sit at the far end of the foot and make up the tips of the toes.

Proximal phalanges
These bones link the metatarsals and the distal phalanges and stretch from the base of the toes.

Metatarsals
The five, long bones that are the metatarsals are located between the tarsal bones and the phalanges. These are the equivalent of the metacarpals in the hand.

Cuneiforms bones (three)
Three bones that fuse together during bone development and sit between the metatarsals and the talus.

Navicular
This bone, which is so named due to its resemblance to a boat, articulates with the three cuneiform bones.

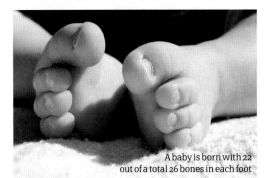

A baby is born with 22 out of a total 26 bones in each foot

© DK Images

Cuboid
One of five irregular bones (cuboid, navicular and three cuneiform bones) which make up the arches of the foot. These help with shock absorption in locomotion.

Talus
The talus is the second largest bone of the foot, and it makes up the lower part of the ankle joint.

Calcaneus
This bone constitutes the heel and is crucial for walking. It is the largest bone in the foot.

The human skeleton explained

Without a skeleton, we would not be able to live. It is what gives us our shape and structure and its presence allows us to operate on a daily basis. It's also a fascinating evolutionary link to all other living and extinct vertebrates

The human skeleton is crucial for us to live. It keeps our shape and muscle attached to the skeleton allows us the ability to move around, while also protecting crucial organs that we need to survive. Bones also produce blood cells within bone marrow and store minerals we need released on a daily basis.

As a fully grown adult you will have around 206 bones, but you are born with over 270, which continue to grow, strengthen and fuse after birth until around 18 in females and 20 in males. Human skeletons actually do vary between sexes in structure also. One of the most obvious areas is the pelvis as a female must be able to give birth, and therefore hips are comparatively shallower and wider. The cranium also becomes more robust in males due to heavy muscle attachment and a male's chin is often more prominent. Female skeletons are generally more delicate overall. However, although there are several methods, sexing can be difficult because of the level of variation we see within the species.

Bones are made up of various different elements. In utero, the skeleton takes shape as cartilage, which then starts to calcify and develop during gestation and following birth. The primary element that makes up bone, osseous tissue, is actually mineralised calcium phosphate, but other forms of tissue such as marrow, cartilage and blood vessels are also contained in the overall structure. Many individuals think that bones are solid, but actually inner bone is porous and full of little holes.

As we age, so do our bones. Even though cells are constantly being replaced, and therefore no cell in our body is more than 20 years old, they are not replaced with perfect, brand-new cells. The cells contain errors in their DNA and ultimately our bones therefore weaken as we age. Conditions such as arthritis and osteoporosis can often be caused by ageing and cause issues with weakening of bones and reduced movement ability. ✿

"As a fully grown adult you will have around 206 bones, but you are born with over 270, which continue to grow and fuse after birth"

Mandible

Collarbone

Scapula

Sternum

Carpals

Radius/Ulna
The radius and ulna are the bones situated in the forearm. They connect the wrist and the elbow.

Rib cage
This structure of many single rib bones creates a protective barrier for organs situated in the chest cavity. They join to the vertebrae in the spine at the back of the body, and the sternum at the front.

Patella

Tarsals

Phalanges

Inside our skeleton

How the human skeleton works and keeps us upright

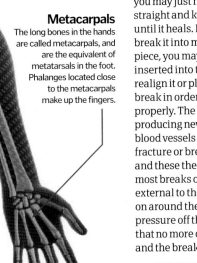

Cranium
The cranium, also known as the skull, is where the brain and the majority of the sensory organs are located.

Metacarpals
The long bones in the hands are called metacarpals, and are the equivalent of metatarsals in the foot. Phalanges located close to the metacarpals make up the fingers.

Vertebrae
There are three main kinds of vertebrae (excluding the sacrum and coccyx) – cervical, thoracic and lumbar. These vary in strength and structure as they carry different pressure within the spine.

Pelvis
This is the transitional joint between the trunk of the body and the legs. It is one of the key areas in which we can see the skeletal differences between the sexes.

Femur
This is the largest and longest single bone in the body. It connects to the pelvis with a ball and socket joint.

Fibula/Tibia
These two bones form the lower leg bone and connect to the knee joint and the foot.

Metatarsals
These are the five long bones in the foot that aid balance and movement. Phalanges located close to the metatarsals are the bones which are present in toes.

Breaking bones

Whether it's a complete break or just a fracture, both can take time to heal properly

If you simply fracture the bone, you may just need to keep it straight and keep pressure off it until it heals. However, if you break it into more than one piece, you may need metal pins inserted into the bone to realign it or plates to cover the break in order for it to heal properly. The bone heals by producing new cells and tiny blood vessels where the fracture or break has occurred and these then rejoin up. For most breaks or fractures, a cast external to the body will be put on around the bone to take pressure off the bone to ensure that no more damage is done and the break can heal.

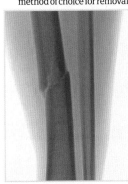

A typical cast for when someone has managed to break a bone. Unbelievably, a saw is the method of choice for removal!

Skull development

When we are born, many of our bones are still soft and are not yet fused – this process occurs later during our childhood

The primary reasons for the cranium in particular not to be fully fused at birth is to allow the skull to flex as the baby is born and also to allow the extreme rate of growth that occurs in the first few years of childhood following birth. The skull is actually in seven separate plates when we are born and over the first two years these pieces fuse together slowly and ossify. The plates start suturing together early on, but the anterior fontanel – commonly known as the soft spot – will take around 18 months to fully heal. Some other bones, such as the five bones located in the sacrum, don't fully fuse until late teens or early twenties, but the cranium becomes fully fused by around age two.

How our joints work

The types of joints in our body explained

Ball and socket joints
Both the hip and the shoulder joints are ball and socket joints. The femur and humerus have ball shaped endings, which turn in a cavity to allow movement.

Skull sutures
Although not generally thought of as a 'joint', all the cranial sutures present from where bones have fused in childhood are in fact immoveable joints.

Vertebrae
Vertebrae fit together to support the body and allow bending movements. They are joined by cartilage and are classified as semi-mobile joints.

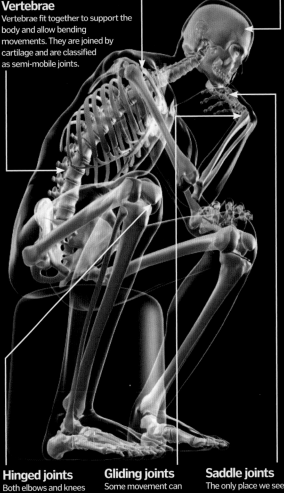

Hinged joints
Both elbows and knees are hinged joints. These joints only allow limited movement in one direction. The bones fit together and are moved by muscles.

Gliding joints
Some movement can be allowed when flat bones 'glide' across each other. The wrist bones – the carpals – operate like this, moved by ligaments.

Saddle joints
The only place we see this joint in humans is the thumb. Movement is limited in rotation, but the thumb can move back, forward and to the sides.

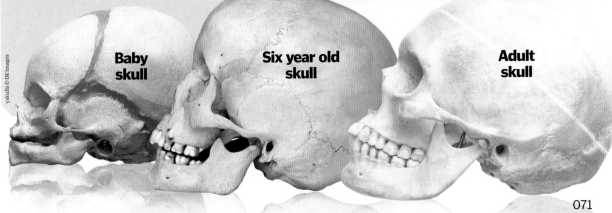

Baby skull

Six year old skull

Adult skull

3 skulls © DK Images

Deep flexor

Greater pectoral

Obliquus externus abdominis

MUSCLE POWER

Why are some people strong but others weak, and how does exercise and training increase muscle strength?

Muscles are often taken for granted. Responsible for every move you make, the primary goal of a muscle is to turn energy into motion. Muscles are broken down into three categories. Skeletal are the type that people in the gym train and what individuals are most commonly aware of. Smooth are the involuntary muscles such as blood vessels, airways and your bladder. The final category is cardiac, the muscles of the heart. It is skeletal muscle, however, that allows humans to both shape their bodies and increase their strength.

Skeletal muscles are complex, designed to contract when asked to perform any action. If you performed a bicep curl, for example, your brain will send a signal to the nerve cells indicating that it's time for the biceps to engage. It's the same process for each muscle that's within the skeletal category, but it's the way these are constructed that allows us to develop them.

A muscle is made up of fibres – each muscle will boast a higher or lower amount – that fall into two distinct groups: slow twitching (type I fibres) and fast twitching (type II fibres).

Type I muscles utilise the oxygen in your body better to generate more fuel, also known as adenosine triphosphate (ATP). They can take extra strain and, more often than not, fatigue slower. Type II muscles, on the other hand, are the opposite. Not needing oxygen to generate fuel, they create spurts of strength and exhaust far quicker. The distinctions are similar to that of a marathon runner and a sprinter, with the former relying on their muscles taking longer to break down and the latter using the intensity and force of the faster twitching fibres to peak quickly.

It's these processes that allow us to both manipulate a muscle and make it stronger. Every time you lift a weight you're tearing these muscle fibres apart, forcing the body to repair them. Once healed, the fibres are thicker than before, a process that can be manipulated with the right diet. Bodybuilders get protein into their system as soon as possible after a workout, as the substance is

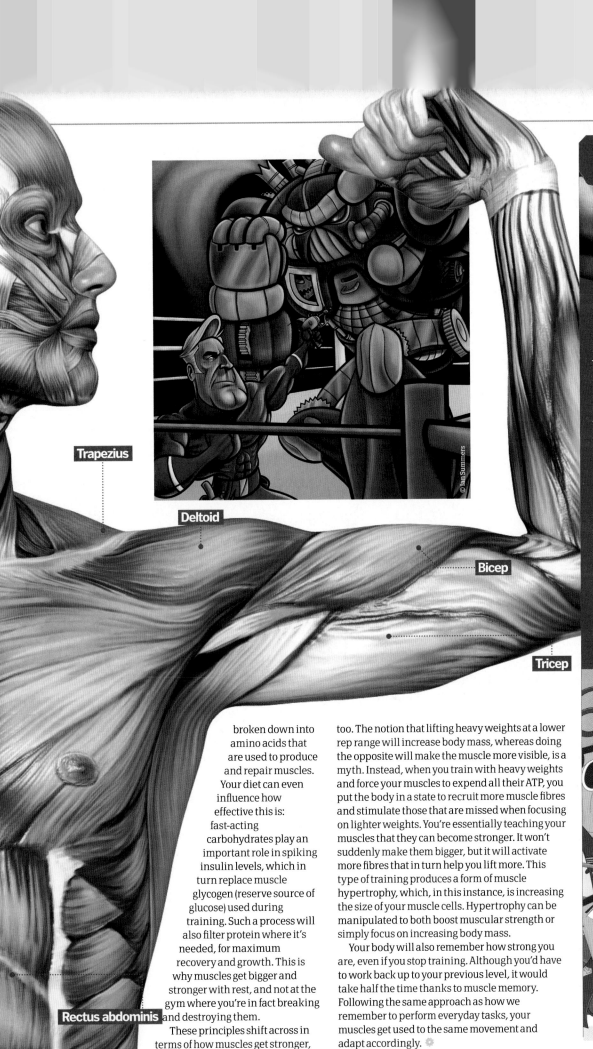

Trapezius

Deltoid

Bicep

Tricep

Rectus abdominis

© Ian Summers

broken down into amino acids that are used to produce and repair muscles. Your diet can even influence how effective this is: fast-acting carbohydrates play an important role in spiking insulin levels, which in turn replace muscle glycogen (reserve source of glucose) used during training. Such a process will also filter protein where it's needed, for maximum recovery and growth. This is why muscles get bigger and stronger with rest, and not at the gym where you're in fact breaking and destroying them.

These principles shift across in terms of how muscles get stronger,

too. The notion that lifting heavy weights at a lower rep range will increase body mass, whereas doing the opposite will make the muscle more visible, is a myth. Instead, when you train with heavy weights and force your muscles to expend all their ATP, you put the body in a state to recruit more muscle fibres and stimulate those that are missed when focusing on lighter weights. You're essentially teaching your muscles that they can become stronger. It won't suddenly make them bigger, but it will activate more fibres that in turn help you lift more. This type of training produces a form of muscle hypertrophy, which, in this instance, is increasing the size of your muscle cells. Hypertrophy can be manipulated to both boost muscular strength or simply focus on increasing body mass.

Your body will also remember how strong you are, even if you stop training. Although you'd have to work back up to your previous level, it would take half the time thanks to muscle memory. Following the same approach as how we remember to perform everyday tasks, your muscles get used to the same movement and adapt accordingly. ✿

The bigger they are...

Just because you look like The Hulk doesn't mean you're going to have the comic book character's strength. If you lift heavy weights for a low number of repetitions, you're training the muscle to take a more intense load due to the formation of new fibres. That doesn't mean you'll have the size to back it up, however, as mass corresponds to the number of calories consumed. The more food that's eaten, the quicker and more efficiently the muscle will be repaired. This is why plenty of power lifters who can pick up an incredible amount don't look like bodybuilders. Not only do they concentrate on pure strength, they also consume a massive number of calories. A bodybuilder, meanwhile, will sculpt his diet to shape and increase muscle size.

Not as strong as you might think...

FIGHT!

GO PLASTIC MAN

© The Boy Fitz Hammond

Shoulders

Exercise name: Military press

How to do it: Using weights, bend your legs, lift up the bar in line with your shoulders and push from your deltoids until your arms are straight. Repeat.

Details: With the correct weight and intensity, it'll tear many muscles apart and increase your strength.

STRENGTH RATING: 🏋️🏋️🏋️

Mid-section

Exercise name: Side plank

How to do it: Lay on your side and hoist your body up using the leg and arm you're resting on. Hold this position for as long as you can.

Details: The side plank will trigger both abdominals and mid-section, for a more efficient centre of gravity.

STRENGTH RATING: 🏋️🏋️🏋️

Calves

Exercise name: Calve raise

How to do it: Using a Smith machine, stand under the barbell and place it on your trapezius muscles. Push from calves and stand on your tiptoes.

Details: Extremely difficult to enhance, the calve raise when done with a barbell will target this muscle.

STRENGTH RATING: 🏋️🏋️🏋️

MUSCLES IN FRONT

Trapezius
A superficial muscle that moves the scapulae (in the rotator cuff) and supports the arm.

Biceps brachii
Consists of a long and short head to, among other things, allow rotation of the forearm and elbow.

Rectus abdominus
Known to the greater world as 'abs' or a 'six-pack', it is possible to possess an eight-pack, or even ten-pack.

Vastus lateralis
The largest part of your quadriceps muscle, the quad also has the rectus femoris, vastus medialis and vastus intermedius.

Gastrocnemius
Meaning 'stomach of leg', the calve is incredibly hard to develop due to the pressure it is put under on a daily basis.

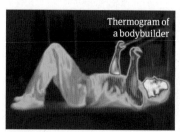

Thermogram of a bodybuilder

© SPL

Deltoid
Formed round the shoulder, it has anterior, posterior and lateral fibres to support rotation and the pectorals and lats.

Pectoralis major
A gym favourite, the pectorals also have the pectoralis minor near the upper chest.

Forearm
Consisting of 20 different muscles, your lower arm is one of the most complex parts of the entire body.

Chest

Exercise name: Bench press

How to do it: Lie on a bench and grab a barbell, hands about shoulder width. Bring the bar to chest level and lower until arms are at 90°. Push upwards.

Details: The bench press isn't merely beneficial for your chest; it also works your shoulders and triceps.

STRENGTH RATING: 🏋️🏋️🏋️

Biceps

Exercise name: Bicep curl

How to do it: Raise a dumbbell from your side up to your shoulder rotating the arm so the palm with the weight faces up. Then lower and repeat.

Details: The biceps' relatively small size compared to other muscle groups means they're quite easy to target.

STRENGTH RATING: 🏋️🏋️🏋️

Forearms

Exercise name: Hammer curls

How to do it: Hold a dumbbell in each hand with palms facing your body. Curl the weight up to your chest, keeping elbows locked. Lower down.

Details: Performed with a heavy weight, you can improve your grip and increase arm strength.

STRENGTH RATING: 🏋️🏋️🏋️

Inside your muscle

A muscle contracts when a fibre is kicked into gear as tension is put upon it. Myofibrils, which are found within a fibre, are made up of actin and myosin. When these two threads join the myofibril shortens, or contracts. If you straighten your arm, keeping your palm facing up, and measure the length of your bicep muscle, you'll find it will become a lot smaller if you curl your hand towards the shoulder.

There are multiple types of contractions, though. Isometric contractions occur when the angle of the joint or length of muscle do not change, for example holding a dumbbell at arm's length and fighting the resistance. Such exercises are usually adapted to try and increase strength. Isotonic contractions are the opposite and more common, such as traditional weightlifting where, as mentioned, the muscle shortens with contraction. Although this can also be used for strength training, it's beneficial for expanding muscle size.

Myofibril
Housing the two filaments actin and myosin, this is what's found inside a muscle fibre. When the myofibril shortens, a muscle contracts.

Muscle fibres
This is a skeletal muscle cell and will fall into the mentioned 'type' categories. There can be far more than just types I and II.

Fascicle
A bundle of muscle fibres is known as a fascicle. Surrounded by perimysium – the connective tissues that groups individual fibres together – this collection makes up a muscle.

Actin
Found in muscle tissue, actin is a strand of protein. When this and myosin interlock with each other and pull, it activates the shortening of the myofibril.

Myosin
Myosin is also an important protein strand and reacts first when a muscle contracts, subsequently activating the actin thread.

MUSCLES BEHIND

Triceps
As the name suggests there's three parts to the muscle: the long, lateral and medial head.

Latissimus dorsi
Meaning 'broadest of the back', the lats, as they're commonly called, are an essential muscle for strengthening the entire body.

Muscle mass corresponds to calories consumed

External oblique
The largest and outermost of the three muscles of the lateral anterior abdomen.

Splenius
Located in the neck, the splenius is responsible for head extension.

Rhomboideus
Working in conjunction with the trapezius, the rhomboids connect the scapula (shoulder blade) with the vertebrae.

Gluteus maximus
The largest muscle in the body, your bottom has to be strong to keep the lower part in a correct position.

Biceps femoris
Containing two parts, the long head is an integral and important part of the hamstring.

© SPL

Hamstrings
Exercise name: Hamstring curls

How to do it: Use a hamstring curl machine and lock legs into position. Push against the foam pad until your legs are at 90° and go back to the start.

Details: Curls will provide extra support to squats, meaning you'll be able to lift more weight from your legs.

STRENGTH RATING:

Upper arms
Exercise name: Tricep kickback

How to do it: Take one dumbell and hold it by your side. With the elbow locked pointing to the ceiling, extend your arm behind you till it's straight.

Details: Tricep extensions hit the three different heads that make up a large part of the upper arm at once.

STRENGTH RATING:

Back
Exercise name: Deadlift

How to do it: Lay barbell on the floor. Put shins to the bar, bend knees and push from the legs. When bar passes hips, straighten back and stand up.

Details: The deadlift utilises every muscle in your body, from your back to your hamstrings.

STRENGTH RATING:

Quadriceps
Exercise name: Squats

How to do it: Using barbell in a squat rack, place bar on trapezius. Back straight, bend knees until hamstrings parallel with floor. Push from legs.

Details: Squats target all of your leg muscles, as well as most of your upper ones too.

STRENGTH RATING:

Hysterical strength – fact or fiction?

Believe it or not, on occasion a desperate mother has found the strength to lift a car to save her threatened child. Seems impossible, right? Although there's no scientific evidence to support it, the most common theory is that the rush of adrenaline from the situation increases muscle twitching, enabling the recipient to be stronger and work harder for a very short period of time. When such an event occurs, though, what you don't hear about is the damage and injuries that these heroes usually suffer. It's why the body produces lactic acid in most cases, in order to stop the body from overdoing it.

© Ian Summers

What's inside your head?

A look at how our thinking machines are put together

From birth, the head of a baby will grow very rapidly. By the age of two the bones will have fused together, although growth continues until the age of seven during which the shape and size of the skull are altered. An adult human head is made from 22 bones. Eight are present in the cranium, and 14 form the face. Together they make the skull, which provides a framework for all the features of our head.

The primary purpose of the skull is to prevent damage to the brain. Without it, even a small force against the head could cause serious brain damage. Before birth, the skull develops holes in which are found the various features of the head.

The skull has three main structural features. Cavities known as orbits contain the eyes, providing protection but also allowing muscles, nerves, blood supply and tissue to reach the eyes. Paranasal sinuses house the nasal cavity and also contain air-filled spaces, which are responsible for making people sound different. Finally, the head is held together by sutures, which are soft fibres at birth but later harden to give the appearance of stitches. They become immovable joints which stop the head falling apart.

The muscles of the head are stretched over the bones in the cranium and face like sheets. There are two main categories of muscles. The muscles of facial expressions are responsible for moving the mouth, altering the chin and moving the cheeks to assist eating and breathing. Muscles of mastication directly control eating, opening and closing the jaw and allow sideways movements. Smaller muscles control other portions of the face including the inner ear and the eye. ✿

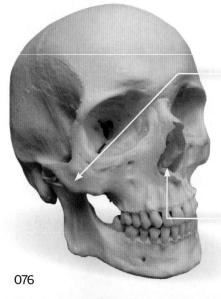

The bones of the skull

The purpose of all the bones in our head

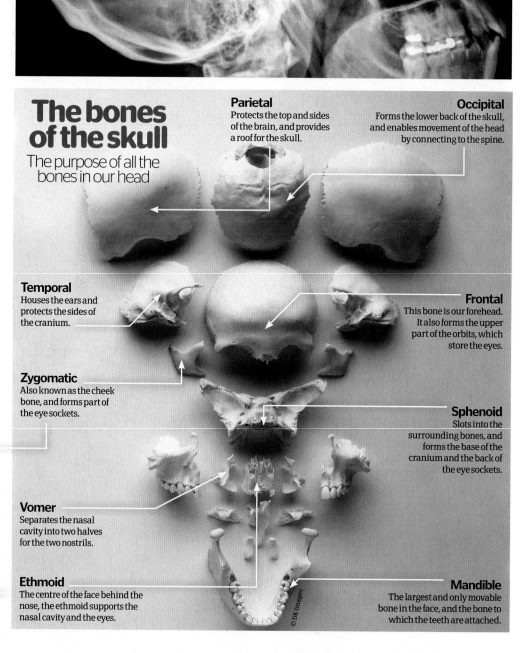

Parietal
Protects the top and sides of the brain, and provides a roof for the skull.

Occipital
Forms the lower back of the skull, and enables movement of the head by connecting to the spine.

Temporal
Houses the ears and protects the sides of the cranium.

Frontal
This bone is our forehead. It also forms the upper part of the orbits, which store the eyes.

Zygomatic
Also known as the cheek bone, and forms part of the eye sockets.

Sphenoid
Slots into the surrounding bones, and forms the base of the cranium and the back of the eye sockets.

Vomer
Separates the nasal cavity into two halves for the two nostrils.

Ethmoid
The centre of the face behind the nose, the ethmoid supports the nasal cavity and the eyes.

Mandible
The largest and only movable bone in the face, and the bone to which the teeth are attached.

© DK Images

Head anatomy
The main features of the head that keep us operational

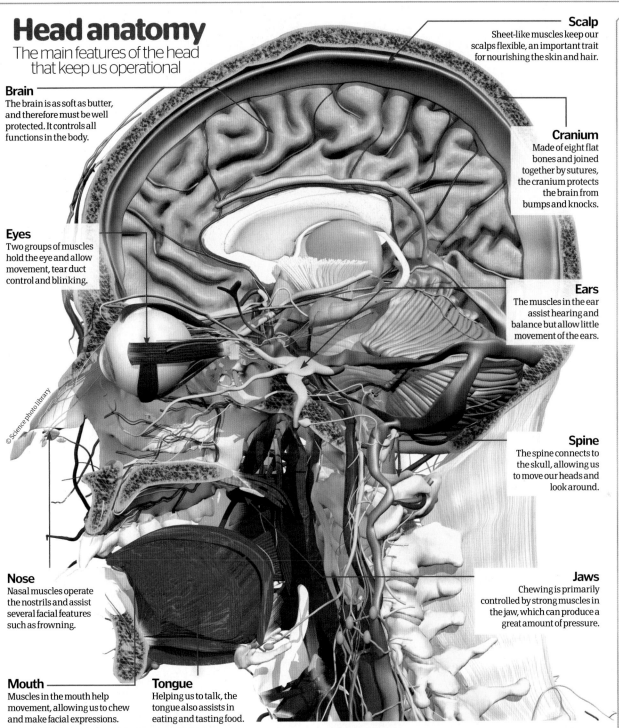

Brain
The brain is as soft as butter, and therefore must be well protected. It controls all functions in the body.

Eyes
Two groups of muscles hold the eye and allow movement, tear duct control and blinking.

©Science photo library

Nose
Nasal muscles operate the nostrils and assist several facial features such as frowning.

Mouth
Muscles in the mouth help movement, allowing us to chew and make facial expressions.

Tongue
Helping us to talk, the tongue also assists in eating and tasting food.

Scalp
Sheet-like muscles keep our scalps flexible, an important trait for nourishing the skin and hair.

Cranium
Made of eight flat bones and joined together by sutures, the cranium protects the brain from bumps and knocks.

Ears
The muscles in the ear assist hearing and balance but allow little movement of the ears.

Spine
The spine connects to the skull, allowing us to move our heads and look around.

Jaws
Chewing is primarily controlled by strong muscles in the jaw, which can produce a great amount of pressure.

Head injuries must always be taken very seriously

What's a knockout?

When the head is struck hard enough, a person can become unconscious. This can cause long-lasting head injuries and must be treated immediately. As the head is struck, the brain processes all the information it receives from the sensory nerves to formulate an appropriate response, be it forcing the person to withdraw, pushing their aggressor or holding the injured area. However, the brain also has a limit on how much it can process, and a hard enough blow may overload it with information.

To prevent any further damage to the head, the brain stops communicating with the body, causing unconsciousness. Although it may seem similar to sleep, an unconscious person will not respond to people or noises and will only wake up once the brain begins communicating with the body again.

Your eyes are held in place but with the freedom to move

A strong jaw and teeth allow us to chew and digest food

Epidermis
This is the top layer of skin through which the hair penetrates.

Dermis
The dermis is the layer of skin below the epidermis, in which the hair follicles, blood vessels and sweat glands are situated.

Hair follicle
The sac-like structure from which the hair grows.

Hair and the skin it's in

Hair shaft
The fibrous part of the hair, technically defined as 'dead', which protrudes from the skin.

Blood vessels
These vessels supply the skin and the hair follicles with needed minerals and energy to grow and replace dead cells.

Sensory nerve
This sensory receptor is situated in the dermis and detects pressure on the skin and hair.

© Science Photo Library

Sebaceous gland
These microscopic glands secrete an oily substance called sebum to lubricate the skin and hair.

Sweat gland
This gland, situated near to the hair follicle, releases sweat when the body is overheating to cool the body.

How does hair grow?

Hair is a key characteristic of mammals, but what is it made of?

Your hair is primarily made up of keratin, which is a form of protein. It grows from follicles situated in the dermis – a specific layer of the skin found below the epidermis but above the subcutaneous tissue – and is exclusive to mammals.

The human body is nearly entirely covered in hair, although some of it is so fine you cannot see it unless you look very closely. This fine hair is called vellus hair and the thicker, pigmented hair that is more visible is called either terminal or androgenic hair, dependent on location. Ratios of

each will depend on the individual, heavily influenced by their sex.

The biology of both types of hair is quite similar, with each containing a cuticle, cortex and medula, which together form the shaft, bulb and follicle. The major difference between vellus and androgenic or terminal hair is the pigmentation, which is determined by melanin situated in the cortex, and thickness of the hair. There are two types of melanin – eumelanin and pheomelanin – and the levels of these types determine the colour of the hair. Although colour is primarily determined by genetics,

grey hair results from a disappearance of melanin from the hair.

Hair can grow up to 5.5 metres long in some individuals that see high levels of hair growth in the active phase, but most hair reaches a set length and will then rest before shedding. The length of the phases differ depending on the type of hair, with head hair having a long growth period of around a year and body hair having a much shorter period of growth, but an extended resting period before shedding.

Whether hair is curly or straight is determined by the shape of the hair

fibre – if it is circular it will be straight, but if it is oval it will be wavy or curly. The degree of curliness is determined by how stretched the oval shape is.

Functions of hair and fur in mammals are wide ranging, with thermoregulation being among the most important, alongside sensory function. As humans have evolved, we've seen a massive reduction in the thickness of hair covering our bodies, as we've found other ways to keep warm. The hair on our heads is retained to aid thermoregulation and in other areas, the functions of which are debated. ✿

Hair growth
Your hair grows in a cycle of growth and rest phases

Growth phase (anagen)
This is the phase when hair grows out from the follicle. The length of this phase can vary quite dramatically, dependent on where the hair is growing and what type of hair it is. Vellus hair grows for a short period of time, whereas the terminal hair situated on the head can grow for up to a year and can grow up to 5.5 metres long.

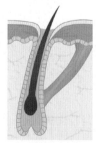

Regeneration phase (catagen)
In this phase, the hair detaches from the follicle and the blood supply and is pushed up through the skin out of the follicle. The follicle renews itself in readiness for another new hair to grow once the present hair has shed from the skin.

Resting phase (telogen)
The hair rests for between one and four weeks before a new hair pushes the present hair out. This will happen all across the body and with all types of hair.

The five basic human tastes

Building a map of the tongue

There is general agreement that humans have five basic tastes, although the fifth taste 'primary' has only been recently officially recognised. Sweetness, bitterness, sourness and saltiness were joined by savouriness in 2002. Several other sensations that the tongue can recognise have been identified but are not classified as tastes.

Sweetness is associated primarily with simple carbohydrates – of which sugar is one of the most common. The way sweetness is detected is complex and only recently has the current model of multiple binding sites between the receptors and sweet substance itself been proposed and accepted. A sweet taste infers that the substance is high in energy and studies have shown that newborns in particular, who need a high calorie intake to grow, demonstrate a preference for sugar concentrations sweeter than lactose, which is found in breast milk.

Bitterness can be detected in very low levels and is generally perceived to be an unpleasant or sharp taste. Many toxic substances in nature are known to be bitter and there is an argument proposed by evolutionary scientists that bitterness sensitivity is an evolutionary defence mechanism. Humans, however, have now developed various techniques to make previous inedible bitter substances edible through reducing their toxicity, often through cooking.

The taste of saltiness is produced by the presence of sodium ions, or other closely related alkali metal ions. Potassium and lithium produce a similar taste as they are most closely related to sodium.

Sourness detects acidity. The way we measure the degree of sourness is through rating sour substances against dilute hydrochloric. The mechanism involved in detecting sourness is similar to saltiness in that taste is caused by a concentration of ions – in this case hydrogen ions. Savouriness is the newest of the recognised basic tastes and the taste is produced by fermented or aged foods. Glutamate is a common compound that can cause this taste and consequently savouriness is considered fundamental to Eastern cuisine.

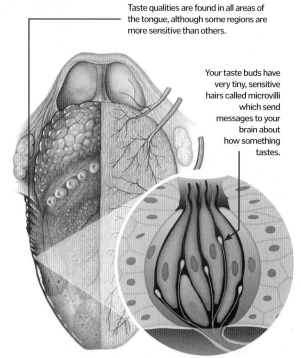

Taste qualities are found in all areas of the tongue, although some regions are more sensitive than others.

Your taste buds have very tiny, sensitive hairs called microvilli which send messages to your brain about how something tastes.

How cells work

The building blocks of life explained

Cells are the building blocks of all living organisms. Individual cells are classified as living things, and there are millions of organisms which are unicellular across the planet.

As they are living units, cells consequently need energy, and therefore respire to survive. Parts of the cell, called organelles, work like organs of a body. Energy for the cell to process can be provided by the cell, such as through photosynthesis in plants, or absorbed into the cell through cell membranes and then processed within it by the mitochondrion. Single cells operate like this, and there are billions of unicellular organisms that survive independently or within multicellular organisms. These single cell organisms are generally prokaryotic cells, which are much smaller and have fewer organelles, most importantly lacking a nucleus. Multicellular organisms are primarily made up of eukaryotic cells which are more complex and can therefore specialise so the organism can become more complex. They do this by grouping together to form tissues, which then group to form organs within the organism.

Cells reproduce to replace old, damaged cells in an organism, to allow growth or growth of a new individual. In unicellular organisms, cell reproduction is obviously the only way a population will grow. Prokaryotes favour binary fission, where all genetic information is doubled and then the cell divides into two new, identical cells. Eukaryote cells use either mitosis, which results in two identical organisms or cells, or meiosis, which results in each new cell having half the number of chromosomes of the original cell.

Nucleus
The nucleus is often referred to as the brain of the cell. DNA is stored here and cell metabolism, movement and reproduction are all controlled from here.

Ribosomes
Ribosomes are spherical bodies composed of RNA and protein enzymes which are the site of protein synthesis for the cell.

Mitochondria
Mitochondria are small, bean-shaped organelles which release chemical energy for the cell by processing glucose that is provided for, or produced by, the cell.

Cell membrane
Present in animal and plant cells, this acts as a boundary layer to protect the cell from unwanted chemicals.

Cytoplasm
The cytoplasm is a thick, almost jelly-like material which supports and protects organelles of the cell.

Animal cells
A typical, non-specialised animal cell

What are moles?

These small skin blemishes are common, but what are they and why must we keep a close eye on them?

A mole on the skin, or a melanocytic naevus, is an abnormal collection of the pigment cells called melanocytes. Some moles can be present at birth (congenital melanocytic naevi) but most develop spontaneously later in life, usually as a result of exposure to sunlight. Moles are often brown or black (pigmented naevi) and are most commonly round or oval, but they can be a variety of different shapes and sizes. Growth and change over time is quite normal.

Moles sound pretty unremarkable and are harmless in nature, and yet we must be vigilant if a new one appears on the skin or if an existing mole begins to change. A malignant melanoma is a rare kind of skin cancer that can occur in melanocytes. Although rare, malignant melanomas cause the majority of the deaths related to skin cancer. If you are particularly moley you're more susceptible to melanoma and should try to avoid too much sunlight.

Moles to watch are dysplastic naevi, which are large, irregularly shaped moles of mixed colouration. They often have paler, jagged edges with darker centres and tend to be accompanied by a lot of other moles on the body. ✿

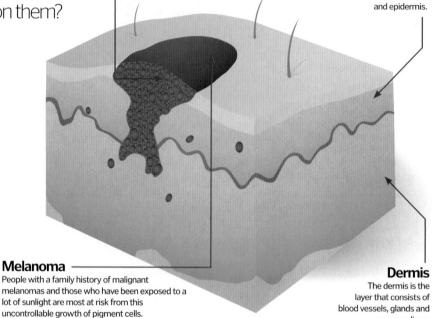

Melanocyte
The skin's natural pigment, melanin, is a protein produced in cells called melanocytes. Melanocytes are usually spread evenly throughout the skin for even colour. Melanin also absorbs UV radiation.

Epidermis
This is the outer layer of your skin and it contains tough, flat cells. Melanocytes are located in the dermis and epidermis.

Melanoma
People with a family history of malignant melanomas and those who have been exposed to a lot of sunlight are most at risk from this uncontrollable growth of pigment cells.

Dermis
The dermis is the layer that consists of blood vessels, glands and nerve endings.

Why do we get spots?

Find out what causes pimples to form on the surface of human skin

Pimples are caused by sensitivity to the testosterone hormone present in both males and females, which can trigger the overproduction of an oily substance called sebum. Sebum, which is produced by sebaceous glands attached to hair follicles in the dermis, helps keep hair and skin waterproof.

Your skin is constantly renewing itself, and while new cells are produced in the lower layers of skin, the old dead cells are sloughed away from the surface. This, together with excessive sebum production, can lead to acne and pimples.

Sebum normally travels through the hair follicle to the surface of the skin. However, if a pore becomes blocked by a few dead skin cells that haven't been shed properly, the sebum can begin to build up inside the hair follicle. This oily buildup is the perfect breeding ground for bacteria, which then accumulate and multiply around the area, making the skin inflamed and infected. This results in the pimple.

Whiteheads and blackheads are types of acne pimples known as comedones. Blackheads are open comedones, which means the blockage of sebum is exposed to the air, causing oxidation of the sebum (like when an apple browns). Whiteheads, on the other hand, are closed comedones and are not exposed to air as they're covered by a layer of skin. ✿

Inflammation
The trapped sebum attracts bacteria that build up and cause a pustule, which can grow inflamed.

Blackhead
When the blockage is nearer the surface, the accumulation of sebum can be exposed to the air, causing oxidation which turns the substance black.

Whitehead
Blockages can occur beneath a layer of skin that prevents air from coming into contact with the sebum which results in it staying white.

Epidermis
Sebum helps slough away the cells on the surface of the skin as they die to make room for the fresh cells generated in the dermis.

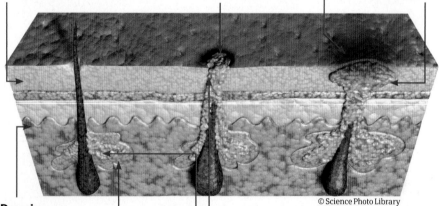

© Science Photo Library

Dermis
New skin cells are created in the lower layers of skin.

Sebaceous gland
Attached to the hair follicle, the sebaceous gland produces an oily, waxy substance called sebum.

Sebum
The sebum travels up the hair follicle to waterproof the hair and protect the surface of the skin.

Blockage
If dead skin cells fail to be shed properly, they can become blocked inside pores. When this happens sebum is plugged behind a barrier, which can lead to a spot forming.

How do we smell?

The ability to smell is one of our most crucial senses and can influence the food we eat and the people we date...

Smell, or olfaction to use the proper terminology, is a very direct sense, in that we actually breathe in microscopic bits of the substance that we smell. These hit the olfactory epithelium, a mucus membrane in the nasal cavity, which contains millions of olfactory receptor neuron cells. Each of these sensory cells is covered in small hair-like structures, called cilia, which react to the odour and send signals to the olfactory nerve, which relays this information to the brain so it is then perceived as smell. Humans can recognise around 10,000 different odours and no two individuals can sense anything exactly the same. ☼

5 TOP FACTS SMELL

1 Women smell better!
Consistently, women out-perform men in smelling ability tests, and research has shown that women can recognise the smell of their baby only days after birth.

2 Smell affects taste
The human nose is actually the main organ involved in perceiving taste. Taste buds can only distinguish sweet, sour, bitter and salt, everything else perceived comes from smell!

3 Blind people can't smell better
It's a common myth that blind people can smell better than sighted. However, this has never been proven and most studies refute the fact.

4 Smelling ability doesn't improve after childhood
At about eight, sense of smell reaches its full potential. Smelling ability reduces as you age.

5 Your sense of smell improves throughout the day
When you first wake up, your sense of smell is far less acute than in the evening, when it is at its peak.

Olfactory bulb
This area of the brain is where signals are processed and smell is perceived. Other animals have a much larger area as they can perceive wider ranges of smells and use their sense of smell more.

Olfactory nerves
The olfactory nerves pass information about the particles sensed in the nasal cavity to the brain, where these signals are perceived as a certain smell.

Nasal cavity
This is where air and microscopic molecules of substances we are to smell enter. Air is pulled into this area to pass through into the lungs by diaphragm movements.

Olfactory epithelium
This is where the olfactory nerve cells are located. In a human, this area is around 10cm squared.

We can detect 10,000 different odours!

Cells that smell
The patch of sensory cells located in the nasal cavity are made up of several different parts

Mucosa
Mucosa lines the epithelium inside the nasal cavity, and catches the particles to be sensed by the receptor neuron cells.

Olfactory receptor neuron cells
These are odour-sensitive cells that are stimulated by the cilia. They then send messages through to the brain.

Olfactory cilia
These sense the particles in air. There are 8-20 of these on each olfactory nerve cell which line the epithelium.

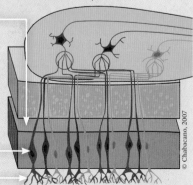

How vision and sight works

An eye-opening look at how we see...

Retina
The retina is the light sensitive area which processes light admitted into the eye and converts it into electrical impulses which are transmitted to the brain via the optic nerve.

Optic nerve
After the retina has processed light into electrical impulses, the optic nerve transports this information to the brain.

The biology of the eye is an extremely complex one, especially when you consider that the human eye only has the rough diameter of 2.54cm and weighs approximately 7.5 grams. It is made up of around 15 distinct parts, which all have different roles to play in receiving light into the eye and transmitting the electrical impulses, which ultimately relay image information to our brains, out of the eye, so that we can perceive the world we live in.

The eye is often compared to a basic camera, and indeed the very first camera was designed with the concept of the eye in mind. We can reduce the complex process that occurs to process light into vision within the eye to a relatively basic sequence of events. First, light passes through the cornea, which refracts the light so that it enters the eye in the right direction, and aqueous humour, into the main body of the eye through the pupil. The iris contracts to control pupil size and this limits the amount of light that is let through into the eye so that light-sensitive parts of the eye are not damaged.

The pupil can vary in size between 2mm and 8mm, increasing to allow up to 30 times more light in than the minimum. The light is then passed through the lens, which further refracts the light, which then travels through the vitreous humour to the back of the eye and is reflected onto the retina, the centre point of which is the macula.

The retina is where the rods and cones are situated, rods being responsible for vision when low levels of light are present and cones being responsible for colour vision and specific detail. Rods are far more numerous as more cells are needed to react in low levels of light and are situated around the focal point of cones. This focal gathering of cones is collectively called the fovea, which is situated within the macula. All the light information that has been received by the eye is then converted into electrical impulses by a chemical in the retina called rhodopsin, also known as purple visual, and the impulses are then transmitted through the optic nerve to the brain where they are perceived as 'vision'. The eye moves to allow a range of vision of approximately 180 degrees and to do this it has four primary muscles which control the movement of the eyeball. These allow the eye to move up and down and across, while restricting movement so that the eye does not rotate back into the socket. ✿

Rods and cones

Rods are the light-sensitive cells in our eyes that aid our vision in low levels of light. Rods are blind to colour and only transmit information mainly in black and white to the brain. They are far more numerous with around 120 million rods present in every human eye compared to around 7 million cones. Cones are responsible for perceiving colour and specific detail. Cones are primarily focused in the fovea, the central area of the macula whereas rods mainly surround the outside of the retina. Cones work much better in daylight as light is needed to perceive colour and detail.

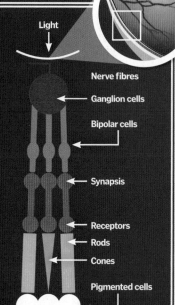

Light

Nerve fibres

Ganglion cells

Bipolar cells

Synapsis

Receptors

Rods

Cones

Pigmented cells

Inside the human eye
How an eye sees

Lens
The lens is a transparent disc in the eye which, with the cornea, refracts light that enters the eye so that it is received by the retina.

Sclera
This is the fibrous, white exterior of the eye that is an important protective layer for the more delicate insides of the eye.

Cornea
The cornea is a transparent layer, covering the pupil, iris and aqueous humour. It helps refract the light towards the retina so that light is received in the correct area.

Iris
The Iris is the coloured part of the eye which contracts to control the level of light admitted into the eye. The hole which light enters through is called the pupil.

How do we see in colour?

Colour is not actually inherent in any object. We only see colour because objects absorb some colour from light, and reflect others. It is the reflected ones that we see and that give an object a set 'colour'. Therefore, for example, grass is not green, it purely absorbs all other colours in light and reflects back green. If an object reflects all colours we will see it as white, if it absorbs all colours we see it as black. We use cones to perceive colour as rods are blind to colour.

"The pupil can vary in size between 2mm and 8mm, increasing to allow up to 30 times more light in than the minimum"

How ears work

The human ear performs a range of functions, sending messages to the brain when a sound is made while also providing your body with a sense of balance

The thing to remember when learning about the human ear is that sound is all about movement. When someone speaks or bangs a drum or makes any kind of movement, the air around them is disturbed, creating a sound wave of alternating high and low frequency. These waves are detected by the ear and interpreted by the brain as words, tunes or sounds.

Consisting of air-filled cavities, labyrinthine fluid-filled channels and highly sensitive cells, the ear has external, middle and internal parts. The outer ear consists of a skin-covered flexible cartilage flap called the 'auricle', or 'pinna'. This feature is shaped to gather sound waves and amplify them before they enter the ear for processing and transmission to the brain. The first thing a sound wave entering the ear encounters is the sheet of tightly pulled tissue separating the outer and middle ear. This tissue is the eardrum, or tympanic membrane, and it vibrates as sound waves hit it.

Beyond the eardrum, in the air-filled cavity of the middle ear, are three tiny bones called the 'ossicles'. These are the smallest bones in your entire body. Sound vibrations hitting the eardrum pass to the first ossicle, the malleus (hammer). Next the waves proceed along the incus (anvil) and then on to the (stapes) stirrup. The stirrup presses against a thin layer of tissue called the 'oval window', and this membrane enables sound waves to enter the fluid-filled inner ear.

The inner ear is home to the cochlea, which consists of watery ducts that channel the vibrations, as ripples, along the cochlea's spiraling tubes. Running through the middle of the cochlea is the organ of Corti, which is lined with minute sensory hair cells that pick up on the vibrations and generate nerve impulses that are sent to the brain as electrical signals. The brain can interpret these signals as sounds. ✿

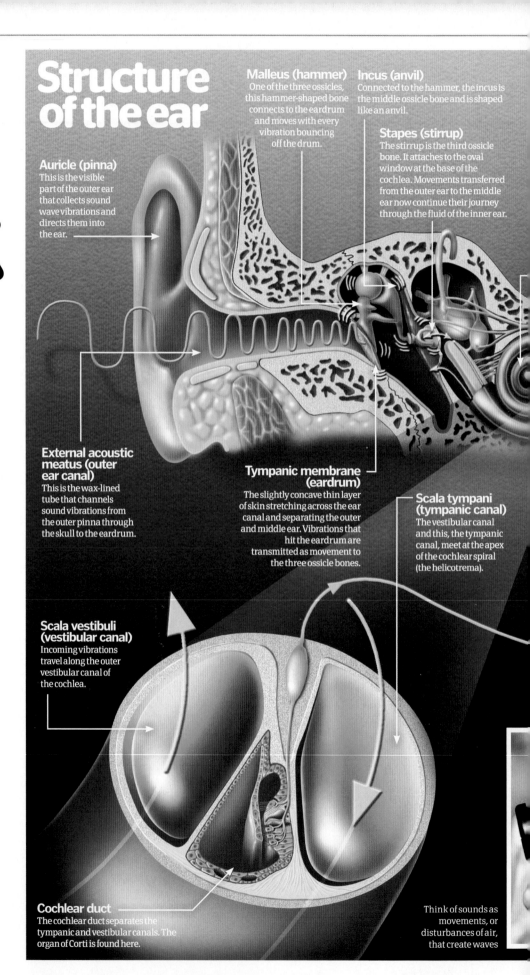

Structure of the ear

Malleus (hammer)
One of the three ossicles, this hammer-shaped bone connects to the eardrum and moves with every vibration bouncing off the drum.

Incus (anvil)
Connected to the hammer, the incus is the middle ossicle bone and is shaped like an anvil.

Stapes (stirrup)
The stirrup is the third ossicle bone. It attaches to the oval window at the base of the cochlea. Movements transferred from the outer ear to the middle ear now continue their journey through the fluid of the inner ear.

Auricle (pinna)
This is the visible part of the outer ear that collects sound wave vibrations and directs them into the ear.

External acoustic meatus (outer ear canal)
This is the wax-lined tube that channels sound vibrations from the outer pinna through the skull to the eardrum.

Tympanic membrane (eardrum)
The slightly concave thin layer of skin stretching across the ear canal and separating the outer and middle ear. Vibrations that hit the eardrum are transmitted as movement to the three ossicle bones.

Scala tympani (tympanic canal)
The vestibular canal and this, the tympanic canal, meet at the apex of the cochlear spiral (the helicotrema).

Scala vestibuli (vestibular canal)
Incoming vibrations travel along the outer vestibular canal of the cochlea.

Cochlear duct
The cochlear duct separates the tympanic and vestibular canals. The organ of Corti is found here.

Think of sounds as movements, or disturbances of air, that create waves

The vestibular system

Cochlea
A bony snail-shaped structure, the cochlea receives vibrations from the ossicles and transforms them into electrical signals that are transmitted to the brain. There are three fluid-filled channels – the vestibular canal, the tympanic canal and the cochlea duct – within the spiral of the cochlea.

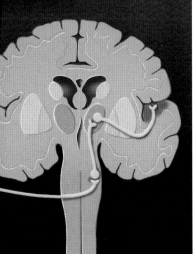

Organ of Corti
The organ of Corti contains rows of sensitive hair cells, the tips of which are embedded in the tectorial membrane. When the membrane vibrates, the hair receptors pass information through the cochlear nerve to the brain.

Cochlear nerve
Sends nerve impulses with information about sounds from the cochlea to the brain.

Inside the inner ear are the vestibule and semicircular canals, which feature sensory cells. From the semicircular canals and maculae, information about which way the head is moving is passed to receptors, which send electrical signals to the brain as nerve impulses.

Macula
A sensory area covered in tiny hairs.

Crista
At the end of each semicircular canal there are tiny hair-filled sensory receptors called cristae.

Semicircular canal
These three loops positioned at right angles to each other are full of fluid that transports sound vibrations to the crista.

Vestibular nerve
Sends information about equilibrium from the semicircular canals to the brain.

Vestibule
Inside the fluid-filled vestibules are two chambers (the utricle and saccule), both of which contain a structure called a macula, which is covered in sensory hair cells.

© DK Images

A sense of balance

The vestibular system functions to give you a sense of which way your head is pointing in relation to gravity. It enables you to discern whether your head is upright or not, as well as helping you to maintain eye contact with stationary objects while your head is turning.

Also located within the inner ear, but less to do with sound and more concerned with the movement of your head, are the semicircular canals. Again filled with fluid, these looping ducts act like internal accelerometers that can detect acceleration (ie, movement of your head) in three different directions due to the positioning of the loops along different planes. Like the organ of Corti, the semicircular canals employ tiny hair cells to sense movement. The canals are connected to the auditory nerve at the back of the brain.

Your sense of balance is so complex that the area of your brain that's dedicated to this one role involves the same number of cells as the rest of your brain cells put together.

The surfer's semicircular canals are as crucial as his feet when it comes to staying on his board

© Science Photo Library

Learn about teeth

The biological structures that are so versatile they enable us to eat a varied diet

The primary function of teeth is to chew food. For this reason, teeth are made of strong substances – namely calcium, phosphorus and various mineral salts. The main structure of the tooth is dentine, this itself is enclosed in a shiny substance called enamel. This strong white coating is the hardest material found in the human body.

Humans have different types of teeth that function in various ways. Incisors tear at food, such as the residue found on bones, while bicuspids have long sharp structures that are also used for ripping. Bicuspids tear and crush while molars, which have a flatter surface, grind the food before swallowing. This aids digestion. Because humans have a varied array of teeth (called collective dentition) we are able to eat a complex diet of both meat and vegetables. Other species, such as grazing animals, have specific types of teeth. Cows, for example, have large flat teeth, which restricts them to a simple diet.

Teeth have many functions, in some cases they aid hunting but they also have strong psychological connotations. Both animals and humans bare their teeth when faced with an aggressive situation. Teeth are the most enduring features of the human body. Mammals are described as 'diphyodont', which means they develop two sets of teeth. In humans the teeth first appear at six months old and are replaced by secondary teeth after six or seven years. Some animals develop only one set of teeth, while sharks, for instance, grow a new set of teeth every two weeks.

With humans, tooth loss can occur through accident, gum disease or old age. From ancient times healers have sought to treat and replace the teeth with false ones. Examples of this practice can be seen from ancient Egyptian times and today, we see revolutionary new techniques in the form of dental implants, which are secured deep within the bone of the jaw.

The trouble with teeth

Tooth decay, also often known as dental caries, affects the enamel and dentine of a tooth, breaking down tissue and creating fissures in the enamel. Two types of bacteria – namely Streptococcus mutans and Lactobacillus – are responsible for tooth decay.

Tooth decay occurs after repeated contact with acid-producing bacteria. Environmental factors also have a strong effect on dental health. Sucrose, fructose and glucose create large problems within the mouth, and diet can be an important factor in maintaining good oral health.

The mouth contains an enormous variety of bacteria, which collects around the teeth and gums. This is visible in the form of a sticky white substance called plaque. Plaque is known as a biofilm. After eating, the bacteria in the mouth metabolises sugar, which subsequently attacks the areas around the teeth.

Medication can also affect oral health, reducing the production of saliva, which offers natural protection and works against acidic matter. Various treatments can be applied to teeth that are damaged or decayed, these include extraction, filling or the replacement of teeth in the form of either dentures and implants.

Tooth anatomy

The tooth is a complex structure. The enamel at the surface of the tooth is highly visible while the dentine is a hard but porous tissue found under the enamel. The gums provide a secure hold for the tooth, while the root is anchored right into the jawbone. In the centre of the tooth there is a substance called 'pulp' which contains nerves and blood vessels, the pulp nourishes the dentine and keeps the tooth healthy.

Tooth formation begins before birth. Normally there are 20 primary teeth (human baby teeth) and later, 28 to 32 permanent teeth, which includes the wisdom teeth. Of the primary teeth, ten are found in the maxilla (the upper jaw) and ten in the mandible (lower jaw), while the mature adult has 16 permanent teeth in the maxilla and 16 in the mandible.

Enamel
The white, outer surface of the tooth. This can be clearly seen when looking in the mouth.

Pulp
The pulp nourishes the dentine and keeps the tooth healthy – the pulp is the soft tissue of the tooth, which is protected by the dentine and enamel.

Cementum
The root coating, it protects the root canal and the nerves. It is connected to the jawbone through collagen fibres.

Blood vessels and nerves
The blood vessels and nerves carry important nourishment to the tooth and are sensitive to pressure and temperature.

Bone
The bone acts as an important anchor for the tooth and keeps the root secure within the jawbone.

Inside your mouth

The upper and lower areas of the mouth are known as the maxilla and the mandible. The upper area of the mouth is attached to the skull bone and is often called the upper arch of the mouth, while the mandible is the v-shaped bone that carries the lower set of teeth.

Maxilla

A layout of the upper area of your mouth

Canine teeth
Long, pointed teeth that are used for holding and tearing at the food within the mouth.

Wisdom teeth
Usually appear between the ages of 17 and 25, and often erupt in a group of four.

Mandible

A look inside your lower jawbone

First and second premolar teeth
The premolar or bicuspids are located between the canine and molar teeth. They are used for chewing.

Lateral and central incisors
Incisor comes from the Latin word 'to cut', they are used to grip and bite.

"Both animals and humans bare their teeth when faced with an aggressive situation"

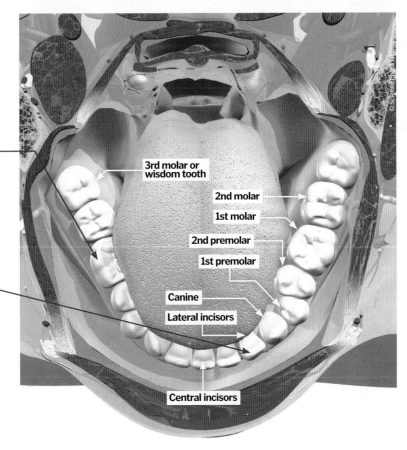

Central incisors
Lateral incisors
Canine
1st bicuspid
2nd bicuspid
1st molar
2nd molar
3rd molar or wisdom tooth

3rd molar or wisdom tooth
2nd molar
1st molar
2nd premolar
1st premolar
Canine
Lateral incisors
Central incisors

Adult teeth start coming through early on

Eruption of teeth

The approximate ages at which the permanent teeth begin to erupt

Age 6
First molar

Age 7
Central incisor

Age 9
First premolar

Age 10
Second premolar

Age 11
Canine

Age 12
Second molar

Age 17 to 21 or not at all
Third molar (wisdom teeth)

Why does it rain? p114

What is a rainforest? p90

What are the Northern lights? p127

© NASA

© Science Photo Library

Planet

What happens when a volcano erupts? p96

How are rivers formed? p120

Earth

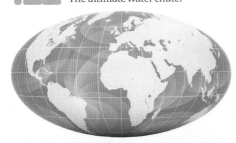

Rainforests are found mainly in tropical regions near the equator where the climate is consistently hot and wet, allowing the rapid and prolific expansion of all forms of life, be it flora or fauna. From the heartlands of South America, through the jungles of Africa and India, to the north coast of Australia, the rainforests are a phenomenal breeding ground for evolutionary processes and major players in maintaining the world's natural cycles, responsible for over 28 per cent of its oxygen turn over.

However, despite their massive selection of indigenous life forms and overall importance to the Earth's oxygen production, the rainforests cover less than six per cent of its surface, a number that thanks to perpetual deforestation is reducing daily, causing many species to be driven to extinction and the climate of many parts of the globe to change radically. This is because despite initial appearances, rainforests are highly complex and intricate systems, consisting of multiple layers that shroud the plethora of activity that is undertaken in each. Indeed, it has only been thanks to recent advances in science and technology that scientists and biologists have been able to study the rainforests in their full glory, recording footage, imagery and results that have highlighted, if anything, how much we still don't understand about them.

Luckily, many discoveries have already been made in the rainforests of the Earth, each providing a snapshot into this alien world. Here we take a closer look at how the rainforests tick, with specific emphasis on their makeup, diverse species of plants and animals, natural processes and the threat to them from deforestation. ✿

Lying around is just so tiring

Explaining rainforests

Receiving up to 2,000 millimetres of rainfall annually, as well as home to over 50 per cent of all Earth's species, the rainforests of our planet are a unique and life-abundant environment which still remain largely unobserved

Many species of parrot dwell in rainforests

ON THE MAP

Where do the rainforests grow?

There are two types of rainforest, tropical and sub-tropical. Where they are situated on Earth can be seen on the adjacent map.

■ Sub-tropical
■ Tropical

The layers of rainforests
Uncovering life below the surface

EMERGENT LAYER Height: 70-80m

The emergent layer boasts the tallest trees, stretching up over 80 metres high

The highest level of any rainforest is the emergent layer, consisting of large (70-80 metre tall), spaced-out trees that reach far above the general canopy. These giants of the forest are characterised by their umbrella-type tops, perfect for catching light, as well as their super-thick trunks, ideal for keeping them upright when strong winds hit their exposed upper extremities. The emergent layer is home to many species of bird, insect and mammal, including eagles, monkeys and butterflies. However, due to its height and direct exposure to the Sun and high winds, the emergent layer houses only a fraction of the life to be found in a rainforest.

CANOPY LAYER Height: 35-40m

Estimated to house over 50 per cent of all plant species on Earth, the canopy layer is one of the densest layers of biodiversity to be found in a rainforest. The canopy layer is similar in fauna to the emergent layer, but far more diverse due to shade, moisture and moderate temperatures. It mainly consists of a thick-layered system of vines and branches where animals shelter from the Sun's rays. Examples of animals that live in the canopy layer include sloths, parrots and toucans.

UNDERSTORY LAYER Height: 0.5-35m

Directly beneath the canopy layer and on top of the forest floor lies the understory layer, a dark, dense, humid maze of shrubs, vines and broadleaf trees. Home to animals such as the snakes, jaguars and lizards the understory layer is one of the most hostile of all, where the battle for survival is fierce. Very little light manages to break down to this level thanks to the overarching canopy, causing many plants and trees to grow large leaves to maximise whatever light they can get. Insect life is prolific at this level, with leaf-cutter ants, spiders, mosquitos and moths a common sight.

FOREST FLOOR Height: 0-0.5m

The lowest layer in any rainforest is the forest floor, a ground layer where the soil quality is exceptionally poor due to the almost total lack of sunlight. This level is prolific, however, in mosses, fungi and microorganisms (such as termites and earthworms).

The animals of the rainforests

The rainforests of the globe are inhabited by some of its most amazing creatures

Rainforests are tremendously rich in animal life thanks to their humid, life-abundant climates. A usual population for an area of rainforest can contain insects, reptiles, amphibians, birds, arachnids and mammals, with a diversity across all its layers unmatched anywhere else on the planet.

Among the most exotic include toucans, brightly coloured birds characterised by their enormous rainbow bills, ideal for reaching for fruit and other food in hard-to-reach places, as well as to intimidate potential predators.

Another species of animal the eastern rainforests boast is the endangered Bengal tiger, of which there are only about 2,000 left in the wild. The second largest tiger on Earth, Bengal tigers can grow up to over three metres and their average weight is 221 kilograms. As obligate carnivores, the amount of meat required to feed a Bengal is staggering (20kg in a single sitting), something that they achieve through a consistent diet of boars, deer, monkeys, birds and, in extreme circumstances, elephants, bears, leopards, wolves and even humans.

Three-toed sloths can also be found in the rainforest. Famously slow moving (they have a top speed of just 0.24km/h), it is an almost totally tree-dwelling species, with its entire body built to hang. These sloths tend to inhabit the understory layer of the forest.

Never one to rush through a meal…

Numerous frogs live in rainforests; many are poisonous

A Bengal tiger stalks through the rainforest

The swampy and sun-deprived understory

The plants of the rainforests

Known as the 'world's largest pharmacy', many of the natural medicines we use originate here

The amounts of chemicals that can be found in the plants of the rainforests are quite staggering. Take the cocoa tree for example, which produces more than 150 chemicals in its leaves, fruit, seeds and bark. The chemicals of this highly medical plant have been used to treat anxiety, fever and kidney stones among other things, as well as holding polyphenols that reduce the chance of cardiovascular disease and even cancer.

Another much-used medicinal plant from the Amazonian rainforest is the Achiote. Parts of this small shrub/tree can be used to make medical remedies for conditions such as leprosy, tonsillitis, pleurisy and apnoea. In addition, the sap from the Achiote's fruit is

Deforestation and climate change

Rainforests deforestation is escalating at an alarming rate

The Amazon Rainforest

Systematic
Square kilometres of forest are systematically dismantled to be sold on to logging and construction firms.

Roads
Roads snake through many areas of the rainforest, allowing heavy logging machinery to be brought in.

Barren
The bare land left by logging causes massive flooding problems as there are no longer trees to absorb rainfall slowly.

The effects on the Earth that deforestation brings are severe, with regional and global climate changing wildly, flooding more frequent, and the extinction of thousands of species of animals and plants. The causes of this destruction are many, with logging and cattle ranching the most serious.

Logging is the systematic processing of hectares of trees to be used in local and international markets, and it is estimated by conservationists that over 75 per cent of the world's forests have been destroyed or degraded by logging.

Cattle ranching also massively eats away at the borders of rainforests, and is increasing flood-prone areas greatly. This is because when ranchers cut down trees to create areas for their animals to pasture, they remove the sponge effect the rainforest provides, so instead of absorbing the large amount of rain the forest receives and distributing slowly, the newly stripped area just floods and channels quickly off into nearby rivers which then also flood.

The reduction in trees also has an impact on the local and global climate, as each time a part of rainforest is lost the net oxygen output from the area, due to photosynthesis, is reduced. Biosequestration (the capture and storage of greenhouse gases) is also reduced, as is the excess quantities of carbon produced under the rainforest, an important source of fuel for the future wellbeing of Earth.

"Pitchers have evolved this taste for blood due to the harsh conditions in which they grow"

used frequently to treat type 2 diabetes. Historically, records have shown that the native peoples of South America used the properties of the Achiote to lower blood pressure and as an insect repellent.

However, not all plants are medicinal, with many of the most aggressive and carnivorous species thriving in the humid, moisture-abundant conditions. Among the most famous of these are the carnivorous Venus flytrap and Pitcher plant, both of which devour numerous insects, reptiles and small mammals.

The Pitcher plant, which can be found mainly on the island of Borneo, traps its prey by luring insects and small animals into its conical body through its attractive appearance and corpse-like smell. Once inside the victim slips into a pool of lethal liquid at its bottom due to slick inner walls, before drowning and being slowly digested. Pitchers have evolved this unnatural taste for blood due to the harsh conditions in which they grow, only found on the forest floor layer of a rainforest.

The Venus flytrap, on the other hand, devours prey in a far more elegant manner. Luring prey into its waiting jaw through the sweet sticky nectar within, the flytrap then snaps shut on its prey when minuscule hairs are brushed against. The closing of its two leaves over the insect takes only a fraction of a second, and while certain bugs may escape, the majority get encased and slowly digested.

There are even plants that can eat rats whole!

The Earth's s

We take an in-depth look at the hidden world beneath our feet

We take the world around us for granted, but the Earth that we walk upon is a complex blend of layers that together create our planet. Thanks to research in the field of seismology, we now know the makeup of the Earth, its distances and measurements and can even compare it to other planets in our solar system.

Essentially, the internal structure of the Earth is made up of three core elements: the crust, the mantle and the core. The crust is the hard outer shell that we live on, split into Oceanic and Continental crusts, and it is comparatively thin. The first layer, the Oceanic crust, is around four to seven miles thick, made up of heavy rocks, whereas the lighter Continental crust is thicker, at approximately 19 miles.

Below the crust is the mantle, and again this is divided into two distinct layers: the inner and outer mantle. The outer mantle is the thinner of the two layers, occurring between seven miles and 190 miles below the Earth's surface. The outer mantle is made up of a bottom layer of tough liquid rock, with a temperature of somewhere between 1,400 degrees Celsius and 3,000 degrees Celsius, and a thinner, cooler upper layer. The inner mantle is deep into the Earth's structure, at between 190 and 1,800 miles deep, with an average temperature of 3,000 degrees Celsius.

Finally, we reach the Earth's core, which is 1,800 to 3,200 miles beneath our feet. The outer core is around 1,370 miles thick, encasing the inner core, which falls down to 3,960 miles below the Earth's surface. The inner core reaches a temperature high of 6,000 degrees Celsius and is made up of iron, nickel and other elements. While the outer core is liquid, the inner core is solid, and the two work together to cause the Earth's magnetism.

> "The internal structure of the Earth is made up of three core elements: the crust, the mantle and the core"

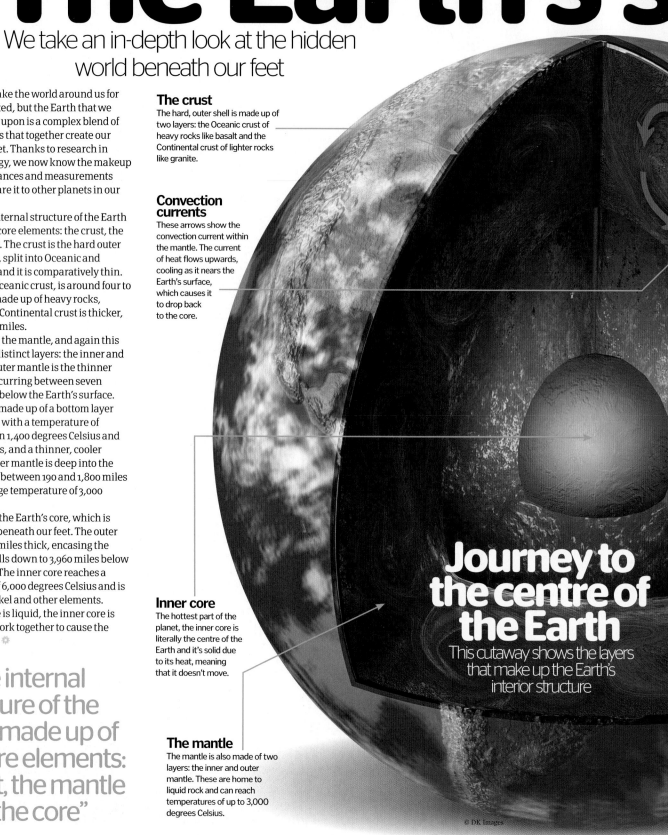

The crust
The hard, outer shell is made up of two layers: the Oceanic crust of heavy rocks like basalt and the Continental crust of lighter rocks like granite.

Convection currents
These arrows show the convection current within the mantle. The current of heat flows upwards, cooling as it nears the Earth's surface, which causes it to drop back to the core.

Inner core
The hottest part of the planet, the inner core is literally the centre of the Earth and it's solid due to its heat, meaning that it doesn't move.

Journey to the centre of the Earth
This cutaway shows the layers that make up the Earth's interior structure

The mantle
The mantle is also made of two layers: the inner and outer mantle. These are home to liquid rock and can reach temperatures of up to 3,000 degrees Celsius.

© DK Images

tructure

Oceanic crust
As suggested by its name, this lies underneath the Earth's oceans and commonly includes basalt in its makeup.

Water
Covering 70 per cent of the Earth's surface, resting on top of the crust, is water in the form of oceans, lakes and so on.

Landmasses
The remaining 30 per cent of the Earth's surface is made up of land – seven continents.

Mantle
Continuing down to the outer core, this shows the mantle, which gets hotter as you get closer to the centre.

Continental crust
The exposed crust that is part of the landmasses that cover the Earth and exposed to the atmosphere, containing rocks like granite.

Upper mantle
Also known as the asthenosphere, this is the thicker, liquid part of the mantle.

Outer core
The liquid, outer core is made up of iron, nickel, sulphur and oxygen. This outer core spins as the Earth rotates.

© DK Images

The Earth's surface
The surface of the Earth is just as complex as the interior structure

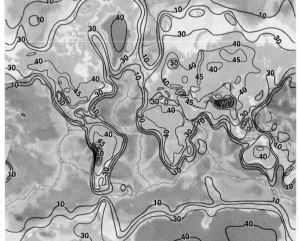

Crust thickness
A contour map of the globe, showing the thickness of the Earth's crust, with the numbers in kilometres.

How the Earth formed
A complicated procedure brought together the many elements of the Earth and even today the planet is adapting and changing

Accretion
Accretion describes the gradual increase in size of an object through the accumulation of additional layers. In the case of Earth, this is how rocks and metals built upon each other to form the core.

Heating and cooling
The process of creating planets via accretion causes friction and collisions that create a heat, which partly explains the temperature at the Earth's core. As this cooled in the planet's formation, the crust hardened.

Oceans and atmosphere
Steam from the crust combined with gases from volcanoes to create the atmosphere and water. As the planet cooled, clouds formed, causing rain, which in turn caused the oceans.

Today's Earth
Though we rarely see the results, the Earth's surface continues to change as landmasses collide and break apart, thanks to the dynamic properties of the Earth's interior structure, which can move land by centimetres each year.

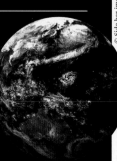

© Side bar images: DK Images

Inside a volcano

Around the world, sleeping giants lie in wait for their 15 megatons of fame

 Imagine the Earth as a giant ripe orange. Beneath the thin, dimpled peel is a thick layer of pulp and juice, 90 per cent of it liquid. The Earth's peel is called the lithosphere, a fragile crust of rock – 75-150km thick – that floats on a massive sea of impossibly hot, semi-fluid magma that extends 5,000km below the surface.

When German meteorologist Alfred Wegener first proposed his theory of "continental drift" back in 1912, people thought he was crazy. How could a colossal hunk of solid rock such as Asia or Africa possibly drift? As we now know, the continents are indeed solid, but they are fragmented into seven major plates and seven minor plates that eternally jostle for position like buoys on troubled water.

The engines that power this perpetual tectonic dance are giant convection currents in the Earth's molten mantle that slowly push magma upward and outward. Wherever rising magma manages to break through the thin lithosphere, it's called volcanism, but the vast majority of volcanoes aren't the explosive, violent variety. Instead, they are slow-bubbling cauldrons along a 60,000km underwater seam called the mid-ocean ridge.

The mid-ocean ridge is like an open, oozing wound in the crust where two oceanic plates diverge. The plates are pulled away from each other by the slow and steady convection currents and the gap between them is constantly refilled by thousands of unknown, unnamed underwater volcanoes. As this underwater lava cools, it creates new ocean floor covering 60 per cent of the Earth's surface.

Forget the orange analogy and think of the Earth's crust like a giant moving walkway in an airport. The walkway emerges from below the floor, travels a set distance and then rolls back underground. The divergent plate boundaries along the mid-ocean ridge are where the Earth's "moving walkway" begins. The diverging plates are carried along this magma conveyor belt – travelling only three to four centimetres per year – until they meet a plate moving in the other direction.

When two plates converge, something has to give. An incredible 90 per cent of earthquakes occur along convergent plate boundaries and so do the world's biggest and deadliest volcanoes. The prime example is the Ring of Fire, the unbroken string of seismic and volcanic activity that encircles the Pacific Ocean. The Ring of Fire is a giant subduction zone, where oceanic plates "dive" below

continental plates and are melted back into magma in the blazing hot forge of the mantle.

Ocean sediment holds tons of water, carbon dioxide, sodium and potassium. When oceanic crust enters the blast furnace of the mantle, these sea-borne elements lower the melting point of surrounding rock, forming a gaseous, yet viscous magma that rises quickly toward the surface. If the rising magma reaches an obstacle – an impenetrable thick layer of solid rock – it pools below the surface, building increased pressure as more gaseous, volatile molten materials push up from below.

And then one day – boom! All it takes is a weak point in the cap of rock holding back the magma. On Mount St. Helens, a landslide cleared a swath of rock from the north flank of the mountain, lowering the downward pressure on the boiling pot of magma below. The result was an explosion that produced a monstrous pyroclastic surge – a wall of searing hot fluidised gas, debris and ash – that vaporised everything within a 500-square-kilometre area.

Some of the most famous and infamous eruptions came from subduction zone volcanoes ▶

> ## "90 per cent of earthquakes occur along convergent plate boundaries and so do the world's biggest and deadliest volcanoes"

Why volcanic eruptions can spark lightning

The mesmerising lightning storms that danced among the ash clouds of Iceland's Eyjafjallajökull volcano were caused by the same conditions that trigger regular thunderstorms. High in the black clouds of a rainstorm, hail and water droplets whirl and collide, freeing large amounts of electrons. Newly charged positive ions congregate in the upper portion of the clouds while the negative particles drift downward. When the charge separation becomes too great, a spark of lightning releases the pent-up energy, bringing the system back to equilibrium.

In a volcanic lightning storm, the same principles are at work. In this case, the colliding particles include ash, water and even hail. Electrical fields form within the ash cloud and the frequent and eye-popping lightning strikes (often in vivid purple and orange colours) resolve the charge separations. Another ingredient of volcanic lightning is electrically charged silica particles that are blown airborne from deep in the earth.

© Science Photo Library

© Science Photo Library

097

▶ along the Ring of Fire: Tambora in Indonesia, Pinatubo in the Phillipines, Gagxanul in Guatemala, Mount Pelée in Martinique, the list of killer volcanoes goes on. In fact, 400 of the world's 500 known active volcanoes occur along subduction boundaries.

But not all famous volcanoes are of the subduction variety. The volcanoes of the Hawaiian Islands are an example of something called hot spot volcanism. Think back to those powerful convection currents in the mantle that push magma upward toward the crust. In certain 'hot spots' around the entire planet, convection currents are able to ooze magma to the surface with very little resistance.

Picture the hot spot under the Hawaiian Islands as a giant tube of toothpaste. Squeeze the tube and the little dollop of paste becomes the first Hawaiian Island, Kauai. Now keep the tube in the same place while the ocean plate travels a few hundred kilometres northwest. Squeeze the tube again and you've created the second island, Oahu. Hawaii, the Big Island, is still sitting over that magma pump, fuelling magnificent, slow-boiling eruptions that are literally building the island.

The intensity and duration of a volcanic eruption depends mostly on the consistency of the magma rising to the surface and the obstacles preventing the magma from reaching the surface. Subduction volcanoes are so ear-poppingly explosive because the magma fuelling them is loaded with gas bubbles and silica from sea floor sediments. The high silica content makes the magma more viscous, preventing gas bubbles from easily escaping. The result is like shaking a bottle of soda. When that pressure is released – pop!

Egmont
The Space Shuttle Atlantis exposed this image of the Mount Egmont volcano, New Zealand.

Young!
Egmont is a young stratovolcano that began to form 70,000 years ago.

© NASA

© U.S. Geological Survey/photo by Cyrus Rea

The hot spot volcanoes of Hawaii, on the other hand, feature highly fluid magma formed from basaltic rock with low silica content. The 'watery' quality of Hawaiian magma allows gas to escape easily. After an initial, relatively calm eruption, Hawaiian volcanoes spew fountains of lava forming large river-like flows that creep slowly to the sea.

The Hawaiian volcanoes Mauna Loa, Kilauea and Mauna Kea are the most closely studied volcanoes in the world, which is why different varieties of lava are classified with Hawaiian names. Pahoehoe is a highly fluid basaltic lava that cools with a smooth, ropy surface. A'a is a thicker lava carrying large chunks of pyroclastic debris like lava blocks and bombs. The result is a slow, jagged flow that cools with a very rough-looking texture.

Lava flow crossing a road during volcanic activity on Reunion, an island in the Indian Ocean

Types of volcanic eruption

Oozing, bubbling, spraying, fountaining, splattering, exploding! When magma reaches the surface, it's sure to be a memorable event. Check out the many different kinds of volcanic eruptions.

Eruption type: Magmatic

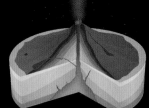

Strombolian
Huge gas bubbles rise and explode at the surface, shooting fast-cooling projectiles like lava bombs, glassy spatter and ash.

Vulcanian
Caused by the sudden release of a lava plug, these violent bursts of lava can send molten material several kilometres in the air.

Pelean
Incredibly deadly, a towering wall of rock, debris and lava pour down the slope of a volcano at speeds upwards of 150km/h.

Mount Redoubt
Mount Redoubt, Alaska. The glacier that filled the crater is collapsing because of the increase in ground temperature underneath.

Colima
The summit crater dome of Colima shows the pyroclastic flows that ran down the slopes during past eruptions.

© Matti Paavola

A colourful stromboli eruption

© Wolfgang Meyer

When a lava flow meets water, you get some lovely rounded formations called pillow lava, but if freshly emerging magma meets water, the results are far more explosive. A phreatic or 'steam blast' eruption discharges large rock fragments and ash, but little lava. The monstrous ash cloud that grounded flights across Europe for weeks was the product of magma meeting glacial ice. The ash from such an eruption isn't the soft, fluffy stuff that gets in your eyes when you have a campfire. Volcanic ash particles are hard, jagged fragments of rock, minerals and glass that can be up to 2mm in diameter.

The effect of a large-scale volcanic eruption is both local and global, immediate and long-term. Pyroclastic surges travelling 150km/h can obliterate an entire city in a matter of seconds, while a massive ash storm can block the Sun's rays so thoroughly that the Earth's surface temperature lowers for months, if not years. The 1815 eruption of Tambora in Indonesia spewed so much ash into the global atmosphere that it created a "year without a summer", complete with June snow storms in New York. ✿

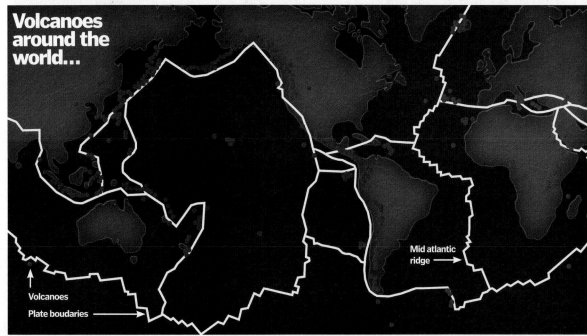

Volcanoes around the world...

Mid atlantic ridge →

Volcanoes →
Plate boudaries →

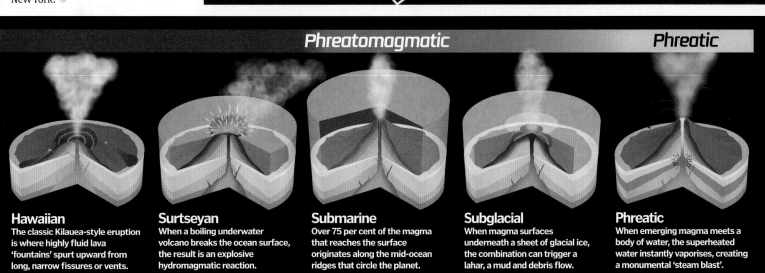

Phreatomagmatic

Phreatic

Hawaiian
The classic Kilauea-style eruption is where highly fluid lava 'fountains' spurt upward from long, narrow fissures or vents.

Surtseyan
When a boiling underwater volcano breaks the ocean surface, the result is an explosive hydromagmatic reaction.

Submarine
Over 75 per cent of the magma that reaches the surface originates along the mid-ocean ridges that circle the planet.

Subglacial
When magma surfaces underneath a sheet of glacial ice, the combination can trigger a lahar, a mud and debris flow.

Phreatic
When emerging magma meets a body of water, the superheated water instantly vaporises, creating a monumental 'steam blast'.

ON THE MAP

10 major mountain ranges

1. Ural Mountains
TYPE: Fold mountain range in Russia and Kazakhstan

2. Altai Mountains
TYPE: Fault-block mountain range in Central Asia

3. Tian Shan
TYPE: Fault-block mountain range in Central Asia

4. Sumatra-Java range
TYPE: Discontinuous mountain range system containing active volcanoes, ranging the length of Sumatra (the Barisan Mountains) and Java

5. Serra do Mar
TYPE: Discontinuous mountain range system on east coast of Brazil, fault-block formation

6. Transantarctic Mountains
TYPE: Fault-block mountain chain that serves as a division between East and West Antarctica

7. Eastern Highlands
TYPE: Discontinuous fold mountain range system dominating eastern Australia

8. Himalayas
TYPE: Fold mountain range system in Asia between India and the Tibetan Plateau

9. Rocky Mountains
TYPE: Fold mountain range in western North America

10. Andes
TYPE: Fold mountain range in South America

Mountain formation

How many ways can you make a mountain?

Mountains are massive landforms rising high above the Earth's surface, caused by one or more geological processes: plate tectonics, volcanic activity and/or erosion. Generally they fall into one of five categories – fold, fault-block, dome, volcanic and plateau – although there can be some overlap.

Mountains comprise about 25 per cent of our land mass, with Asia having more than 60 per cent of them. They are home to 12 per cent of the Earth's population, and they don't just provide beauty and

The Himalayas are home to the world's highest peaks

© NASA

Lithosphere
This rocky, rigid layer includes the oceanic and continental crusts and part of the mantle. Tectonic plates reside in this layer.

Continental crust
The outermost shell of the planet comprises sedimentary, igneous and metamorphic rock.

Fault-block mountains
Fractures in the tectonic plates create large blocks of rock that slide against each other. Uplifted blocks form mountains.

Asthenosphere
This semiplastic region in the upper mantle comprises molten rock and it's the layer upon which tectonic plates slide around.

recreation; more than half of the people on Earth rely on the fresh water that flows from the mountains to feed streams and rivers. Mountains are also incredibly biodiverse, with unique layers of ecosystems depending on their elevation and climate.

One of the most amazing things about mountains is that although they look solid and immovable to us, they're always changing. Mountains rising from activity associated with plate tectonics – fold and fault-block – form slowly over millions of years. The plates and rocks that initially interacted to form the mountains continue to move up to 2cm (0.7in) each year, meaning that the mountains grow. The Himalayas, for example, grow about 1cm per year.

The volcanic activity that builds mountains can wax and wane over time. Mount Fuji, the tallest mountain in Japan, has erupted 16 times since 781AD. Mount Pinatubo in the Philippines erupted in the early-Nineties without any prior recorded eruptions, producing the second largest volcanic eruption of the 20th Century. Inactive volcanic mountains – and all other types of mountains, for that matter – are also subject to erosion, earthquakes and other activity that can dramatically alter their appearances as well as the landscape around us. There are even classifications for the different types of mountain peaks that have been affected by glacial periods in Earth's history. The bare, near-vertical mountaintop of the Matterhorn in the Alps, for example, is known as a pyramidal peak, or horn.

Types of mountain

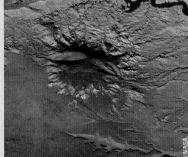

Fold
This most common type of mountain is formed when two tectonic plates smash into each other. The edges buckle and crumble, giving rise to long mountain chains.
Examples: Mount Everest, Aconcagua

Volcanic
These mountains are created by the buildup of lava, rock, ash and other volcanic matter during a magma eruption.
Examples: Mount Fuji, Mount Kilimanjaro

Dome
These types of mountain also form from magma. Unlike with volcanoes, however, there is no eruption; the magma simply pushes up sedimentary layers of the Earth's crust and forms a round dome-shaped mountain.
Examples: Navajo Mountain, Ozark Dome

Plateau
Plateau mountains are revealed through erosion of uplifted plateaux. This is known as dissection.
Examples: Catskill Mountains, Blue Mountains

Fault-block
Fault-block mountains form when cracked layers of crust slide against each other along faults in the Earth's crust. They can be lifted, with two steep sides; or lifted, with one gently sloping side and one steep side. **Examples:** Sierra Nevada, Urals

Mountains made from below

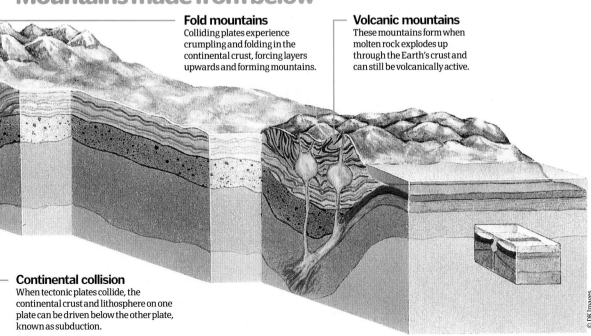

Fold mountains
Colliding plates experience crumpling and folding in the continental crust, forcing layers upwards and forming mountains.

Volcanic mountains
These mountains form when molten rock explodes up through the Earth's crust and can still be volcanically active.

Continental collision
When tectonic plates collide, the continental crust and lithosphere on one plate can be driven below the other plate, known as subduction.

Mountains are home to 12 per cent of the world's population

How plants work

Could you stay put in your birthplace for hundreds of years, surviving off whatever happens to be around?

Truly, it's not easy being green. But plants not only survive, they thrive all over the globe, without the benefit of muscles, brains or personalities. It's a good thing they do: plants head up nearly all food chains, pump out the oxygen we breathe, hold off erosion and filter pollutants out of the atmosphere. Over the past 3.5 billion years, they've diversified into an estimated 320,000-430,000 separate species, with more coming to light every year.

All this stems from one neat trick: harnessing the Sun's energy to power a built-in food factory. Through this process, called photosynthesis, plants combine carbon dioxide with water to create carbohydrates that they use to grow and reproduce.

The earliest plants, similar to today's algae, didn't do much other than photosynthesise. They floated around in the ocean, soaking up water and rays and reproducing asexually when the mood struck them. Then, around 500 million years ago, plants evolved to live on the land, to obtain the power boost of more abundant sunlight. The first landlubber plants still needed to stay wet all over, however, so they were confined to perpetually damp areas. Today's mosses, liverworts, and hornworts have the same limitations.

Things got more exciting 90 million years later, when plants went vascular. Vascular plants have tissue structures that can distribute water and nutrients absorbed by one part of the body to the rest of the body. Instead of

spending its days soaking in a puddle, a vascular plant can grow roots down into the ground to soak up water and minerals while sending shoots up into the dry air, topped with leaves that soak up sunshine to power the food factory.

Plants can store this food in their roots, in the form of root tubers, like carrots and sweet potatoes. Above ground, vascular plants protect themselves and retain their water supply with a waxy, waterproof covering called cuticle. Cuticle makes plants hearty enough to reach high into the air or spread far along the ground.

Plants grow at meristems, areas with cells that are capable of division – that is, making new cells. Hormones control this cell division to grow particular forms, like leaves, as well as controlling the

direction of growth, guided by what the plant 'senses'. Based on the settling of starch grains that indicate the direction of gravity, the growth hormone auxin drives stems to grow up towards the sky and roots to grow down towards water. Then, plants actually turn leaves toward the Sun. Triggered by light-sensitive cells that effectively 'see' light, the hormone auxin causes more cells to grow on the dimmer side of a stem, making the stem and attached leaf bend towards sunlight. Similarly, vines automatically curl when they come across a larger plant, causing them to wrap and climb.

Plants switch sexual orientation every generation. Each sporophyte generation produces male and female spores, which asexually yield male and female plants. In this gametophyte generation, males produce sperm and females produce eggs, which join up to create new sporophyte plants. Typically, the sporophyte generation is a large, familiar plant, while the gametophyte generation is tiny. For example, pollen is tiny male plants in the gametophyte generation. The tiny males and females produce an embryo, or seed.

When you can't walk, spreading your seed requires kinky creativity. For example, flowering plants attract insects with nectar, and then coat their legs with pollen to carry to the next plant. Plants also develop tasty fruits around plant seeds to entice animals to swallow seeds, and then defecate those seeds miles away.

Plants enrich every corner of human life, even beyond food and oxygen. From invaluable herbs – plants with medicinal or flavour value – to towering trees made from woody tissue, our original go-to construction material, plants prop up our civilisation. High-five one today. ✿

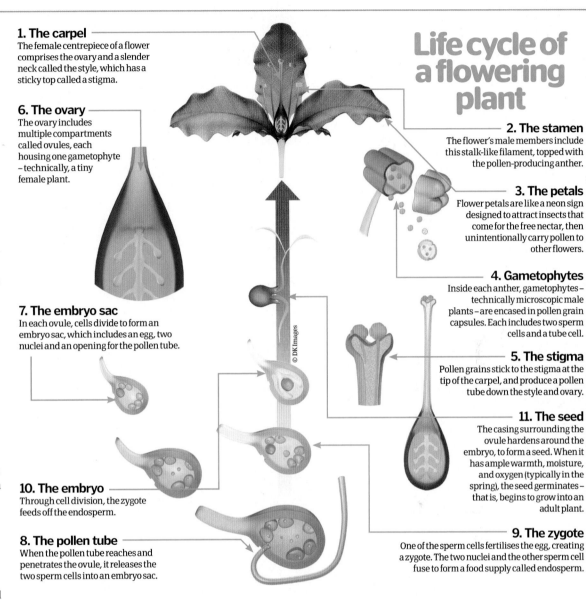

1. The carpel
The female centrepiece of a flower comprises the ovary and a slender neck called the style, which has a sticky top called a stigma.

6. The ovary
The ovary includes multiple compartments called ovules, each housing one gametophyte – technically, a tiny female plant.

7. The embryo sac
In each ovule, cells divide to form an embryo sac, which includes an egg, two nuclei and an opening for the pollen tube.

10. The embryo
Through cell division, the zygote feeds off the endosperm.

8. The pollen tube
When the pollen tube reaches and penetrates the ovule, it releases the two sperm cells into an embryo sac.

2. The stamen
The flower's male members include this stalk-like filament, topped with the pollen-producing anther.

3. The petals
Flower petals are like a neon sign designed to attract insects that come for the free nectar, then unintentionally carry pollen to other flowers.

4. Gametophytes
Inside each anther, gametophytes – technically microscopic male plants – are encased in pollen grain capsules. Each includes two sperm cells and a tube cell.

5. The stigma
Pollen grains stick to the stigma at the tip of the carpel, and produce a pollen tube down the style and ovary.

11. The seed
The casing surrounding the ovule hardens around the embryo, to form a seed. When it has ample warmth, moisture, and oxygen (typically in the spring), the seed germinates – that is, begins to grow into an adult plant.

9. The zygote
One of the sperm cells fertilises the egg, creating a zygote. The two nuclei and the other sperm cell fuse to form a food supply called endosperm.

© DK Images

Ferns reproduce in a different way from flowering plants

4. Prothallus
Each spore grows into a type of gametophyte called a prothallus. This is much bigger than the gametophytes in flowering plants.

1. The adult fern
Ferns date back 360 million years, making them more than 2.5 times older than flowering plants.

3. Spores
When enough spores form, they burst open the pod and disperse.

2. Sporangia
Inside these hard pods on the underside of fern fronds, spore cells multiply.

6. Archegonia
Sperm from another prothallus fertilises the egg inside the archegonia, to form a zygote.

5. Mature gametophyte
The prothallus grows both a female sex organ (the archegonia) and a male sex organ (the antherida), which produces sperm.

7. Young fern
The zygote grows into a young fern, and the prothallus structure withers away.

© DK Images

Most unusual plants

The sensitive plant

Touch a leaf on the sensitive plant, also known as mimosa pudica, and an electrical current activates sudden water loss, causing leaves to drop abruptly. This imitation of an animal scares pests away.

Myrmecophytes

Many species, collectively known as myrmecophytes, have evolved to be ideal homes for ant colonies. In return, the ants viciously attack any threats to the plant.

Sumatran corpse flower

The world's largest flower can grow to be 0.9m (3ft) wide and 24 pounds. It mimics the smell of rotting meat in order to attract carrion-eating insects, which then spread its pollen.

Snowdonia hawkweed

This Welsh flower is possibly the world's rarest plant. Botanists thought it extinct in the early-Fifties, but in 2002 it made a surprise reappearance near Bethesda.

Plant plumbing: How transport works

Internal transportation systems in plants move water, food and other nutrients between roots, stems and leaves. This system is the key adaptation that allowed plants to evolve elaborate shapes and towering forms.

Upper epidermis
The waxy cuticle on the epidermis keeps the plant from drying out.

Palisade mesophyll
These cells are rich in chloroplasts, which are integral in photosynthesis.

Xylem vessel
These vessels carry water, with dissolved minerals, from the roots to leaves.

Phloem vessel
These carry food created in photosynthesis from leaves to the rest of the plant.

Diffusion
This water vapour exits the plant through leave openings called stomata. This continual exit of water creates negative pressure, which effectively pulls water up the xylem from the roots.

Movement of water
Water moves from the xylem vessels, which run from the roots to leaves, into the mesophyll cells.

Evaporation
Water along the walls of the mesophyll cells evaporates, forming water vapour.

Spongy mesophyll
Mesophyll cells fit together to form most of the tissue in a leaf.

Lower epidermis
The lower epidermis can be thinner than the upper epidermis, since it doesn't get direct sunlight.

Stoma
Guard cells alongside each stoma (pore in the leaf) open when sunlight and humidity are high.

Flower stigmas come in various shapes

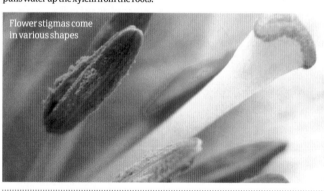

Insects seeking nectar pick up pollen on their legs

The root of it: How absorption works

Roots soak up water through osmosis – the drive for water to move through a cell membrane from a less concentrated solution to a more concentrated solution, in order to achieve equilibrium. Cells in roots have a higher concentration than the surrounding water in the soil, so the water flows into the root.

3. Water enters the stem
Water continues flowing through the xylem, up into the above-ground stem, helped along by negative pressure in the leaves, created by evaporating water.

2. Water enters xylem
Pressure from osmosis pushes water into xylem vessels in the root core.

1. Root hairs
Thin hairs extending from the root increase the surface area for osmosis, and so handle most water absorption.

Inside the food factory:
How photosynthesis works

In Greek, photosynthesis means 'putting together' (synthesis) using 'light' (photo), and that's a decent summary of what it's all about. However, photosynthesis doesn't actually turn light into food, as you sometimes hear; it's the power source for a chemical reaction that turns carbon dioxide and water into food.

The energy of light protons temporarily boosts the electrons in pigment molecules to a higher energy level. In other words, they generate an electrical charge. The predominant pigment in plants – chlorophyll – primarily absorbs blue, red, and violet light, while reflecting green light (hence, the green colour). In some leaves, chlorophyll breaks down in the autumn, revealing secondary pigments that reflect yellows, reds, and purples. Pigments are part of specialised organelles called chloroplasts, which transfer the energy of excited electrons in pigments to molecules and enzymes that carry out the photosynthesis chemical reaction.

Harnessing sunlight
Chlorophyll and other pigments absorb energy of light photons from the Sun.

Expelling oxygen
The oxygen from the water isn't necessary to make food, so the plant releases it through pores called stomata.

Nucleus
The cell nucleus houses genetic instructions (DNA) and relays instructions to the rest of the cell.

Vacuole
Among other things, this organelle contains water that helps maintain the turgor pressure that keeps plants erect.

Breaking water down
The energy from light breaks water molecules down into hydrogen and oxygen.

Making food
Through additional reactions, the plant converts glucose into a range of useful compounds. Sucrose acts as plant fuel, starches store energy for later, protein aids cell growth, and cellulose builds cell walls.

Chloroplast
These are the engines for photosynthesis. A typical leaf palisade cell includes up to 200 chloroplasts.

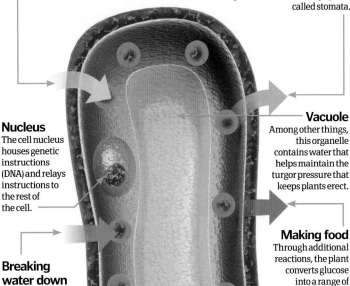

© DK Images

Adding carbon dioxide
Plants get all the CO_2 they need from the air. CO_2 combines with hydrogen to make glucose, a simple sugar.

Colourful petals are designed to attract insects

ON THE MAP

How much of the planet is covered by forest?
40 million sq km (15,444,100 sq miles), or a third of the Earth's land area, is covered by forests.

1 34% Rest of the world
2 20% Russian Federation
3 12% Brazil
4 8% US
5 8% Canada
6 5% China
7 4% Australia
8 3% Democratic Republic of Congo
9 2% India
10 2% Indonesia
11 2% Peru

© Walter Oedmund 2009

Bunchberry dogwood
This shrub holds the 'fastest plant' record. When its flower opens, stamens fling out like a catapult, propelling pollen at 800 times the g-force astronauts experience.

Parachute flowers
The different species of parachute flower have long flower tubes lined with inward pointing hairs that temporarily hold insects trapped, to ensure they end up covered in pollen before exiting.

Welwitschia mirabilis
This so-called 'living fossil' plant of the Namib desert in Africa grows only two leaves, over hundreds of years. They grow continuously, however, and can extend more than 4 metres (13 feet).

© Science Photo Library

Flypaper plants
Also known as butterworts, these plants are coated in super-sticky digestive enzymes that absorb nutrients from all manner of bugs that happen to get trapped.

Compound leaf
Compound leaves are divided into smaller leaflets. There is a single bud at the base of the petiole stalk.

Terminal buds
A bud found at the tip of the stem is called a terminal bud and will allow the stem to grow in length.

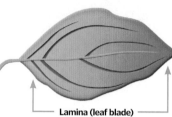

Inside a leaf
UPPER EPIDERMIS   **PALISADE CHLOROPHYLL**

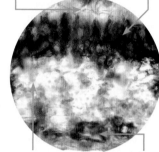

SPONGY MESOPHYLL   **LOWER EPIDERMIS**

Leaves
These green fleshy parts are vital to the plant's ability to create its own food. The process of photosynthesis enables a plant to produce carbohydrates from the Sun's energy. The leaves therefore expose as much surface area as possible in order to absorb the most sunlight, they will even turn towards the Sun for maximum absorption.

Lamina (leaf blade)

Simple leaf
Consisting of a flat and solid blade, a simple leaf is supported by and attached to the stem by a small petiole stalk.

Lateral buds
Axillary buds are those located on the area between the upper side of the leafstalk and the stem.

Stem
The plant's strong stem offers support for the leaves and other above-ground parts. It is made up of nodes and internodes, with the nodes representing the site where the leaves are attached and the internodes, predictably, indicating the area of the stem between nodes. Green stems are photosynthetic, they just don't produce as much carbohydrate as the leaves. The stem is a vascular system, which means they transport water and minerals to the leaves and the roots.

Leaf veins

Plant anatomy

Explaining the parts of a plant and their functions

Plants feature two main systems: the roots and the shoots. Above ground the shoot system comprises the food-making leaves, buds, stem, and any flowers or fruit the plant may have. Below ground the food-storing root system, which anchors the plant in the soil and prevents it from blowing away, features nutrient-absorbing roots, tubers, and rhizomes. Let's start from the top and work down. ☼

Node, point of attachment of branch or leaf

Vascular tissue   Epidermis layer

Stem cross section
Stems consist of a thin transparent epidermis layer that produces a juicy substance that can attract insects, a vascular tissue layer made up of xylem and phloem (the transport tissues that move water and sugars through the plant), and providing the bulk of the stem's mass is the ground tissue, in which starch can be stored.

Ground tissue

Root cap
Right at the end of the root is a thimble-shaped cap that protects and lubricates the root as it grows through the soil.

Root tip
This is the area of the root where cell division takes place.

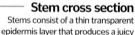

Shoot system

Primary root

Roots
The roots permeate the soil, anchoring the plant. The part of the plant embryo that sprouts into a root (the radicle) immediately gets to work securing the plant by growing downwards and branching off to grow secondary roots.

Many plants develop structures that are not roots but specialised stems. Rhizomes, for example, are horizontal plant stems that grow underground and can develop new roots and shoots. Below the surface you may also find tubers, which are thickened swollen plant stems (such as potatoes).

Root system

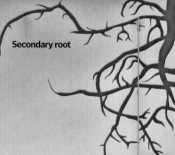

Secondary root

Adventitious buds
These unruly buds will develop anywhere but where they're meant to, such as on the root.

Root hairs
The hairs on a root have a huge surface area, enabling it to more efficiently soak up water and minerals – especially nitrogen and sulphur – by way of either osmosis, diffusion or active transport.

How cacti survive

Taking a closer look at the materials and mechanisms cacti use to survive in the world's harshest environments

Spines gather moisture and also serve as a defence mechanism

© Science Photo Library

Flowers
All cacti have a floral tube that grows above a one-chamber ovary. Cacti flowers tend to be solitary, large and very colourful, and are pollinated by both wind power and animals. After pollination, the entire floral tube detaches from the body.

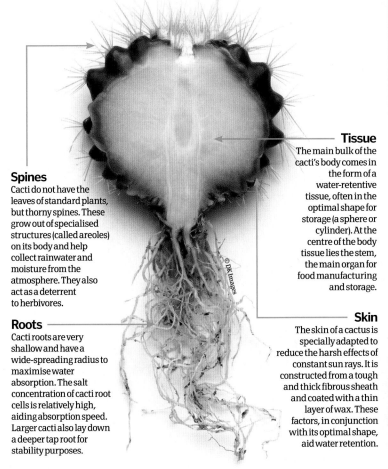

© DK Images

Spines
Cacti do not have the leaves of standard plants, but thorny spines. These grow out of specialised structures (called areoles) on its body and help collect rainwater and moisture from the atmosphere. They also act as a deterrent to herbivores.

Roots
Cacti roots are very shallow and have a wide-spreading radius to maximise water absorption. The salt concentration of cacti root cells is relatively high, aiding absorption speed. Larger cacti also lay down a deeper tap root for stability purposes.

Tissue
The main bulk of the cacti's body comes in the form of a water-retentive tissue, often in the optimal shape for storage (a sphere or cylinder). At the centre of the body tissue lies the stem, the main organ for food manufacturing and storage.

Skin
The skin of a cactus is specially adapted to reduce the harsh effects of constant sun rays. It is constructed from a tough and thick fibrous sheath and coated with a thin layer of wax. These factors, in conjunction with its optimal shape, aid water retention.

Cacti are hardy, flowering plants in the caryophyllales order that have evolved to survive in some of the Earth's driest and most barren landscapes. This unceasing survival is achieved through the specialised tailoring of two main principles: form and function.

First, all cacti have developed optimal forms for retention of internal water supplies (spheres and cylinders), combining the highest possible volume for storage with the lowest possible surface area for loss. This allows cacti to store vast quantities of water for elongated

periods – for example, the species carnegiea gigantea can absorb 3,000 litres in a mere ten days. This ability directly correlates to the typical weather patterns of Earth's barren, dry environments, with little water being deposited for months on end, only for a short monsoon to follow in the rainy season. Optimal structural form also grants much-needed shadow for lower areas of the plant.

Second, cacti have evolved unique mechanisms and adapted traditional plant functions to grow and thrive. Foremost among these changes are the cacti's spines, elongated spiky structures that grow out from its

central body though areoles (cushion-like nodes). These act as a replacement for leaves, which would quickly die if exposed to high levels of sun rays. The spines have a membranous structure and can absorb moisture directly from the atmosphere (especially important in foggy conditions) and also from deposited rainwater, capturing and absorbing droplets throughout the body's spiny matrix. In addition, due to the lack of leaves, cacti have evolved so as to undertake photosynthesis directly within their large, woody stems, generating energy and processing stored water safely away from the intense sunlight.

Finally, cacti have modified their root structures to remain stable in brittle, parched earth. Cacti roots are very shallow compared with other succulents and are spread out in a wide radius just below the Earth's crust. This, in partnership with an intense salt concentration, allows cacti to maximise their access to and absorbability speed of ground water, sucking it up before it evaporates or trickles down deeper into the Earth. For stability, many cacti also extend a main 'tap root' further into the Earth, in order to act as an anchor against high winds and attacks by animals. ✿

Coffee plants

From seed to a steaming hot cup of tasty beverage, we explain how coffee is grown and cultivated

Coffee production starts with the plantation of a species of coffee plant, such as the arabica species. Plants are evenly spaced at a set distance to ensure optimal growing conditions (access to light, access to soil nutrients, space to expand). Roughly four years after planting, the coffee plant flowers. These flowers last just a couple of days, but signal the start of the plant's berry-growing process.

Roughly eight months after flowering, the plant's berries ripen. This is indicated by the change in shade, beginning a dark-green colour before changing through yellow to a dark-red. Once dark-red, the berries are then harvested by strip picking or selective picking. The former is an often mechanised technique where an entire crop is harvested at once, regardless of being fully ripe or not. By doing this, the producer can quickly and cheaply strip a plantation but at the expense of overall bean quality. The latter technique is more labour-intensive, where workers handpick only fully ripe berries over consecutive weeks. This method is slower and more costly, but allows a greater degree of accuracy and delivers a more consistent and quality crop.

Once the berries have been harvested, the bean acquisition and milling process begins. Processing comes in two main forms, wet and dry. The dry method is the oldest and most predominant worldwide, accounting for 95 per cent of arabica coffee. This involves cleaning the berries whole of twigs, dirt and debris, before spreading them out on a large concrete or brick patio for drying in the sun. The berries are turned by hand every day, to prevent mildew and ensure an even dry. The drying process takes up to four weeks, and the dried berry is then sent to milling for hulling and polishing.

The wet method undertakes hulling first, with the beans removed from the berries before the drying process. This is undertaken by throwing the berries into large tanks of water, where they are forced through a mesh mechanically. The remainder of any pulp is removed through a fermentation process. As with

Workers pick large quantities of coffee berries

the dry method, the beans are then spread out on a patio for drying.

The final stage is milling. This is a series of four processes to improve the texture, appearance, weight and overall quality. Beans that have been prepared the dry way are first sent for hulling to remove the remaining pulp and parchment skin. Next, the beans are sent for polishing. This is an optional process, in which the beans are mechanically buffed to improve their appearance and eliminate any chaff produced during preparation. Third, the beans are sent through a battery of machines that sort them by size and density (larger, heavier beans produce better flavour than smaller and lighter ones). Finally the beans are graded, a process of categorising beans on the basis of every aspect of their production.

Anatomy of a coffee plant

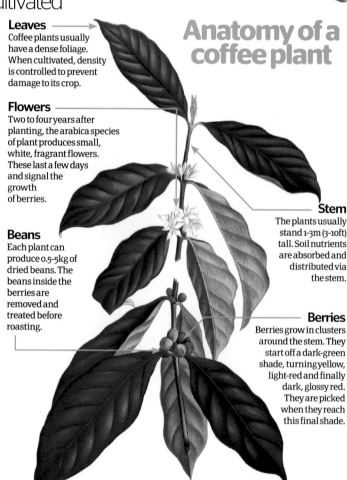

Leaves
Coffee plants usually have a dense foliage. When cultivated, density is controlled to prevent damage to its crop.

Flowers
Two to four years after planting, the arabica species of plant produces small, white, fragrant flowers. These last a few days and signal the growth of berries.

Beans
Each plant can produce 0.5-5kg of dried beans. The beans inside the berries are removed and treated before roasting.

Stem
The plants usually stand 1-3m (3-10ft) tall. Soil nutrients are absorbed and distributed via the stem.

Berries
Berries grow in clusters around the stem. They start off a dark-green shade, turning yellow, light-red and finally dark, glossy red. They are picked when they reach this final shade.

Anatomy of a coffee berry

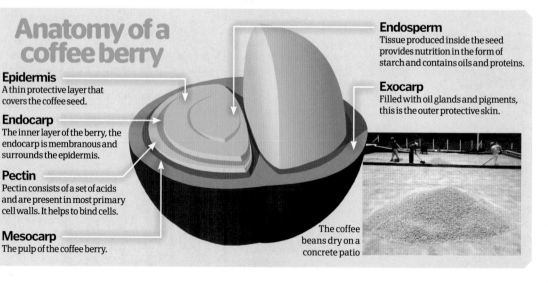

Epidermis
A thin protective layer that covers the coffee seed.

Endocarp
The inner layer of the berry, the endocarp is membranous and surrounds the epidermis.

Pectin
Pectin consists of a set of acids and are present in most primary cell walls. It helps to bind cells.

Mesocarp
The pulp of the coffee berry.

Endosperm
Tissue produced inside the seed provides nutrition in the form of starch and contains oils and proteins.

Exocarp
Filled with oil glands and pigments, this is the outer protective skin.

The coffee beans dry on a concrete patio

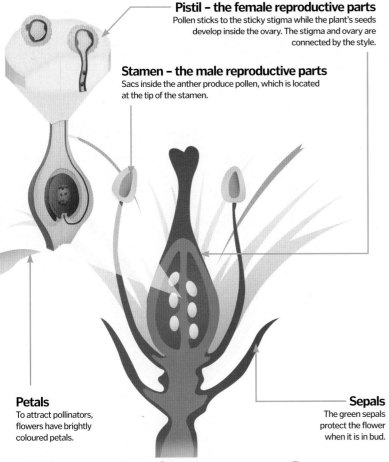

Pistil – the female reproductive parts
Pollen sticks to the sticky stigma while the plant's seeds develop inside the ovary. The stigma and ovary are connected by the style.

Stamen – the male reproductive parts
Sacs inside the anther produce pollen, which is located at the tip of the stamen.

Petals
To attract pollinators, flowers have brightly coloured petals.

Sepals
The green sepals protect the flower when it is in bud.

Pollination

Plants: the facts of life

Flowering plants propagate by way of pollination. Just as in human reproduction, there are male and female sex organs. This process, however, is much less strenuous than in animal intercourse; the male parts of the flower barely do anything.

The male parts of the flower, which produce pollen, are called stamens, and each one consists of a stalk, or filament, with what's known as an anther at the tip. The anther is full of tiny sacs in which the pollen grains develop and eventually break free.

The female reproductive organs are called pistils, and these consist of a sticky stigma at the tip, which the pollen sticks to, and an ovary, which is a bulbous structure full of ovules where seeds develop at the base of the pistil. The stigma and ovary are connected by a stalk called a style.

Pollen itself is produced by the male organs and is transferred to the female parts in order to form seeds. Self-pollination can occur when pollen sticks to the stigma of a flower of the same plant. Alternatively pollen can be transferred to another plant altogether, and this can either be as a result of the wind blowing the pollen through the air, or by the pollen getting stuck to industrious insects attracted by the blooms' colourful petals, who then roam from flower to flower unknowingly distributing pollen as they go.

When a male pollen grain lands on the female stigma of a plant of the same species, the grain develops a pollen tube that leads to an ovule within the ovary. The male cells then travel through the tube into the ovule, where it can proceed to fertilise the female egg inside. Once fertilisation has occurred, a seed forms in the ovary. Meanwhile, the ovary surrounding the seed becomes a fruit, which protects the seed and helps it develop into a plant itself. ✿

Photosynthesis

Plants need to eat but how do they do it?

Photosynthesis is the process plants use to make food to live. Plants take carbon dioxide from the air and water (from rain) to make an organic chemical glucose – a food which plants absorb to survive. The process requires an input of energy and that is where sunlight comes in. Plants capture the energy from sunlight using a pigment called chlorophyll which converts light energy into chemical energy. Oxygen is released as a waste chemical. The formula is noted as:

Carbon dioxide + water – (sunlight) – Glucose + Oxygen, or:

$6CO_2 + 6H_2O - (sunlight) - C_6H_{12}O_6 + 6O_2$

The process occurs in the leaves of the plant and each variety has evolved to make sure as much photosynthesis happens as possible, because the more a plant photosynthesises, the more food it can make and the faster and stronger it will grow – optimising its chances of survival. The leaf exhibits a waxy outer shell to restrict the loss of water as this is a crucial substance in the process.

The three ingredients a plant needs for photosynthesis to occur are carbon dioxide, water and light. The three factors which affect the rate at which a plant can produce glucose via this method is the concentration of carbon dioxide, temperature and light intensity. A plant will use glucose as a storage food substance such as starch – as in the case of potatoes or rice, or lipids in the case of seeds. It may convert the glucose into cellulose to make or repair cell walls and in other cases it forms amino acids which are used to produce proteins or chlorophyll to trap more sunlight to perpetuate the cycle. ✿

"Plants capture the energy from sunlight using chlorophyll"

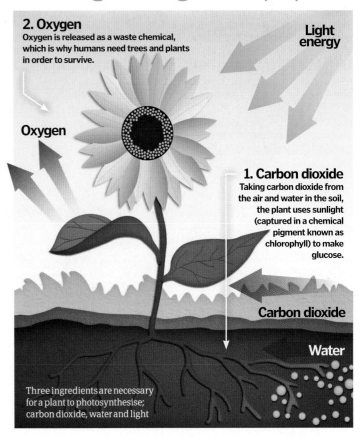

2. Oxygen
Oxygen is released as a waste chemical, which is why humans need trees and plants in order to survive.

Light energy

Oxygen

1. Carbon dioxide
Taking carbon dioxide from the air and water in the soil, the plant uses sunlight (captured in a chemical pigment known as chlorophyll) to make glucose.

Carbon dioxide

Water

Three ingredients are necessary for a plant to photosynthesise; carbon dioxide, water and light

The water

Rain falling today has spent billions of years travelling between Earth's clouds, oceans and ice

The water – or hydrological – cycle is the Earth's water recycling system. Since water rarely escapes the planet or arrives from space, the water cycle keeps rivers relentlessly flowing into the oceans and the atmosphere supplied with clouds and rain. Without it, life simply couldn't exist.

The water cycle circulates water between the oceans and atmosphere, sometimes via the land. When ocean water is heated, it turns into water vapour, which rises into the atmosphere and is carried by winds. The vapour cools at some point and forms clouds. Around 78 per cent of the rain, snow and other forms of precipitation falling from these clouds goes straight back into the ocean. The rest falls over the Earth's continents and islands.

Some of this water runs into rivers and lakes and is carried back to the sea. Water also seeps back to the oceans through deep soil and rocks, becoming the Earth's groundwater. Water falling as snow over the polar ice sheets can be buried, sometimes for millions of years, until it reaches the sea via slow-moving glaciers. Water that stays in shallow soil can be lifted back into the atmosphere when it warms. Alternatively, plants may suck up soil water through their roots and return it to the atmosphere through their leaves. When animals eat plants, they take the water into their bodies and expel it into the air in their breath.

Humans are increasingly altering the water cycle on land by building cities and flood controls, and capturing water for drinking, agriculture and industry.

How the water cycle works

Ocean water evaporation
Ocean water is heated, evaporates and rises into the atmosphere as water vapour. The vapour cools as it rises and, at some point, condenses and forms clouds.

Loss from vegetation
Plants contribute about ten per cent of the water in the atmosphere by losing water drawn from the ground through their leaves by transpiration.

Water processes explained

Condensation
When you breathe on a cold window and it fogs up, you're seeing condensation in action. It's the process by which water vapour in the air turns back into liquid water when it cools down. Atmospheric water vapour condenses on salt, smoke and dust particles to form clouds.

Infiltration
Infiltration is where water seeps into the ground rather than running across it. Once in the ground, the water stays in shallow soil layers or moves deeper to form groundwater. Dry, loose soils on flat ground will absorb more water than steeply sloping hard surfaces or already wet soil.

cycle

Water vapour transport
Around eight per cent of the water evaporated from the oceans is carried over the land by winds circulating through the atmosphere.

Snowfall
Snow melts immediately or when the weather warms, but if it falls on glaciers or ice sheets, it can be locked up for hundreds or even millions of years.

Rainfall
Rain runs off into rivers or infiltrates into the ground where it is taken up by plants or moves into groundwater.

Surface water evaporation
Around 14 per cent of evaporation occurs over land from lakes, rivers, ice and the ground. Ice also turns straight into water vapour without melting, a process called sublimation.

Groundwater
Water infiltrating into the soil can seep into the ground where it flows towards streams and the ocean, or enters deep underground stores called aquifers.

© DK Images

The River Indus reached 30 kilometres wide in places

When the water cycle lets us down

Floods affect tens of thousands of people each year, as is evident from 2010's devastating monsoon flooding across Pakistan. The flood, which affected some 20 million people, was the result of the heaviest monsoon rains in the area for generations. On 8 August 2010 the River Indus burst its banks, sweeping away entire communities. While it's normal for Pakistan to receive half its annual rainfall (250-500mm) during the monsoon months of July and August, the country was reportedly bombarded with 300mm on 29 July alone. The Met Office suggests several possible reasons for the unusually heavy rains, including changes to upper atmosphere airflow, active monsoon systems, and La Niña (El Niño in reverse).

Serious floods, like those seen in Pakistan during July and August 2010, can cause catastrophic destruction

Runoff

Water flowing down tarmac roads into curb-side drains after a storm is an example of the process of runoff. Rain that doesn't evaporate or infiltrate into soil or rock also flows down small channels as runoff. The channels merge into streams that, eventually, join rivers flowing downhill to the sea.

Evaporation
Wet clothes hung outside dry by evaporation, the process by which liquid water turns into vapour when  heat energy breaks bonds between its water molecules. Soaking a T-shirt keeps you cool on a hot day because since evaporation uses up heat energy from the air, it reduces nearby temperatures.

Precipitation
Precipitation is a catch-all term for water falling from clouds to the earth. It covers rain, snow, hail and so on. Precipitation happens when water vapour condenses on airborne particles as droplets. These grow bigger by, for example, collisions until they become so heavy they fall to the ground.

Transpiration

Plants – like humans – breathe out water vapour, a process called transpiration. During transpiration, water drawn into a plant's roots is carried to the leaves where it evaporates. How much plants transpire varies depending on air temperature, humidity and incoming sunlight. Higher temperatures and stronger sunlight mean more transpiration.

The Earth's atmosphere

It's all around us, but how much do we know about our atmosphere?

Our atmosphere (made up of 78 per cent nitrogen and 21 per cent oxygen, with other gases making up the last per cent) is held in place by gravity and consists of a number of different layers that work together to protect us from solar radiation and to keep consistent temperatures. The atmosphere gets thinner with altitude, with 80 per cent of its mass in the first layer closest to the Earth's surface. There are five main layers that make up the atmosphere. The troposphere is the first layer (and is where our weather occurs), followed by the stratosphere, mesosphere, thermosphere and exosphere. There is no definite boundary between where the atmosphere ends and outer space begins, though the Kàrmàn line at 100km above sea level is often regarded as a the boundary.

There are other layers that exist alongside the five main layers. The lowest of these is the 'planetary boundary', which is within the troposphere and closest to the Earth's surface

and its depth can vary widely between 100m to 3,000m as it is directly affected by conditions on the surface. The ozone layer is the one that most of us will be familiar with and this is contained within the stratosphere, in its lower portion. Around 90 per cent of the ozone in the atmosphere lies here. The ionosphere is what causes auroras, such as the northern lights, as it is ionised by solar radiation and stretches from 50 to 1,000km, overlapping the exosphere and thermosphere.

Finally, the homosphere and the heterosphere run from the Earth's surface to around 80km and from 80km upwards respectively. They are so-named because of the way the gases within them are mixed. The heterosphere has a chemical composition that changes with height, whereas the homosphere's make-up remains more constant. The five main layers are based on the thermal structure of the atmosphere, whereas the additional layers mentioned here are classified according to composition. ✿

The northern lights are caused partly by the atmosphere

Atmospheric water vapour

Moisture in the air

The gaseous water vapour in our atmosphere is responsible for our rain, snow, hail, fog, and clouds. If the vapour was to fall evenly over the planet as precipitation, each year 25mm of water will have fallen.

7.5
6.0
4.5
3.0
1.5
0.0cm

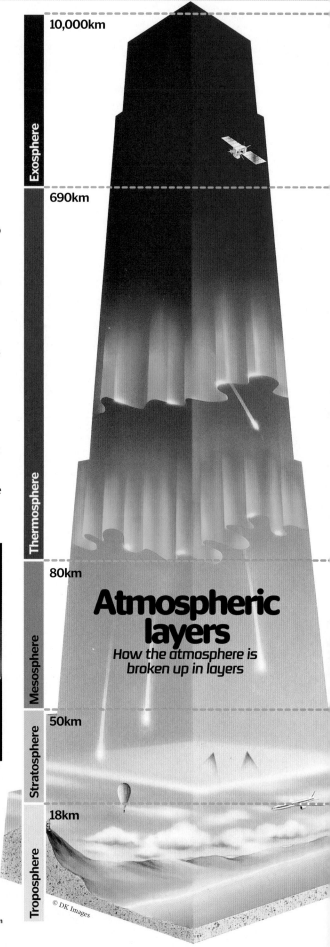

10,000km

Exosphere

690km

Thermosphere

80km

Atmospheric layers

How the atmosphere is broken up in layers

Mesosphere

50km

Stratosphere

18km

Troposphere

© DK Images

5. Exosphere

The final layer where particles are widely spaced and can travel hundreds of kilometres before colliding with another particle. The makeup of this layer is mainly hydrogen and helium.

© NASA

4. Thermosphere

Temperatures start to increase with height. This is also the layer in which the International Space Station orbits, between 320 and 380km, and shuttles fly into. It extends up to the base of the exosphere, called the exobase.

This rock made it through the mesosphere

3. Mesosphere

Extends from the stratopause (again, the layer boundary) to a height of 80-85km and is notably the layer in which meteors burn up when entering the atmosphere. Temperatures decrease with height, and in the mesopause is the coldest place on Earth (around -100°C).

2. Stratosphere

Starts from the tropopause (the boundary between the first two layers) up to around 51km, with temperatures increasing with height. This is where you'll find things like weather balloons.

1. Troposphere

The first layer of atmosphere, starting at the Earth's surface and extending to between 7km and 17km. It is heated by a transfer of energy from the Earth's surface, so it gets cooler as it goes higher.

Pollution in the air

The effects of pollution include smog, acid rain, the greenhouse effect, and holes in the ozone layer. Each problem has implications for both our health and the environment.

The carbon dioxide gas produced when fuel is burned may contribute to the greenhouse effect. Plants can convert CO_2 back to oxygen, but the human production of CO_2 currently exceeds the amount the plants can convert back.

Rife in cities, smog is the result of smoke, fog, and chemical fumes caused when different pollutants combine.

Acid rain occurs when a pollutant, such as sulfuric acid combines with droplets of water in the precipitation and becomes acidified.

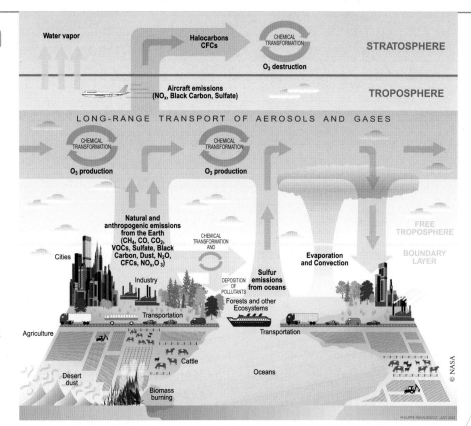

STRATOSPHERE
TROPOSPHERE
Water vapor
Halocarbons CFCs
CHEMICAL TRANSFORMATION
O_3 destruction
Aircraft emissions (NOx, Black Carbon, Sulfate)
LONG-RANGE TRANSPORT OF AEROSOLS AND GASES
CHEMICAL TRANSFORMATION
O_3 production
CHEMICAL TRANSFORMATION
O_3 production
FREE TROPOSPHERE
BOUNDARY LAYER
Natural and anthropogenic emissions from the Earth (CH_4, CO, CO_2, VOCs, Sulfate, Black Carbon, Dust, N_2O, CFCs, NO_x,O_3)
CHEMICAL TRANSFORMATION AND
DEPOSITION OF POLLUTANTS
Sulfur emissions from oceans
Evaporation and Convection
Cities
Industry
Forests and other Ecosystems
Transportation
Transportation
Agriculture
Cattle
Oceans
Desert dust
Biomass burning
© NASA
PHILIPPE REKACEWICZ - JULY 2005

The greenhouse effect

The 'greenhouse effect' is what keeps our planet warm. The atmosphere contains gases that absorb and emit infrared radiation. These gases trap heat within the troposphere layer of the atmosphere and this heats the planet's surface. Without the greenhouse effect, the Earth's mean temperature would be around a very inhospitable -18 or -19°C instead of the comfortable 14°C we're used to.

The Sun

Reflected by atmosphere
Incoming solar energy
Reflected by clouds
Reflected from Earth's surface
Radiated to space from clouds and atmosphere
Radiated directly to space from Earth
Absorbed by atmosphere
Absorbed by clouds
Radiation absorbed by atmosphere
Absorbed by land and oceans

1. Solar radiation
The Sun produces solar radiation, which is absorbed by the Earth, causing the surface to be warmed to an average temperature of 14°C.

2. Thermal radiation
Part of the Sun's solar radiation is reflected back into space away from the Earth.

3. Greenhouse gases
Gases in the lower atmosphere absorb solar radiation and create heat and energy, which is used to warm the Earth's surface.

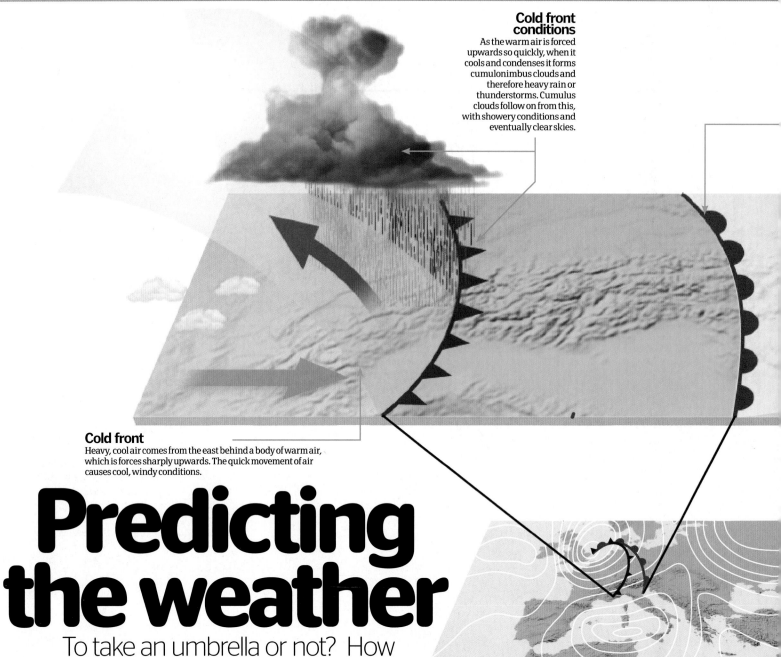

Cold front conditions
As the warm air is forced upwards so quickly, when it cools and condenses it forms cumulonimbus clouds and therefore heavy rain or thunderstorms. Cumulus clouds follow on from this, with showery conditions and eventually clear skies.

Cold front
Heavy, cool air comes from the east behind a body of warm air, which is forces sharply upwards. The quick movement of air causes cool, windy conditions.

Predicting the weather

To take an umbrella or not? How we get those all-important forecasts...

The simple fact of the matter is that weather is unpredictable. So how is it that we can gather information and make predictions about what conditions on Earth will be like?

Most weather phenomena occur as a result of the movement of warm and cold air masses. The border between these bodies of air are known as 'fronts', and it's here that the most exciting weather, including precipitation and wind, occurs.

As a body of air passes across different types of terrain – such as over the oceans, low-lying areas or even mountainous regions – air temperature and moisture levels can change dramatically. When two air masses at different temperatures meet, the less dense, warmer of the two masses rises up and over the colder. Rising warm air creates an area of low pressure (a depression), which is associated with unsettled conditions like wind and rain.

We know how a frontal weather system will behave and which conditions it will produce down on the ground. The man who first brought the idea of frontal weather systems to the fore in the early 20th Century was a Norwegian meteorologist called Vilhelm Bjerknes. Through his constant observation of the weather conditions at frontal boundaries, he discovered that numerical calculations could be used to predict the weather. This model of weather prediction is still used today.

Since the introduction of frontal system weather forecasting, the technology to crunch the numbers involved has advanced immeasurably, enabling far more detailed analysis and prediction. In order to forecast the weather with the greatest accuracy, meteorologists require vast quantities of weather data – including temperature, precipitation, cloud coverage, wind speed and wind direction – collected from weather stations located all over the world. Readings are taken constantly and fed via computer to a central location.

Technology is essential to both gathering and processing the statistical data about the conditions down on Earth and in the upper atmosphere. The massive computational power inside a supercomputer, for example, is capable of predicting the path and actions of hurricanes and issuing life-saving warnings. After taking the information collected by various monitors and sensors, a supercomputer can complete billions of calculations per second to produce imagery that can reveal how the hurricane is expected to develop.

Warm and cold fronts

What do these terms mean and how do they affect us?

Warm front

This is where warm air from the south meets cold air from the north, and the warm air rises gradually above the cold air.

In practice

The red curves of a warm front and blue triangles of a cold front are shown on a map to show where the fronts are, where they're heading and the weather they'll bring.

Warm front conditions

As the warm air slowly rises, it cools and condenses and clouds are formed. These are nimbostratus, causing steady rainfall, then altostratus accompanied by drizzle, and finally cirrus, when clearer skies can be seen.

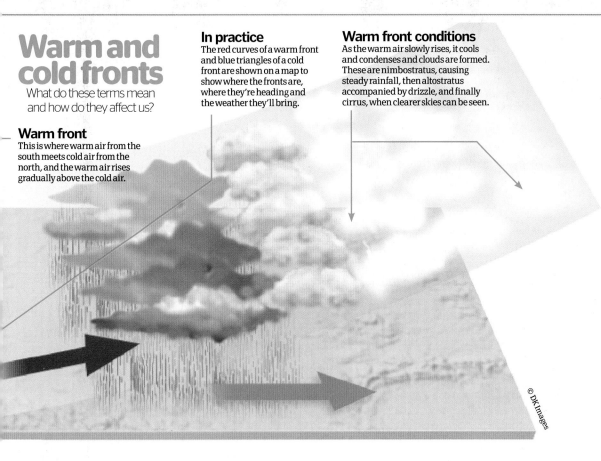

© DK Images

Stormy weather

Hail

The tops of storm clouds are full of tiny ice crystals that grow heavier until they fall through the cloud. The biggest hail stone on record was 17.8cm (7in).

Lightning

A flash of lightning is a giant spark caused when the molecules in a thunder cloud collide and build up static electricity. The flash occurs when a spark jumps through a cloud, or from the cloud to the ground, or from one cloud to another.

Thunder

This is the noise produced by lightning. An increase in pressure and temperature cause the air nearby to rapidly expand, which produces the characteristic sound of a sonic boom.

Storm cloud

Your typical run-of-the-mill cloud can be hundreds of metres high. A storm cloud, however, can reach heights of over ten kilometres (that's six miles).

How many...?

A staggering 16 million thunderstorms occur each year globally.

WEATHER FORECAST MAP

Learn what these weather-related signs and symbols mean

High pressure

Weather here will be clear and dry, due to the high pressure. If this high pressure occurs in summer weather will be warm, whereas in winter it will be cold and crisp.

Wind

The conditions at this point will be windy. This is indicated by the position of the isobars; the closer together they are the windier the conditions.

Low pressure

At the centre of these circular patterns of isobars is where systems of high or low pressure lie. Where there is low pressure conditions will be rainy and windy.

Isobars

These indicate atmospheric pressure. Areas of equal atmospheric pressure are joined together with the lines shown and the numbers indicate pressure measured in millibars. Lower numbers indicate low pressure, while higher numbers indicate high pressure.

Occluded front

This is where one front 'catches up' with another. In this example, the cold has caught up with the warm. Occluded fronts cause the weather to change quite quickly and, in this case, become similar to that of a cold front.

© DK Images

Cold front

As with any cold front, the weather here will be expected to be cool with heavy rainfall and possibly even thunderstorms. This will be followed by showers.

In between

After the passing of the warm front and before the arrival of the cold front conditions should be clear and dry, but normally only for a short period.

Warm front

The warm front will cause steady rainfall, followed by drizzle, accompanied by cloudy skies. These are typical conditions caused by any warm front.

Influencing cloud formation

We explore elemental factors influencing varying cloud types

Look up into the sky above and you will notice that clouds constantly shift in shape and size. This is due to there being numerous common types of cloud formation, with each performing a natural role, which is determined by external factors such as altitude, condensation and disposition. These include stratus, cumulus, stratocumulus, altocumulus, cirrus, cirrocumulus and cumulonimbus.

Most cloud formations are produced in environments that are saturated, or where relative humidity is at 100 per cent. Varying mechanisms can activate this process. For example orographic uplift, which occurs as air is forced up due to the physical presence of elevated landmass. As air rises it cools as a result

of adiabatic expansion, at a rate of approximately ten degrees Celsius per every 1,000 metres, until saturation occurs. Stratus clouds, for example, form when minimal upward vertical air currents lift a thin layer of air high, which is enough to initiate the condensation of excess water vapour.

Altocumulus clouds are part of the middle order of formations, appearing greyish with dark patchy areas. Often these clouds precede a cold front, and on a warm humid morning indicate approaching thunderstorm activity. Altocumulus clouds are often produced due to turbulent updrafts of air, uplifted by terrain barriers such as mountains, composed of super-cooled water, below freezing, which has not yet crystallised around a condensation nucleus.

There are several cloud formations at high altitude. Most notable are cumulonimbus, which form if cumulus congestus clouds continue to grow vertically. Ranging from near ground level up to 50,000 feet, this formation releases enormous amounts of energy by condensated water vapour. Lightning, hail and violent tornadoes are associated with cumulonimbus clouds. During the formation, condensation carries droplets up and down several times before being released and combining to form raindrops. In larger specimens up-currents become extremely severe, splitting raindrops and ice crystals, before re-combining and falling to the ground. This contributes to a build up of electrical charges and therefore the occurrence of lightning. ⚙

Common types of clouds in the troposphere

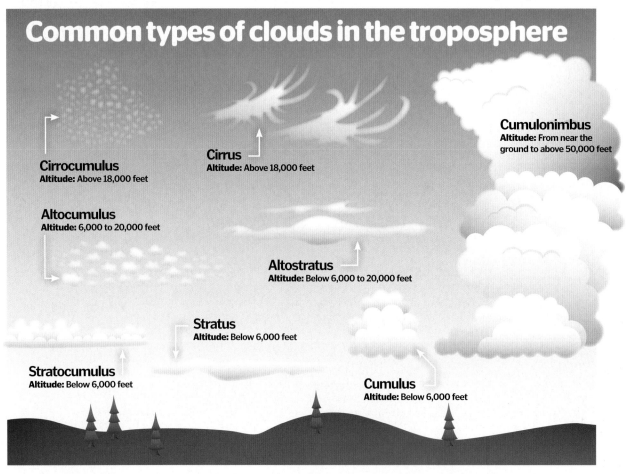
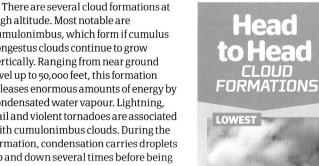

Cirrocumulus
Altitude: Above 18,000 feet

Cirrus
Altitude: Above 18,000 feet

Cumulonimbus
Altitude: From near the ground to above 50,000 feet

Altocumulus
Altitude: 6,000 to 20,000 feet

Altostratus
Altitude: Below 6,000 to 20,000 feet

Stratus
Altitude: Below 6,000 feet

Stratocumulus
Altitude: Below 6,000 feet

Cumulus
Altitude: Below 6,000 feet

Where does acid rain come from?

We've all seen the effects of acid rain on limestone statues, but how does this damaging substance form?

All rainwater is a little bit acidic, because the carbon dioxide present in the atmosphere dissolves in water and forms carbonic acid. Stronger acid rain, however, can damage stone structures and can also be harmful to crops, as well as polluting waterways. It forms in the atmosphere when poisonous gases emitted by human activities combine with the moisture within rain clouds.

Fossil-fuelled power stations and petrol/diesel vehicles give off chemical pollutants – mainly sulphur dioxide (SO_2) and nitrogen oxides (NOx) – which when mixed with the water in the air react and turn acidic.

Acid rain in action

2. Wind
The gases are carried on the wind to higher ground, towards rain clouds.

3. Gasses dissolve
Upon combining with the water vapour (water and oxygen) in the rain clouds, the gasses react to form weak but potentially damaging acid. Sulphur dioxide from industry becomes sulphuric acid.

4. Acid rainfall
When acid rain falls it can damage plant life, infiltrate waterways and erode buildings and statues.

1. Acidic gases
Sulphur dioxide and nitrogen oxides from industry and vehicles are released into the atmosphere.

© Science Photo Library

Oxidation of sulphur and nitrogen
KEY:
Blue: Nitrogen
Yellow: Sulphur
Red: Oxygen

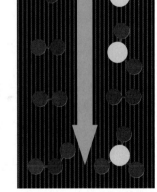

Sulphur dioxide (SO_2)
This is a by-product of heavy industry, such as power stations.

Nitrogen oxides (NOx)
These are released in car exhaust fumes.

> "Stronger acid rain can damage stone structures and be harmful to crops"

Inside a rainbow

A meteorological phenomenon – we investigate how rainbows take shape

Marvelled for their beauty, rainbows have been inspiration for folk tales, but how are they made? Well, rainbows are refractions of light and are made of a series of colours: red, orange, yellow, blue, green, indigo and violet. As light travels in waves the colour of light that is emitted depends on the light's wavelength. When light travels through an object such as crystal or an individual raindrop, it bends and refracts. As light hits the water it bends according to its wavelength and refracts at separate angles. Drops at different angles send different colours to the eye. To see a rainbow you must have your back to the Sun and rain must be falling nearby – since each raindrop is lit by the white light of the Sun a spectrum of colours is produced.

1. Angles
No two observers will witness the exact same rainbow because each will view a different set of drops at different angles.

2. Wave lengths
As light enters a raindrop the different wavelength colours bend at separate angles.

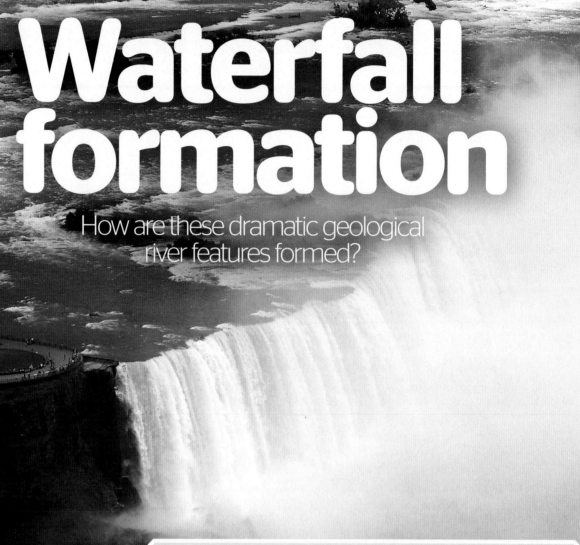

Waterfall formation

How are these dramatic geological river features formed?

The often-breathtaking natural product of vertical erosion, a waterfall occurs in a river's steep upper course high above sea level. A waterfall forms over many thousands of years as river water flows over a band of hard rock lying next to a band of soft rock downstream. The erosive effects of hydraulic action (water pushing air into tiny cracks in the riverbed) and abrasion (rocks scraping over each other) cause the soft rock to erode quicker than the hard. So while the hard rock remains solid for longer, the soft rock below is worn away, lowering the riverbed from that point and forming a step drop.

At the foot of the step, a deep plunge pool forms where water and rocks collect and swirl about, abrading more of the riverbed and less-resistant rock in the process. The harder, overhanging 'cap' rock is gradually undercut and eventually collapses due to its own weight, breaking off into the plunge pool.

Further collapse of the hard rock sees the waterfall itself recede back upstream, creating steep-sided gorges either side of the waterfall. ✿

Niagara: the most famous waterfall in the world

Frozen waterfalls make for a great climbing obstacle

A waterfall formed by volcano

Located on the border between Argentina and Brazil and surrounded by subtropical rainforest, Iguazu Falls is one of the most impressive waterfall systems on the planet. Part of a World Natural Heritage Site, Iguazu is distinctive because it was formed as a result of a massive volcanic eruption, which left a massive crack in the earth. Though there are many taller and more powerful falls, at 1.67 miles Iguazu is one of the widest, making it an undeniably awesome spectacle. The whole area consists of 275 individual waterfalls spread out across the Iguazu River. A mammoth semicircular waterfall lies at the heart of a series of cascading falls, and the main plunge waterfall, known as Garganta del Diablo, or the Devil's Throat, is 82 metres tall.

Iguazu Falls is a major draw for tourists in South America

Waterfalls can be an incredible sight to behold

There are ten different ways to classify waterfalls

1 Block
Occurring over a wide stream where the waterfall is wider than it is tall. It spills over like a wide sheet of water.

2 Cascade
Flows either over a series of small steps in the rock in quick succession, or over a rugged sloping surface.

3 Curtain
Found on a wide section of stream where the fall is taller than it is wide. These falls tend to narrow during periods of low discharge.

4 Fan
Occurring when the width of the water spilling over increases as it descends, making the base appear much wider than the top.

5 Horsetail
Found on vertical waterfalls, the falling water is in constant or semi-constant contact with the bedrock.

6 Plunge
Water spills over vertically, usually losing contact with the bedrock altogether. Often known as a cataract waterfall.

7 Punchbowl
The flow of water is squeezed through a narrow opening and is then blasted out and down into a pool.

8 Segmented
If the stream is broken into multiple channels this will cause several falls to occur side by side.

9 Slide
Slide waterfalls flow down over a smooth, sloping bedrock surface while maintaining contact with the bedrock.

10 Tiered
Tiered waterfalls form when several distinct drops occur one after the other, in close succession.

Waterfall creation
What processes happen to make a waterfall

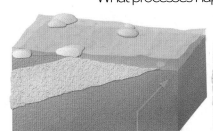

1. Undercutting/ overhanging
A layer of resistant hard rock is undercut by the erosion of the softer rock beneath. This forms a step over which the water flows.

2. Plunging
The force of the falling water hitting the soft rock below creates a plunge pool, which is deepened by the abrasion of fallen angular rocks.

3. Collapsing
Further erosion, worsened by splashback from the falling water in the plunge pool, causes the overhanging hard rock to eventually collapse under its own weight.

4. Receding
As this cycle of erosion and collapsing continues, the waterfall steepens and recedes back upstream, creating a steep-sided gorge and an increasingly tall waterfall.

 Learn more

For some more information about different waterfalls around the world, head on over to **www.world-waterfalls.com/** where you can read about waterfalls from every corner of the Earth, and then choose your favourite!

Beginning life in the mountains, rivers form from streams created through precipitation or springs of water that are sourced from groundwater that has percolated the earth. These streams, known as tributaries, then flow rapidly through V-shaped valleys, over rocky terrain and over rock edges as waterfalls. This is the first of three stages any river goes through and is known as the upper course or youth.

By the second stage, known as the middle course or maturity, many tributaries will have joined together to form the main body of water that makes up the river. The river meanders at a medium speed across narrow flood plains, which are areas of flat land lying either side of a river. Flood plains are formed when successive flooding causes sediment to be deposited on the banks.

As the river follows its course it carries with it a load, which is made up of rocks, stones, sand and other particles. It is the load that causes erosion as the materials crash against the banks of the river. The load is transported down the river in four ways, depending upon the size of the material. Traction is the rolling of the largest particles across the riverbed, whereas saltation is the bouncing of those slightly smaller. Finer materials are carried along through suspension and some are dissolved within the water and are moved through solution.

The final stage of a river is the lower course, predictably sometimes known as old age. By this time the river has slowed considerably as it heads towards the sea across broad flood plains, finally ending at what is known as the mouth – where the river finally joins the ocean. Deltas are formed as the river deposits its load.

How rivers

The river's fascinating processes and intriguing features from start to finish

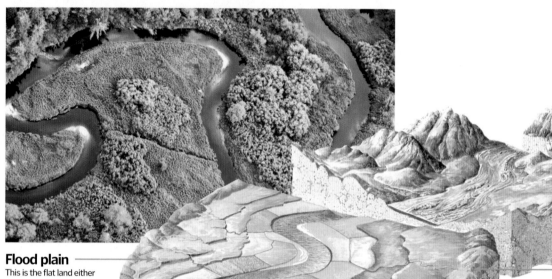

Flood plain
This is the flat land either side of the river, where floodwater goes and sediment is deposited when the river floods.

Meander
As the river travels its course its load erodes the sides and carves out bends known as meanders.

Deltas, estuaries and the river mouth

The mouth of a river signifies the end of its course and is where the river meets the sea. The 'D' shaped area of sediment that forms at the river mouth is called a delta. Deltas are built up from the bed as the river slows and deposits its load as it reaches the end of its course. The river tends to split as it travels over a delta.

Estuaries are also found at the mouth of a river. In these areas the fresh water of the river meets and mixes with the salt water of the sea. Estuaries are affected by the tide, and the combination of salt and fresh water provides a diverse habitat for many plants and animals.

The delta of the Atchafalaya River on the Gulf of Mexico

The river system

Delta
This is where the river slows down as it reaches the sea and as the water slows it deposits its load. This deposited sediment forms the delta.

Mouth
The mouth is the end of the river, where it widens and joins with the sea. All rivers end this way.

work

Source
It is here the river begins its life, in the form of small streams up in the mountains, which eventually come together to form the main body of the river.

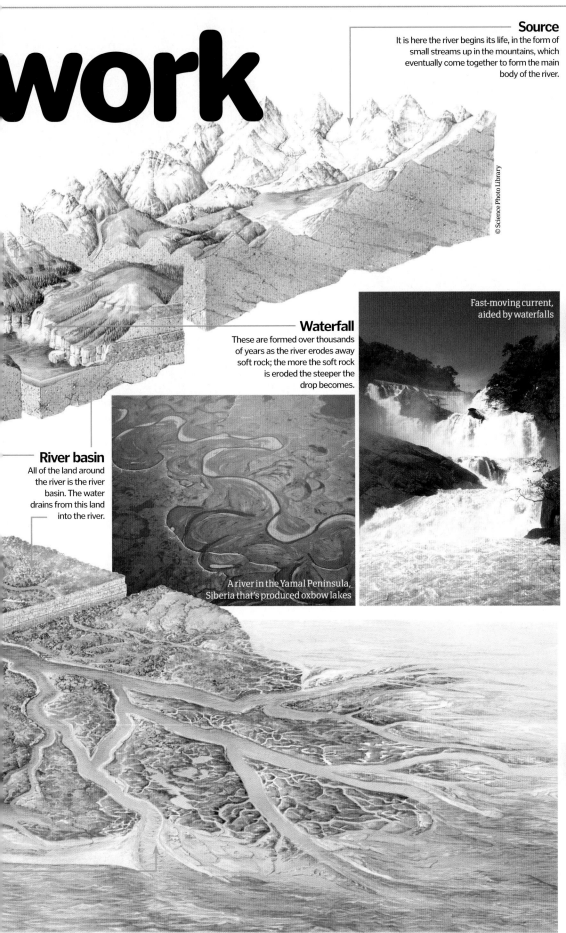

© Science Photo Library

Waterfall
These are formed over thousands of years as the river erodes away soft rock; the more the soft rock is eroded the steeper the drop becomes.

Fast-moving current, aided by waterfalls

River basin
All of the land around the river is the river basin. The water drains from this land into the river.

A river in the Yamal Peninsula, Siberia that's produced oxbow lakes

Oxbow lakes

Oxbow lakes are crescent- or horseshoe-shaped lakes situated at the side of a flowing river. They are formed from river meanders and are the result of lateral erosion cutting into the bends of the river's course where the river is flowing at its fastest. This eventually leads to the two bends joining together and altering the river's course. Deposition also plays a role as sediment builds up on the outside of the bend where the river flow is much slower. As the river breaks through and the bends join, the sediment builds up to cut off the meander and an oxbow lake is formed.

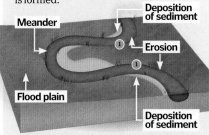

Meander — Deposition of sediment — Erosion

Flood plain — Deposition of sediment

Stage one
As the water flows around the meander it flows fastest at points 1, leading to the materials carried by the river crashing into (and therefore eroding) the bends.

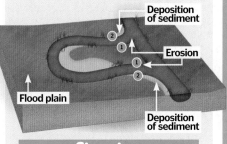

Deposition of sediment — Erosion

Flood plain — Deposition of sediment

Stage two
The river flows slowest at points 2, which leads to deposition of sediment. The continuous erosion at points 1 has led to breakthrough, where the curves of the meander have joined together, changing the flow of the river's course.

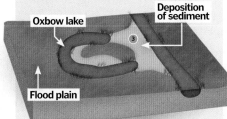

Deposition of sediment

Oxbow lake

Flood plain

Stage three
More deposition at point 3 has led to a crescent-shaped lake being completely separated from the river. This lake is known as an oxbow lake and in time will become a wetland, followed by a meadow where trees and plants will develop.

Geysers

What drives these spectacular fountains of superheated water and steam?

Geysers form when water is superheated by volcanic activity underneath the surface of the Earth, but can't move freely as it circulates towards the surface. Instead, pressure builds up until the water explodes upwards in a giant gush.

Since water needs to encounter hot rock, some geyser fields are found above upwellings of hot rock from deep within the Earth. Others are found near crustal plate boundaries where there is volcanic activity and broken, fractured rock. Rivers, snow or rainwater trickling through the Earth can provide a constant source of water.

Most geysers form where there's a silica-rich rock known as rhyolite. Rising hot water dissolves the silica in the rhyolite and carries it upwards through natural pipes in the rock where it's then deposited as a rock called geyserite. The silica seals the pipe against water pressure and narrows its walls.

Every geyser has a different plumbing and reservoir system, but there are two main types. 'Cone' or 'column' geysers like Old Faithful erupt in a steady column from a beehive-shaped nozzle of geyserite. They tend to have one reservoir of water with a single pipe leading from it to the surface. 'Fountain' or 'pool' geysers erupt from a large pool of water in a series of powerful bursts. They are thought to have a reservoir fed by two water sources – descending shallow, cold water and hot water rising from below.

As geysers need a rare combination of geological conditions to form, there are only around 50 geyser fields worldwide and most have just a few geysers. The biggest – Yellowstone, USA – has almost half the world's geysers.

How do geysers work?

To get geysers, you need four things: a volcanic heat source close to the Earth's surface, a water supply, a plumbing and reservoir system of hard, fissured rock, and a natural pipe that narrows so high water pressures can build up in the reservoir below.

7. A sudden rush
Water pressure mounts below the bottleneck until it can overcome the weight of overlying, colder water and rush to the surface.

8. Sky-high water
The colder water above the superheated water is thrown up into the air as a jet. The pressure lifts, causing the superheated water to turn into steam.

Geyserite is a form of silica found around a geyser

© Science Photo Library

1. Water trickles underground
Snow, rain or river water takes hundreds of years to trickle through fractured rocks to depths of two to three kilometres.

6. Silica seal
Silica dissolved from rhyolite – a volcanic rock – can slowly build up on the pipe walls causing a bottleneck.

© DK Images

3. Superheated water
The water is heated to very high temperatures, but it can't boil because of the pressure of the overlying water and rock. This is called superheating.

4. Plumbing system
The heated water circulates upwards via a complex, natural system of underground pipes and passages. As it does, the overlying pressure lessens and it can expand and boil.

5. High-pressure area
For a geyser to form, there must be a tight spot in the underground pipe system. This acts like a giant pressure cooker.

2. Hot rocks
The water comes in contact with hot rocks surrounding partially molten rock lying only a few kilometres below the Earth's surface.

ON THE MAP

The world's biggest geyser fields
1 Yellowstone National Park, US
2 Kamchatka Peninsula, Siberia
3 Taupo Volcanic Zone, New Zealand
4 El Tatio Geysers, Chile
5 Iceland
6 Umnak Island, Alaska

Hot and steamy

Geysers aren't the only hydrothermal features on Earth. Mudpots, hot springs, fumaroles and hydrothermal vents can also form when water is heated underground. However, unlike geysers, the heated water flows freely to the surface rather than erupting in a jet.

Where lots of water reaches the surface, hot springs form. Bacteria living in the hot water can give hot springs like Grand Prismatic Spring vivid, beautiful colours. Fumaroles – or steam vents – form where all the water is boiled away before reaching the surface. Hydrothermal vents or 'smokers' are like hot springs, but they form in the deep ocean near ridges and rifts.

Avalanche!
What causes these often deadly snow slides?

Although the potential for an avalanche is present wherever you find a mass of snow on a slope, there are three main types of avalanche each dependent on several conditions: the type of snow in the snowpack, the temperature, wind, the steepness and orientation of the slope, and vegetation (or anchors). ✿

1. Trigger
This disturbance is where the avalanche begins to fracture and it tends to be high up the slope but can still occur anywhere on a mountain. 90 per cent of fatal avalanches are triggered by the victims.

The avalanche path
This consists of the starting zone, the track and the run-out zone.

2. Starting zone
The starting zone is the section of the avalanche path at which the avalanche is released sending unsecured snow downhill. It normally occurs on a steep slope of between 30 and 50 per cent.

3. Track
The track is the main path down which an avalanche flows. The snow will either slide down as a sheet or concentrated in gullies. Towards the bottom of a track you may well see large piles of snow, boulders and tree remains.

4. Run-out (debris toe)
As the slope flattens out – or meets another slope – the avalanche will come to rest. This area is the run-out and consists of a pile of snow and debris picked up along the run. Any unfortunate victims would likely be found in this area of deposition. The very end of the deposited snow is referred to as the avalanche toe.

Main types of avalanches

Dry (80mph)
Occurring below freezing, dry avalanches are usually triggered by loading from new snow or blowing snow. These high-speed slides consist of air and powdery snow, beginning at a single point and gathering speed and mass. As it moves downhill, pressure builds ahead of the mass of snow, creating a powerful blast of air capable of destroying most things in its path.

Slab (60-80mph)
The most common – not to mention deadly – type of avalanche occurs when a layer of compacted snow overlies softer snow. When the weaker snow can no longer support the snow above – or if a passing skier adds to the weight – the hard layer (usually 30-80cm) will fracture like a pane of glass and slide away. If a victim is in the middle of the slab, they are unlikely to survive.

Wet (10-30mph)
Wet avalanches move slower than their drier relatives and occur as a result of rain or warmer weather melting the snow. Rain or humidity softens the snowpack, breaking the bonds between water molecules. Although wet avalanches are slower and don't feature a dust cloud, they are still highly destructive, capable of dragging boulders and even trees down the mountainside.

Interview

We spoke to **Cam Campbell**, public avalanche forecaster for the Canadian Avalanche Centre, to find out more

What are the most common avalanche triggers?
Cam Campbell: The most common triggers for all types of avalanches are natural; [including] loading from new snow, rain or blowing snow, rapid warming of the snowpack from an increase in air temperature or intense solar radiation, falling cornices, or other natural snowpack stressors. [...] Most fatal avalanches are human-triggered by the victim or someone in their party.

How and why are avalanches sometimes triggered intentionally?
CC: [Avalanches are triggered intentionally] to reduce the threat of future uncontrolled avalanches. Any time an avalanche is intentionally triggered, strict procedures, such as access closures and spotters are in place to ensure nobody will be adversely affected. Ski resorts or commercial backcountry operations often stabilise slopes by triggering avalanches before opening to the public. Intentional triggering can be achieved safely through remote-controlled explosives well away from the avalanche path, or hand- or helicopter-deployed explosives above the path.

Survival tips
The top ten survival tips for mountaineers and skiers

- ☑ Take avalanche safety course
- ☑ Read avalanche bulletin
- ☑ Choose route or terrain appropriate for conditions
- ☑ Carry and practise using safety gear (transceiver, shovel and probe)
- ☑ Never travel alone
- ☑ Avoid common trigger points such as convexities, thin areas, or below protruding rocks or trees
- ☑ Travel on avalanche prone slopes one person at a time and spot from safe locations
- ☑ If caught do everything in your power to escape the flowing mass
- ☑ If burial is imminent, create an air pocket in front of your face with hands and arms
- ☑ If buried, remain calm and await rescue

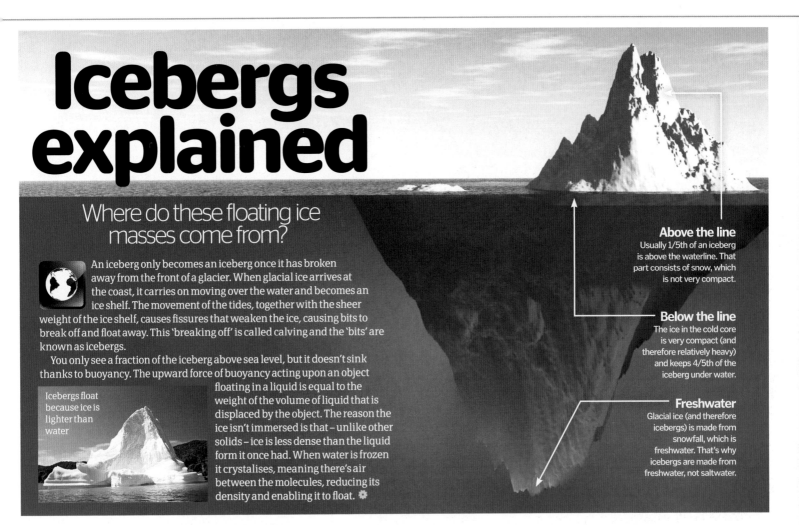

Icebergs explained

Where do these floating ice masses come from?

An iceberg only becomes an iceberg once it has broken away from the front of a glacier. When glacial ice arrives at the coast, it carries on moving over the water and becomes an ice shelf. The movement of the tides, together with the sheer weight of the ice shelf, causes fissures that weaken the ice, causing bits to break off and float away. This 'breaking off' is called calving and the 'bits' are known as icebergs.

You only see a fraction of the iceberg above sea level, but it doesn't sink thanks to buoyancy. The upward force of buoyancy acting upon an object floating in a liquid is equal to the weight of the volume of liquid that is displaced by the object. The reason the ice isn't immersed is that – unlike other solids – ice is less dense than the liquid form it once had. When water is frozen it crystalises, meaning there's air between the molecules, reducing its density and enabling it to float. ✿

Icebergs float because ice is lighter than water

Above the line
Usually 1/5th of an iceberg is above the waterline. That part consists of snow, which is not very compact.

Below the line
The ice in the cold core is very compact (and therefore relatively heavy) and keeps 4/5th of the iceberg under water.

Freshwater
Glacial ice (and therefore icebergs) is made from snowfall, which is freshwater. That's why icebergs are made from freshwater, not saltwater.

Hailstones

The balls of ice that fall to the ground, ruining crops, denting cars and smashing greenhouses

Hailstones form in the upper parts of freezing storm clouds – the cumulonimbus kind – which feature very powerful convection air currents that stretch up to ten kilometres into the atmosphere. They consist of many layers of either clear, hard ice, or softer milky snow, formed under different conditions, which can be seen if you slice a hailstone in half. Most hailstones are about the size of a marble, but can occasionally be as large as oranges.

Water droplets form inside storm clouds and are drawn upwards by strong rising air currents where they turn into ice. On its journey up, an ice particle will bump into even colder water particles – they then stick together and gain in size and weight, creating another layer of ice. As the hailstone grows heavier, it falls back down through the cloud, colliding with yet more ice particles on their way up.

The hailstone can circulate around the cloud many times, gaining more and more layers of ice, until it becomes too heavy for the air current to support. At this point it will drop out of the cloud completely, falling to earth. ✿

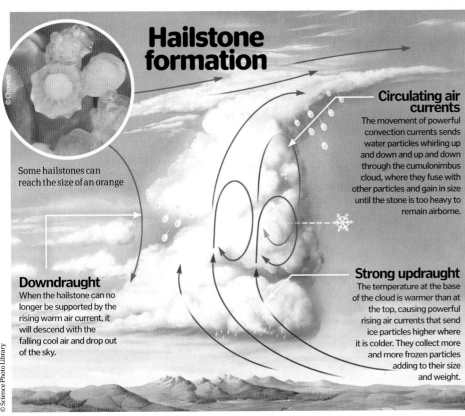

Hailstone formation

Some hailstones can reach the size of an orange

Circulating air currents
The movement of powerful convection currents sends water particles whirling up and down and up and down through the cumulonimbus cloud, where they fuse with other particles and gain in size until the stone is too heavy to remain airborne.

Downdraught
When the hailstone can no longer be supported by the rising warm air current, it will descend with the falling cool air and drop out of the sky.

Strong updraught
The temperature at the base of the cloud is warmer than at the top, causing powerful rising air currents that send ice particles higher where it is colder. They collect more and more frozen particles adding to their size and weight.

Steep shoreline gradient

The gradient of the shoreline affects the swell, forcing it up vertically and increasing wave power and length.

Wave breaking point

When the height of a wave – which is determined largely by wind speed – cannot be sustained and collapses under its own weight.

Surfing is a good way to make the most of giant waves

Wave trough

The wave trough is the lowest point on the ocean surface between two successive wave crests.

Making waves

Circular motion of water particles

As the wind passes across the surface of the ocean it transfers its energy into the water particles, causing them to move in a circular motion.

© DK Images

Wave crest

The peak height of any wave is the wave crest.

Wavelength

The distance between two successive wave crests measures the wavelength.

How waves are formed

Born out of transference of energy from wind to water, waves are a powerful and dangerous natural phenomenon

Waves carry tremendous amounts of energy over large distances

Waves are mainly formed across the surface of the sea through high winds transferring their energy into water particles. This transference of energy causes water particles to move in a repetitive circular motion, merge and then form an ocean swell which, when passed over the steeper gradient of the shore, forces it up to a point where it cannot support its own weight and breaks. Wave formation is effected by factors including current speed, water depth and wind speed.

Waves are also formed through vertical water displacement, the most devastating example of which can be seen in tsunamis. This mass water displacement – generally created by earthquakes or underwater landslides raising the seabed – transfers energy in a different way, passing energy to water particles so their resulting motion isn't circular but consistently forward. This causes tsunami waves not to roll back on themselves when forced over shallow terrain such as shoreline and creates a wave of tremendous length and shallow depth, as well as containing massive stored energy capable of devastating levels of destruction.

An individual wave is characterised through two parts, the trough (the low gap between two vertical waves) and the crest (the peak of a wave). The distance between two subsequent wave crests is the wavelength and the gap between each successive wave is called the wave period. Waves fall into two categories, with the distinction dependent on the ratio between length of wave and depth of water. If the water depth is shallow and the wavelength long, then the wave is classed as a shallow water wave. If it is the inverse of the latter, then it is classed as a deep water wave.

Northern lights

Stormy space weather produces the world's biggest neon sign

Space weather

The cold vacuum of space seems an unlikely place for a storm. But that's exactly what happens when a solar flare explodes into the Sun's upper atmosphere, instantly heating nearby gasses to millions of degrees.

The extreme heat causes gas atoms to split into positively charged ions and negatively charged free electrons. This supercharged soup of ionised gas is called plasma. The Sun emits a constant stream of plasma in all directions at a speed of 500km/s (a million mph). But when the flow of plasma becomes a flood, the Earth is in for some bad space weather.

Geomagnetic storms cause more than the majestic northern lights. They can warp the Earth's magnetic field so badly that satellites are knocked out of orbit and invading electrons overwhelm power grids. In 1989, 6 million people in Montreal, Quebec lost power for nine hours thanks to a particularly strong solar storm.

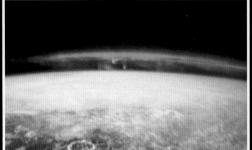

The aurora borealis, or northern lights, taken by astronaut Donald R Pettit, on board the International Space Station (ISS)

"Gentle solar winds turn into geomagnetic storms"

What would the North Pole tourist bureau do without the northern lights? Ten-month winters don't make for good travel brochures. But only here, in this most inhospitable open-air theatre, can you witness the most hauntingly beautiful light show ever conceived. Curtains of shimmering, chameleon-hued light as unpredictable as an artist's temper.

The scientific explanation behind the aurora borealis ('northern dawn' in Latin) is almost as improbable and magical as the lights themselves. The Earth, it turns out, is constantly bombarded by highly charged particles blown around by solar winds. Few of these particles ever reach the atmosphere because they are deflected by the Earth's magnetic field.

But every so often, the gentle solar winds turn into geomagnetic storms. Solar flares and coronal mass ejections (CME) – explosions of solar material into interplanetary space – can send powerful waves of charged particles toward the Earth. As these cosmic electrons collide with the Earth's magnetic field, they generate millions of amps of electric current that arc along the magnetic field toward the poles.

If the force of a geomagnetic storm is severe enough, particles will breach the magnetic field at the poles, creating what is essentially the world's biggest neon sign. As the supercharged electrons pass through the atmosphere, they excite gas atoms like oxygen and nitrogen.

The excited gasses emit different coloured lights depending on their altitude and the power of the surge. Low-altitude oxygen is responsible for the fluorescent green hues and high-altitude oxygen produces those brilliant crimson reds. Nitrogen flares up as shades of blue and purple.

The celestial light show is visible at the South Pole as well (there, it's called the aurora australis), but the Antarctica tourist board is woefully understaffed. ✿

The carbon cycle

You're breathing it out right now, but where has it been before and where is it off to?

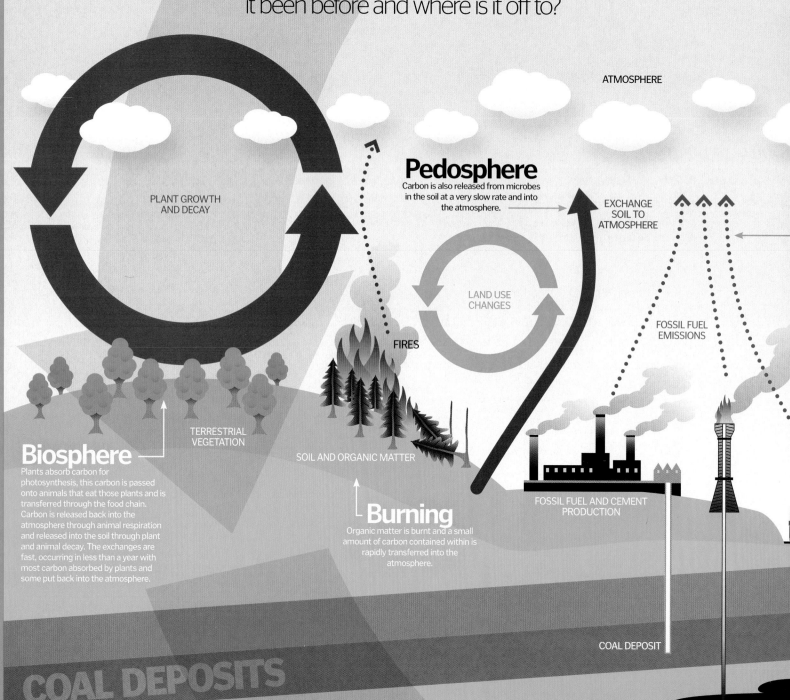

ATMOSPHERE

PLANT GROWTH AND DECAY

Pedosphere

Carbon is also released from microbes in the soil at a very slow rate and into the atmosphere.

EXCHANGE SOIL TO ATMOSPHERE

LAND USE CHANGES

FIRES

FOSSIL FUEL EMISSIONS

TERRESTRIAL VEGETATION

Biosphere

Plants absorb carbon for photosynthesis, this carbon is passed onto animals that eat those plants and is transferred through the food chain. Carbon is released back into the atmosphere through animal respiration and released into the soil through plant and animal decay. The exchanges are fast, occurring in less than a year with most carbon absorbed by plants and some put back into the atmosphere.

SOIL AND ORGANIC MATTER

Burning

Organic matter is burnt and a small amount of carbon contained within is rapidly transferred into the atmosphere.

FOSSIL FUEL AND CEMENT PRODUCTION

COAL DEPOSIT

COAL DEPOSITS

Geosphere

This is the area below the Earth's surface, where carbon is found in the solid form of coal or the liquid form of oil. These are millions of years' worth of dead matter, compacted and preserved to form these fuels which are burnt to provide power.

OIL AND GAS DEPOSIT

Carbon is a greenhouse gas that helps trap heat and keep the Earth warm. Just as water is transferred around the Earth, carbon atoms also follow a cycle and are used again and again. You might not be able to see carbon but it is a vital part of how our world works and it moves around the Earth in a variety of ways.

Carbon moves from the atmosphere into plants. In the atmosphere it is combined with oxygen and found as carbon dioxide. Plant photosynthesis draws the carbon out of the air to make plant food. The carbon then moves from plants into animals as animals eat the plants. The carbon moves up the food chain as each animal is eaten by another. Animals release carbon back into the atmosphere through respiration when they breathe out CO_2. When plants and animals die the carbon is transferred into the soil when decomposition occurs. Some of this carbon will end up buried miles underground and so will eventually make fossil fuels. These fossil fuels are then burned and used for power, in the form of factories, cars and so on, therefore releasing the carbon back into the atmosphere. Some carbon also enters the sea as the ocean absorbs it from the atmosphere.

Although the carbon cycle is a natural process it can be affected by human activity; our burning of fossil fuels means there is 30 per cent more carbon dioxide in the air now than 150 years ago.

Exchange rates ■ VERY FAST (< 1 year) ■ FAST (1 to 10 years) ■ SLOW (10 to 100 years) ■ VERY SLOW (> 100 years)

Fossil fuels

Fossil fuels found deep underground emit carbon, in the form of carbon dioxide, into the atmosphere when used. This includes factory work, cement production and use of vehicles. It is a speedy transmission but is a process that is ever increasing and putting more and more carbon into the atmosphere.

EXCHANGE OCEANS TO ATMOSPHERE

Hydrosphere

Carbon moves between the ocean and the atmosphere through diffusion. Carbon is used by organisms in the ocean food web and re-released. Generally carbon is released into the atmosphere by tropical oceans and absorbed by high-latitude oceans. It is a fast process occurring between one and ten years with a fairly even transferral of carbon being released and absorbed.

"Some carbon also enters the sea as the ocean absorbs it from the atmosphere"

Deep sea

Some carbon is transferred into the deeper ocean where it can stay for 1,000 years. Phytoplankton uses carbon to make shells; when they die they fall to the bottom of the ocean where they are buried and compressed to become limestone, which in time can be used as fossil fuel.

SURFACE WATER

DISSOLVED ORGANIC CARBON

GAS HYDRATES

EXCHANGE SURFACE WATER TO DEEP WATER

MARINE ORGANISMS

INTERMEDIATE AND DEEP WATER

MARINE SEDIMENTS AND SEDIMENTARY ROCKS

SURFACE SEDIMENT

What are fossils?

Obliterating the traditional perception of the origins and evolution of life on Earth, fossils grant us unique snapshots of what once lived on our ever-changing planet

Adpression
A form of fossilisation caused by compression within sedimentary rock. This type of fossilisation occurs mainly where fine sediment is deposited frequently, such as along rivers. Many fossilised plants are formed this way.

Resin
Referred to as amber, fossil resin is a natural polymer excreted by trees and plants. As it is sticky and soft when produced, small invertebrates such as insects and spiders are often trapped and sealed within resin, preserving their form.

Bioimmuration
Bioimmuration is a type of fossil that in its formation subsumes another organism, leaving an impression of it within the fossil. This type of fossilisation usually occurs between sessile skeletal organisms, such as oysters.

Carbon dating

A crucial tool for palaeontologists, carbon dating allows ancient fossils to be accurately dated

Carbon dating is a method of radioactive dating used by palaeontologists that utilises the radioactive isotope carbon-14 to determine the time since it died and was fossilised. When an organism dies it stops replacing carbon-14, which is present in every carbonaceous organism on Earth, leaving the existing carbon-14 to decay. Carbon-14 has a half-life (the time it takes a decaying object to decrease in radioactivity by 50 per cent) of 5,730 years, so by measuring the decayed levels of carbon-14 in a fossil, its time of death can be extrapolated and its geological age determined.

Types of fossilisation

Dependent on climate and ground conditions, deceased animals can be fossilised in many ways

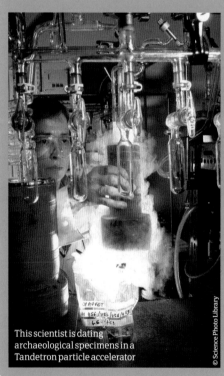

This scientist is dating archaeological specimens in a Tandetron particle accelerator

Permineralisation
A process in which mineral deposits form internal casts of organisms, permineralisation works when a deceased animal dies and then is rapidly submerged with groundwater. The water fills the creature's lungs and empty spaces, before draining away leaving a mineral cast.

Recrystallisation
When a shelled creature's shell, bone or tissue maintains its original form but is replaced with a crystal – such as aragonite and calcite – then it is said to be recrystallised.

Mold
A type of fossilisation process similar to permineralisation, molds occur when an animal is completely dissolved or destroyed, leaving only an organism-shaped hole in the rock. Molds can turn into casts if they are then filled with minerals.

The origin of life on Earth is irrevocably trapped in deep time. The epic, fluid and countless beginnings, evolutions and extinctions are immeasurable to humankind; our chronology is fractured, the picture is incomplete. For while the diversity of life on Earth today is awe-inspiring, with animals living within the most extreme environments imaginable – environments we as humans brave every day in a effort to chart and understand where life begins and ends – it is but only a fraction of the total life Earth has seen inhabit it over geological time. Driven by the harsh realities of an ever-changing environment, Armageddon-level extinction events and the perpetual, ever-present force of natural selection, wondrous creatures with five eyes, fierce predators with 12-inch fangs and massive creatures

twice the size of a double-decker bus have long since ceased to exist. They're forgotten, buried by not just millions, but billions of years. Still, all is not lost. By exploiting Earth's natural processes and modern technology over the last two hundred years, scientists and palaeontologists have begun to

but, in general, it occurs when a recently deceased creature is rapidly buried by sediment or subsumed in an oxygen-deficient liquid. This has the effect of preserving parts of the creature – usually the harder, solid parts like its skeleton – often in the original, living form within the Earth's crust. The softer parts

"The softer parts of fossilised creatures tend not to survive due to the rapidity of decay"

unravel Earth's tree of life and, through the discovery and excavation of fossils – preserved remains and traces of past life in Earth's crust – piece the jigsaw back together.

The fossilisation of an animal can occur in a variety of ways (see 'Types of fossilisation' boxout)

of fossilised creatures tend not to survive due to the speed of decay and their replacement by minerals contained in their sediment or liquid casing, a process that can leave casings and impressions of the animal that once lived, but not its remains. Importantly, however, creature fossilisation tends to ▶

be specific to the environmental conditions in which it lived – and these in themselves are indicative of certain time periods in Earth's geological history. For example, certain species of trilobite (an extinct marine arthropod) are only found in certain rock strata (layers of sedimentary and igneous rocks formed through mineral deposition over millions of years), which itself is identifiable by its materials and mineralogic composition. This allows palaeontologists to extrapolate the environmental conditions (hot, cold, dry, wet, etc) that the animal lived and died in and, in partnership with radiometric dating, assign a date to the fossil and/or the period.

Interestingly, however, by studying the strata and the contained fossils over multiple layers, through a mixture of this form of palaeontology and phylogenetics (the study of evolutionary relatedness between organism groups), scientists can chart the evolution of animals over geological time scales. A good example of this process is the now known transition of certain species of dinosaur into birds. Here, by dating and analysing specimens such as archaeopteryx – a famous dinosaur/bird transition fossil – both by strata and by radiometric methods, as well as recording their molecular and morphological data, scientists can then chart its progress through strata layers to the present day. In addition, by following the fossil record in this way, palaeontologists can also attribute the geophysical/chemical changes to the rise, fall or transition of any one animal/plant group, reading the sediment's composition and structural data. For example, the Cretaceous-Tertiary extinction event is identified in sedimentary strata by a sharp decline in species' diversity – notably non-avian dinosaurs – and increased calcium deposits from dead plants and plankton.

Excavating any discovered fossil in order to date and analyse it is a challenging, time-consuming process, which requires special tools and equipment. These include picks and shovels, trowels, whisks, hammers, dental drills and even explosives. There is also an accepted academic method all professional palaeontologists follow when preparing, removing and transporting any discovered fossil. First, the fossil is partially freed from the sedimentary matrix it is encased in and labelled, photographed and reported. Next, the overlying rock (commonly referred to as the 'overburden') is removed using large tools up to a distance of two to three inches from the fossil, before it is once again photographed. Then, depending on the stability of the fossil, it is coated with a thin glue via brush or aerosol in order to strengthen its structure, before being wrapped in a series of paper, bubble wrap and Hessian cloth. Finally, it is transported to the laboratory.

The fossil record

By examining discovered fossils, it is possible to piece together a rough history of the development of life on Earth over a geological timescale

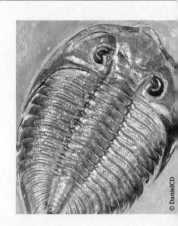

© DanielCD

12 | CAMBRIAN | 542-488.3 Ma

The first geological period of the Paleozoic era, the Cambrian is unique in its high proportion of sedimentary layers and, consequently, adpression fossils. The Burgess Shale Formation, a notable fossil field dating from the Cambrian, has revealed many fossils including the genus opabinia, a five-eyed ocean crawler.

© Wallace65

11 | ORDOVICIAN | 488.3-443.7 Ma

Boasting the highest sea levels on the Palaezoic era, the Ordovician saw the proliferation of planktonics, brachiopods and cephalopods. Nautiloids, suspension feeders, are among the largest creatures from this period to be discovered.

© Jlorenzi

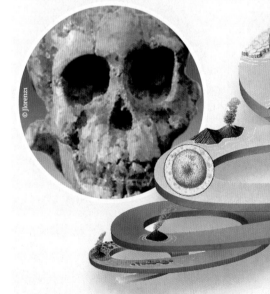

10 | SILURIAN | 443.7-416 Ma

With its base set at major extinction event at the end of the Ordovician, the silurian fossils found differ markedly from those that pre-date the period. Notable life developments include the first bony fish, and organisms with moveable jaws.

9 | DEVONIAN | 416-359.2 Ma

An incredibly important time for the development of life, the Devonian period has relinquished fossils demonstrating the evolution of the pectoral and pelvic fins of fish into legs. The first land-based creatures, tetrapods and arthopods, become entrenched and seed-bearing plants spread across dry lands. A notable find is the genus tiktaalik.

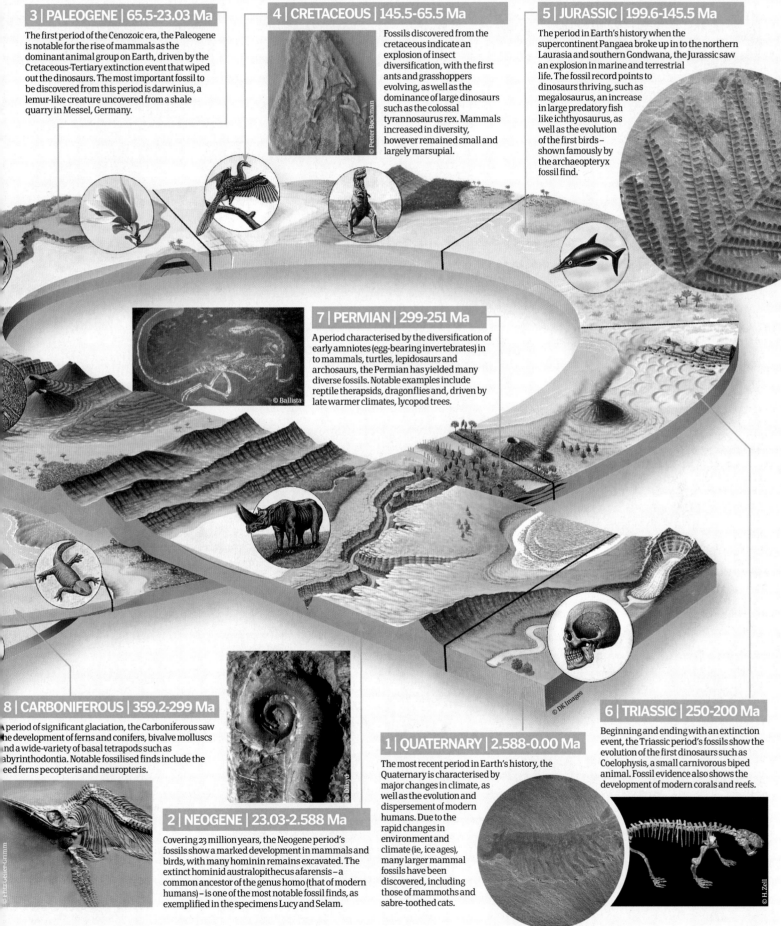

3 | PALEOGENE | 65.5-23.03 Ma

The first period of the Cenozoic era, the Paleogene is notable for the rise of mammals as the dominant animal group on Earth, driven by the Cretaceous-Tertiary extinction event that wiped out the dinosaurs. The most important fossil to be discovered from this period is darwinius, a lemur-like creature uncovered from a shale quarry in Messel, Germany.

4 | CRETACEOUS | 145.5-65.5 Ma

Fossils discovered from the cretaceous indicate an explosion of insect diversification, with the first ants and grasshoppers evolving, as well as the dominance of large dinosaurs such as the colossal tyrannosaurus rex. Mammals increased in diversity, however remained small and largely marsupial.

© Petter Bockman

5 | JURASSIC | 199.6-145.5 Ma

The period in Earth's history when the supercontinent Pangaea broke up in to the northern Laurasia and southern Gondwana, the Jurassic saw an explosion in marine and terrestrial life. The fossil record points to dinosaurs thriving, such as megalosaurus, an increase in large predatory fish like ichthyosaurus, as well as the evolution of the first birds – shown famously by the archaeopteryx fossil find.

7 | PERMIAN | 299-251 Ma

A period characterised by the diversification of early amniotes (egg-bearing invertebrates) in to mammals, turtles, lepidosaurs and archosaurs, the Permian has yielded many diverse fossils. Notable examples include reptile therapsids, dragonflies and, driven by late warmer climates, lycopod trees.

© Ballista

8 | CARBONIFEROUS | 359.2-299 Ma

A period of significant glaciation, the Carboniferous saw the development of ferns and conifers, bivalve molluscs and a wide-variety of basal tetrapods such as labyrinthodontia. Notable fossilised finds include the seed ferns pecopteris and neuropteris.

© Fritz Geller-Grimm

© DJlloyd

2 | NEOGENE | 23.03-2.588 Ma

Covering 23 million years, the Neogene period's fossils show a marked development in mammals and birds, with many hominin remains excavated. The extinct hominid australopithecus afarensis – a common ancestor of the genus homo (that of modern humans) – is one of the most notable fossil finds, as exemplified in the specimens Lucy and Selam.

1 | QUATERNARY | 2.588-0.00 Ma

The most recent period in Earth's history, the Quaternary is characterised by major changes in climate, as well as the evolution and dispersement of modern humans. Due to the rapid changes in environment and climate (ie, ice ages), many larger mammal fossils have been discovered, including those of mammoths and sabre-toothed cats.

© DK Images

6 | TRIASSIC | 250-200 Ma

Beginning and ending with an extinction event, the Triassic period's fossils show the evolution of the first dinosaurs such as Coelophysis, a small carnivorous biped animal. Fossil evidence also shows the development of modern corals and reefs.

© H.Zell

Earth's minerals

Crystals can take many forms, but how they come to be is a mystery for many. We find out exactly how they are made...

The term 'crystal' is used to describe a solid object that has been created by a structured repeating pattern of the same atoms or molecules.

Crystals 'build' using a process known as nucleation, which involves the attraction of molecules to one place to form a cluster. This can be achieved independently, which is referred to as 'unassisted nucleation', where solute (molecules) dissolved in the solvent collect together on their own; gradually attracting and amassing more, therefore growing in size and shape. Assisted nucleation sees the molecules collate using some form of solid matter, such as rock, as a type of collection point.

If the molecules remain joined, undisturbed and don't dissolve back into the surrounding solution, a stable nuclei will form, which attracts more of the same atoms. As this continues to build, the crystal will eventually reach its 'critical cluster size' and will not dissolve back into the solution from which it came.

Environmental factors such as pressure, space, temperature and chemical conditions present in the minerals can influence the way a crystal forms, but ultimately a crystal's shape is formed as molecules collect in a specific pattern that repeats itself over and over. As atoms join to all of its sides in the same pattern, geometric shapes are formed. ✿

Crystals form in a range of elements and conditions, but one of the most prolific areas is in the ftermath of a volcano...

How crystals form
Crystals form with the separation of solids and liquids; therefore molecules bobbing around in the formulated solution cluster together in a repeated pattern over time to become a stable solid.

Size matters
If molten rock cools rapidly only small crystals will be created, which usually happens when lava is ejected from a volcano. However, slowly cooling molten rocks create much larger crystals.

Regularity of eruption 1
According to scientists the number of crystals contained within the magma can determine how frequently it will erupt.

Regularity of eruption 2
Volcanoes exhibiting more viscous magma erupt less often than those with less viscous magma, but with a greater energy.

Cool down
After a volcanic eruption the magma cools and the minerals contained within it begin to crystallise, which are known as 'phenocrysts'.

© Svalnojen

© Science photo library

© Science photo library

Gemstones
Gemstones are precious or semiprecious stones that are commonly used as jewels when cut and polished. They can be formed inorganically (using the methods discussed in this feature) or organically by a living thing; for example amber is formed of sap created by trees and pearls are created by oysters.

Geodes
Geodes look like ugly egg-shaped rocks, but inside are completely constructed with crystals. They take millions of years to form and are commonly created when a magma bubble cools. Dissolved minerals from flowing water etc, seep into this hard shell and attach to the inner wall. Through assisted nucleation, the crystal grows towards the centre. Quartz is the most common crystal to find in this way, but amethyst and other minerals can also be discovered.

Cave of Crystals

The Naica Mine of Chihuahua, Mexico, is a working mine that has become famous for its enormous crystals. 120m below the surface dwells the Cueva de las Espadas (Cave of Swords), discovered in 1912, and so-called because of its metre-long shafts of gypsum. However, the once-amazing find has now been eclipsed by a recent discovery that lies beneath the Cave of Swords: Cueva de los Cristales (Cave of Crystals) where gigantic 11-metre long crystals have been found.

It is believed that the huge beams formed in the 290-metre deep cave owe their size and statue to the fact that they've been allowed to form over hundreds of thousands of years in a very narrow, stable temperature range. It is believed that they were originally created as calcium sulphate found within groundwater filtered down through the caves. Magma from underneath the caves heated the water to a stabilised temperature of around 57°C, at which point the minerals converted to selenite molecules, which clustered over time to form crystals.

© Rob Lavinsky

As conditions remained undisturbed in a perfect environment for millennia the crystals grew much larger, if not more plentiful, than any other in the cave system

Crystal systems

A free-growing crystal always forms a geometric shape with flat faces and all crystals form one of six systems of symmetry which help identify them…

Cubic
Featuring eight or 12 sides these formations are not always square in shape.

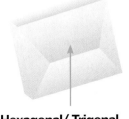

Hexagonal/ Trigonal
Hexagonal crystals are six-sided prisms, whereas trigonal ones have three or quasi-six sides.

Tetragonal
Similar in makeup to cubic formations but longer along one axis that the other.

Monoclinic
Often forming a prism shape, these are often referred to as skewed tetragonal crystals.

Orthorhombic
These are not square in the cross section and instead form rhombic prisms.

Triclinic
Often sporting peculiar shapes, it's unsymmetrical on each side.

135

© James Temple

How do polar bears hunt? p154

© Ansgar Walk 1996

Amazing

How do ladybirds fly? p169

How do whales communicate? p146

How fast is a cheetah? p172

What do pandas eat? p156

animals

Deadly dinosaurs

Until they were wiped out 65 million years ago dinosaurs ruled the Earth. Among them, monstrous beasts stamped their authority over the menagerie, devouring all who stood in their way. These were the dinosaur kings, the largest carnivores the world has ever seen

 Evolving from archosaurs (large lizards) in the latter part of the middle Triassic period, dinosaurs quickly gained a strong and prolific foothold all over Pangaea, the super continent which all our continents were once part of. Indeed, as the dominant terrestrial vertebrates through the Jurassic and Cretaceous periods, thousands of species of dinosaur have been unearthed as fossils by palaeontologists all over the world, with new discoveries being presented every year. Among them, huge behemoths with skeletons over 16 metres long and six metres tall, with skulls the size of bath tubs have surfaced and delivered a scary and disturbing glimpse into the creatures that once prowled the countries we still live in today.

Among the largest of these giants, a group of massive carnivorous theropods (bipedal dinosaurs) emerged throughout the Jurassic and Cretaceous periods, casting a shadow over the rest of the dinosaur population. The most famous of these is the Tyrannosaurus Rex, as made popular by the *Jurassic Park* films, however this type of theropod was but one of a host of killers and, amazingly, not the largest! Historically, of course, the reign of these carnivorous kings was cut short in the mass-extinction of the dinosaur population at the close of the Cretaceous period, when a 110-mile radius asteroid crashed into the Yucatán Peninsula, setting off a chain-reaction (tsunamis, dust clouds, temperature variation, food-chain collapse) of events that eventually led to their extermination.

Here, though, we explore the giddy heights of the pinnacle of dinosaur evolution, the time when nothing living on Earth could match these beasts for size and strength. Better run for cover then, as things are about to get prehistoric... ⚙

"Among them, huge behemoths with skeletons over 16 metres long and six metres tall, with skulls the size of bath tubs have surfaced"

Why the long face?
Spinosaurus had one of the longest skulls of any carnivore, some 1.75m long.

Snout and about
The long, crocodile-like snout suggests it plunged its jaw into water to catch fish.

Sail of the century
The sail of Spinosaurus was formed of very tall neural spines growing on the back vertebrae.

© Bugboy52.4

Image used with kind permission of Jerry Lofaro

CARNIVORE 1

Spinosaurus

Step aside T-Rex, this was the ultimate theropod...

Bigger and arguably meaner than the Tyrannosaurus Rex, the Spinosaurus is thought to be the largest theropod dinosaur to ever roam the planet. Over 16 metres long, six metres high and weighing a monumental 12 tons, the Spinosaurus was a relatively common animal in the late Cretaceous period. Palaeontologists have found fossilised remains of the Spinosaurus in Morocco, Libya and Egypt, including a well preserved but now destroyed (blown-up in a World War II bombing run) specimen that included the lower jaw and vertebrae with complete spines. Spinosaurus was typical for a large theropod but differed in its skull and vertebrae construction. The snout of the 1.75-metre skull was long like a crocodile, with the nostril openings placed well back from the tip. Its teeth were also conical, rounded in a cross section and did not contain any serrations – these features suggest that the Spinosaurus plunged its jaw into water in order to catch fish. However, considering its size, jaw strength and number of teeth, it equally had no trouble in hunting small, medium and other large dinosaurs on land.

Not a dinosaur you'd want to meet down a dark alley...

The Statistics
Spinosaurus

Height: 6 metres
Length: 16 metres
Weight: 12 tons
Head size: 1.75 metres
Interesting fact: The spines on the Spinosaurus grew up to two metres tall
Fear factor: 9/10

CARNIVORE 2

Giganotosaurus

The dinosaur with a big name to live up to, but was it as colossal as it sounds?

Meaning 'giant southern lizard', the Giganotosaurus was roughly the same size as the largest Tyrannosaurus Rexs, measuring over 12 metres long, five metres tall and weighing over eight tons. The skull of the Giganotosaurus was adorned with shelf-like bony ridges, notably above the eye sockets and had low horn-like projections, while the neck was considerably thicker than that of the Spinosaurus, with a stout and powerful head supported by it. Giganotosaurus remains have been found in Argentina and it has been postulated by palaeontologists that it dined mainly on medium-sized dinosaurs such as Andesaurus.

The Statistics
Giganotosaurus

Height: 4.5 metres
Length: 12 metres
Weight: 8 tons
Head size: 1.80 metres
Interesting fact: The Giganotosaurus had a brain half the size of the Tyrannosaurus
Fear factor: 7/10

Ridge too far
Giganotosaurus had bony ridges above the eye sockets.

© Arthur_Weasley

Size comparison
Who was the real king of the dinosaurs...

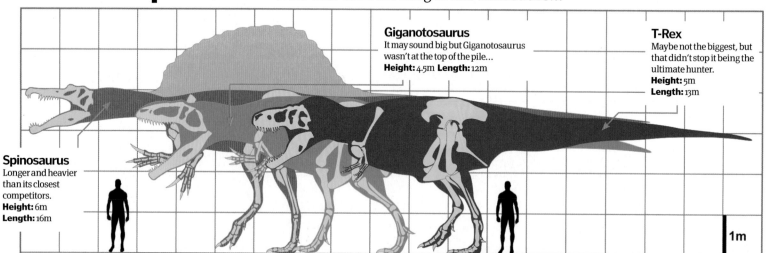

Giganotosaurus
It may sound big but Giganotosaurus wasn't at the top of the pile...
Height: 4.5m **Length:** 12m

T-Rex
Maybe not the biggest, but that didn't stop it being the ultimate hunter.
Height: 5m
Length: 13m

Spinosaurus
Longer and heavier than its closest competitors.
Height: 6m
Length: 16m

1m

CARNIVORE 3

Carcharodontosaurus

Not the world's easiest name to pronounce...

Named in 1931, the African Carcharodontosaurus was a huge theropod with serrated teeth similar to the great white shark. The skull of the Carcharodontosaurus was very narrow although it reached up to 1.6 metres in length, while its body was taller at the back than at the front, giving it a low, streamlined physicality. The thigh muscles of the Carcharodontosaurus were some of the largest of any dinosaur and this, in partnership with its narrow streamlined frame and ferocious sharp teeth, made chasing down and devouring prey elementary. Arguably the quickest of the carnivorous theropods, the archarodontosaurus was a fearsome predator. Fossilised remains have been found in Morocco, Tunisia and Egypt.

This incredible beast was named after its deadly serrated teeth

© Didier Descovens 2010

The Statistics
Carcharodontosaurus

Height: 4 metres
Length: 11 metres
Weight: 6 tons
Head size: 1.60 metres
Interesting fact: The Carcharodontosaurus could run over 20mph
Fear factor: 8/10

Shark-like teeth
The serrations in the teeth are very similar to a shark's.

© F.Fonseca

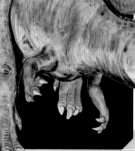

© Arthur_Weasley

© Arthur_Weasley

Mapusaurus

The dinosaur that proved teamwork can be the best way to get a good meal

Dating from the late Cretaceous period and stalking the area that is now Argentina, the Mapusaurus was a close relative of the Giganotosaurus. Despite being one of the smaller giant carnivores, with a length of 12 metres, height of four metres and weight of four tons, it was still a fearsome predator. Interestingly, palaeontologists believe that the Mapusaurus would engage in group hunting activity, allowing groups of them to take down larger foes than they would be able to achieve on their own. The remains of the Mapusaurus were first excavated between 1997 and 2001 and now complete the majority of a full skeleton. Due to its connection to the Giganotosaurus, it shares many of the same characteristics.

The Statistics
Mapusaurus

Height: 4 metres
Length: 12 metres
Weight: 4 tons
Head size: 1 metre
Interesting fact: Unlike other large theropod dinosaurs, Mapusaurus' would often hunt in groups
Fear factor: 6/10

Leg up
Researchers believe that the structure of the femur suggests a close relationship to Giganotosaurus.

Tyrannosaurus Rex

The most famous dinosaur of them all and the ultimate predator

The T-Rex was one of the largest terrestrial carnivores in the world, with the estimated strength of its bite greater than that of any other animal that has ever existed on Earth. Standing at a height of five metres, measuring over 13 metres in length and weighing over nine tons, the T-Rex is considered to be one of the most fearsome hunters ever.

The body of the T-Rex was perfectly balanced, with a horizontal backbone positioned above the hips giving completely equal weight distribution. The head was also colossal, measuring 1.6 metres long and far bulkier than any other theropod, containing 58 serrated teeth and large forward-facing eye sockets giving it acute binocular vision. From fossilised remains of Tyrannosaurus faeces, palaeontologists have discovered that the T-Rex crushed bones of the prey it consumed. The T-Rex was prolific over the entire western North America.

Good eyes
The T-Rex had binocular, colour vision

A nice bit of colour... in case you didn't spot it running at you!

Matter of balance
The massive skull of the T-Rex was balanced by a thick, heavy tail.

Quite a bite
The T-Rex had 58 serrated, banana-shaped teeth.

The Statistics
Tyrannosaurus Rex

Height: 5 metres
Length: 13 metres
Weight: 9 tons
Head size: 1.6 metres
Interesting fact: The Tyrannosaurus Rex could consume 230kg of meat in a single bite
Fear factor: 10/10

How crocodiles hunt prey

They outlived the dinosaurs but these hunters are anything but elderly

Crocodiles are often described as living fossils, but despite the fact that their body shape hasn't changed much in the last 200 million years, they are actually some of the most sophisticated reptiles on Earth.

Like all living reptiles, they are cold blooded but that doesn't make them sluggish. Crocodiles have a four-chambered heart and muscles that mimic our diaphragm to ensure they can quickly pump oxygen around their bodies for explosive bursts of speed. Crocodiles are ambush predators; their preferred tactic is to lurk in the river with just their eyes and nostrils visible above the surface and burst out of the water to surprise animals that have come to the bank to drink. If their initial lunge fails, they can chase prey over land at speeds of 17kph. The galloping gait of the crocodile was dismissed as a folk legend for many years, simply because hardly anyone who witnessed it lived to tell the tale.

Once a crocodile has grabbed its prey, it will drag it into the water and pull it under. Crocodiles need air to breathe but they can hold their breath for 30 minutes and drowning your prey is easier and more reliable than risking it escaping if you unclamp your jaws. Crocodile teeth are only designed for gripping and puncturing; they have no incisors or carnassials to slice meat off a carcass. Instead they will grip a chunk of flesh with the front teeth and spin violently on their long axis to twist off a bite-sized piece. Crocodiles don't have lips so they can't seal their mouth shut when eating. This means they can't swallow food underwater without drowning themselves so each torn off mouthful has to be brought to the surface and tossed into the back of the mouth.

When food is scarce, their cold-blooded metabolism allows crocodiles to go for as long as two years without eating at all. This, combined with their ability to scavenge rotting meat, was probably what allowed them to survive the event that killed the dinosaurs. ✿

A stealthy croc spies its prey from the water

Eyes
Mounted on the top of the head to allow it to watch the bank while almost submerged. A nictitating membrane protects them underwater.

Teeth
Crocodiles have 64 to 70 teeth, which are replaced continuously throughout the animal's life.

Tongue
A crocodile can't stick its tongue out of its mouth because it is anchored to the floor of the mouth all the way along.

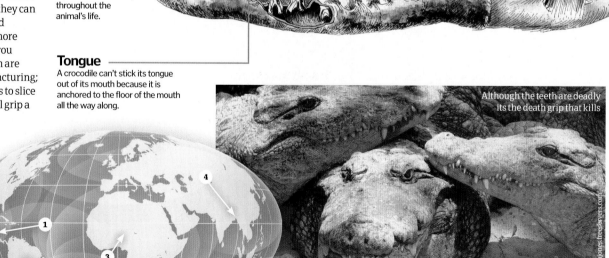

Although the teeth are deadly its the death grip that kills

ON THE MAP

Where to find crocodiles
1 Central America
2 The Amazon Rainforest
3 Sub-Saharan Africa
4 Tropical regions of Asia and the Far East
5 Northern Australia

Anatomy of a river killer
Inside the body of the oldest killer on the planet

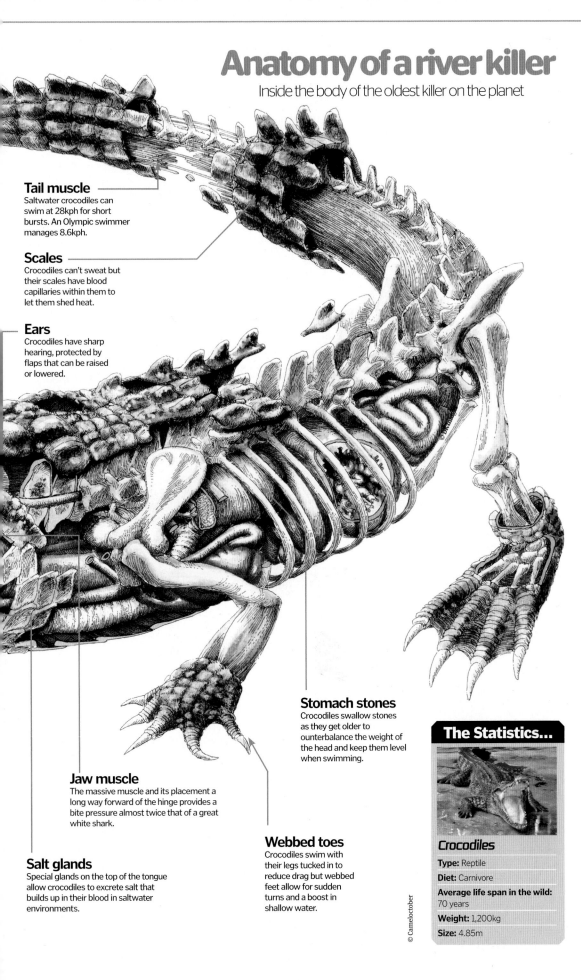

Tail muscle
Saltwater crocodiles can swim at 28kph for short bursts. An Olympic swimmer manages 8.6kph.

Scales
Crocodiles can't sweat but their scales have blood capillaries within them to let them shed heat.

Ears
Crocodiles have sharp hearing, protected by flaps that can be raised or lowered.

Jaw muscle
The massive muscle and its placement a long way forward of the hinge provides a bite pressure almost twice that of a great white shark.

Salt glands
Special glands on the top of the tongue allow crocodiles to excrete salt that builds up in their blood in saltwater environments.

Webbed toes
Crocodiles swim with their legs tucked in to reduce drag but webbed feet allow for sudden turns and a boost in shallow water.

Stomach stones
Crocodiles swallow stones as they get older to ounterbalance the weight of the head and keep them level when swimming.

© Cameloctober

The Statistics...

Crocodiles

Type: Reptile	
Diet: Carnivore	
Average life span in the wild: 70 years	
Weight: 1,200kg	
Size: 4.85m	

Crocodile or alligator?
A field spotter's guide to carnivorous reptiles

Crocodile
Location: Crocodiles live in Africa, Asia, Australia and the Americas, in both fresh and saltwater.

Snout shape: The V-shaped snout is a general-purpose design for catching fish, reptiles and mammals.

Jaws/teeth: The upper and lower jaws are the same width, so the fourth tooth in the lower jaw sticks up.

Colour: Mottled green or sandy yellow, with slightly darker scales along the back and tail.

Skin: Each scale has a pore near the edge, visible even on crocodile handbags and wallets.

Alligator
Location: Alligators are only found in the southern United States and China and vastly prefer freshwater.

Snout shape: A heavier, U-shaped snout provides extra strength for cracking turtle shells.

Jaws/teeth: A wider upper jaw completely covers all the teeth in the lower jaw when the mouth is closed.

Colour: Much darker, sometimes almost completely black, depending on the water quality.

Skin: Alligators only have pores on the scales that are covering the upper and lower jaws.

Other
A crocodile with a very long, thin snout, is actually a gharial. Caimans look like a slightly smaller alligator, but you can tell them apart because the large scales on their head form a four-four-two pattern, instead of two-two-two.

Amphibian skin

Skin is the body's main protective barrier against the outside world, and although an amphibian's skin is only very thin it has many qualities vital to keeping amphibians alive

Amphibians can breathe in and out through their skin – on land and under water – and they take in water not through their mouths but through absorbent skin on their underside called a seat patch. Most adult amphibians have lungs, but additional oxygen is taken in through the skin. Some species of salamander have no lungs or gills and breathe exclusively through their skin.

The reason amphibians feel slippery is that their skin is full of glands that produce mucus, which spreads across the surface of the skin. This mucus moistens the skin,

making it softer and therefore more oxygen absorbent. Although amphibians have few defences against predators, they do have additional poison glands on their skin that secrete irritating toxins for repelling would-be diners. Most are only mildly poisonous, but some species, such as the poison dart frog, are deadly to the touch.

Amphibian skin must stay moist to prevent the body from becoming too hot or cold, and also to avoid desiccation (drying up), which spells the end for Mr Toad. This constant need for moisture means that, as well as producing mucus, amphibians should live close to a water source. ✿

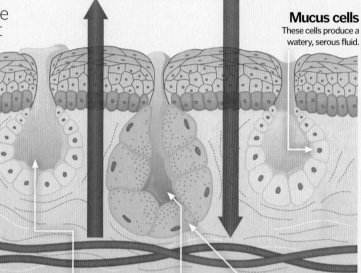

Breathe out
Carbon dioxide leaves the body through the skin.

Breathe in
Oxygen passes into blood vessels via the skin.

Mucus cells
These cells produce a watery, serous fluid.

Mucus gland
Mucus cells group together to form a sac-like gland.

Poison gland
Groups of poison glands are located in areas most likely to be attacked by predators.

Poison cells
The toxicity of the poison secreted is reliant on the amphibian's diet.

Crocodile jaw

A crocodile has the strongest bite of any known creature, producing a force of around 5,000 pounds per square inch. The muscles that control this bite down have evolved and developed to be extraordinarily strong, and alongside relative speed over short distances on land and the immensely sharp teeth that crocodiles prominently display, this forms an immense weapon for the crocodiles to successfully hunt within a competitive environment.

However, although the jaw muscles used to snap the jaw shut are well developed, the muscles used to open the jaw are considerably weaker, so much so that if the jaw is taped shut or a large rubber band is put around it, the muscles are not strong enough to push up against the force created by these. ✿

Why do crocodiles have the strongest bite of any creature known, yet are not able to open their jaw if we place an elastic band around it?

Jaw-dropping strength
A crocodile's bite is immensely powerful, but when it comes to opening its jaw the muscles are very weak.

High strength:
5,000
lbs inch²

Low strength

© Science Photo Library

He hasn't lost a game of snap yet!

Death rolls
How crocs employ this tactic

Commonly misunderstood, the crocodile death roll is a unique method to feed off previously killed prey, not a method to kill them. The most famous user of the death roll is the Nile species of crocodile, common to the Nile River in Egypt. Here, crocodiles use their camouflage and speed to grab large prey and drag them into the water. Once there, the crocodile proceeds to drag the target underwater, holding it there until it drowns. Once the prey is dead, the crocodile then performs the death roll in order to tear large chunks of flesh off its body quickly and efficiently. To do this, it buries its large teeth into the creature's flesh, before rolling its body 360 degrees. The muscular force of the crocodile's body in partnership with the sharpness of its teeth proceed to tear the prey open, something that would prove difficult within the water while stationary.

Marsh crocs basking in the sun

A close-up view of a snake's shedded skin

Why do snakes shed their skin?
How and why do these slippery reptiles moult so frequently?

Snakes shed their skin for two main reasons. The first is to facilitate continued growth. This occurs as snakeskin does not grow in partnership with the snake itself, unlike in humans, where millions of skin cells are shed each year continuously on a microscopic, unseen level. On the contrary, snakes cannot shed skin in this microscopic way, necessitating them to literally outgrow the outer layer of skin whole on a frequent basis. The frequency that snakes shed their skin is largely dependent on the stage of life cycle they are in, with sheddings incredibly frequent during infancy and teenage years (bi-monthly in some species), but slowing to a couple of times per year as adults.

The second reason why snakes shed their skin is to preserve their health. Poor living conditions (lack of humidity, lack of vegetation, excess heat, and so on) as well as an inadequate food source can lead to skin damage and parasites. If left unchecked for a long period of time in the wild, this would be highly detrimental to the snake's well being. By shedding its skin, the snake can mitigate these potentially damaging conditions and start anew.

Interestingly, however, the shedding process brings with it complications. For the week or two preceding the shedding, the snake's vision is impaired due to the loosening of the skin's outer layer, and the week or two after the event, the new outer layer is soft and vulnerable to attack from predators. For this reason, snakes tend to be overly protective around sheddings, and largely inactive if possible. The snake initialises each shedding by rubbing itself against a sharp object such as rock, to pierce the outer layer of skin.

How do snakes bite?
Call them cold-blooded, but snakes have death down to a science

Snakes are highly adapted killers. Non-venomous snakes kill by constriction (suffocation) or swallowing prey alive. Venomous snakes – which make up only ten per cent of the world's snake species – inject their victims with powerful toxins that either paralyse the respiratory system or attack red blood cells, instantly rotting flesh and bone.

Only venomous snakes have fangs, a set of long, hollow teeth in either the front or back of the mouth that act as hypodermic needles. As fangs enter the flesh, the snake flexes its jaw muscle, squeezing toxic saliva out of the venom gland, through the fang's venom canal and deep into the victim's tissue.

Snakes can control the release of venom, so many defensive strikes against humans are non-lethal 'dry bites'. If bitten, never try to cut open the wound or suck out the venom. Keep the victim calm and get to a hospital quickly for a dose of antivenin.

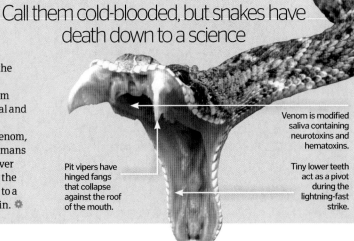

Venom is modified saliva containing neurotoxins and hematoxins.

Pit vipers have hinged fangs that collapse against the roof of the mouth.

Tiny lower teeth act as a pivot during the lightning-fast strike.

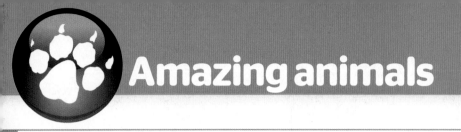
How whales communicate

Whales produce a wide range of complex sounds through differing techniques

Whales communicate by creating sounds through methods that differ depending on their family type. Toothed whales – which include dolphins – produce high-pitched sounds by the manipulation of air stored in their head through their phonic lips, a structure loosely akin to the human nasal cavity. As air is passed through the phonic lips they contract causing vibrations in the surrounding tissue before being consciously streamed by the whale.

Baleen whales differ in their sound creation, as they do not posses a phonic lip structure, doing so through manipulation of air passing through their larynx instead. The larynx works through the vibrations of internal vocal cords when air is passed over them. However, mystery shrouds this method of communication as baleen whales lack vocal cords, so presently scientists are unsure as to the exact manner in which their low-pitched sounds emanate from their larynx. ✿

The world's most venomous fish

Almost invisible among the coral reefs, the Stonefish is a real-life killer

The Stonefish is the world's most venomous fish thanks to its ability to inject deadly neurotoxins from the spines on its dorsal fin into its target. The Stonefish's neurotoxins work by attacking the nerve cells of whatever it is injected into, causing severe pain, sickness, nausea, paralysis and, depending on depth of spine penetration into skin, death within three hours.

Unlike most other poisonous fish who dwell in the dark depths of the ocean - leaving little chance of human contact – Stonefish dwell in shallow waters and are likely to be found anywhere between just beneath the surface down to a depth of three metres. ✿

"The Stonefish's neurotoxins work by attacking nerve cells"

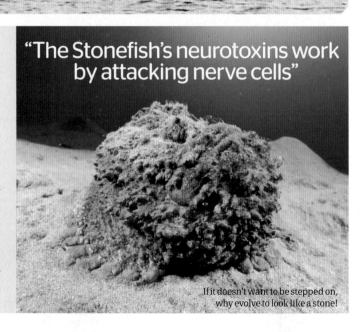

If it doesn't want to be stepped on, why evolve to look like a stone!

The deadly pufferfish

A look at why, despite its size and timid appearance, one type of fish can be extremely deadly when it comes to defending itself

The pufferfish is a group of over 100 species that are so-named for their unique line in defence. When cornered, a puffer's last gasp is to draw in water (or sometimes air) and pump it to the stomach, expanding to three times its normal size; deterring potential predators and when possible, affording it the vital seconds necessary to escape.

To achieve this with the required efficiency and speed, once the puffer has taken on water its gills clamp shut and a powerful bow-door-like valve closes over the inside of the mouth. Once the mouth's cavity is compressed, this forces the water into its stomach.

Despite its resulting comic appearance, the tissues and organs of many a puffer are no joke, laced with the potent poison tetrodotoxin – a single pinhead of which could kill a grown man. This makes it ten times more deadly than the black widow spider. The poison is produced as part of a mutually beneficial relationship by common bacteria where nutrients are exchanged as payment for the ultimate deterrent.

Some species such as the porcupine puffer are more sporting than others, covered with spines that offer added protection and ample warning to any would-be attackers. Each spine is attached to the skin by an ingenious tripod-shaped bony base. When the skin stretches, one of the legs is pushed forward and two are pulled back to snap the spine outwards... a point well made in more ways than one. ✿

The Statistics
Pufferfish

Type: Fish
Diet: Omnivore: algae, molluscs, invertebrates and crustaceans
Average life span: 4-8 years
Power: Pressurised water reactor, fuelled for life
Weight: 150g-30lbs
Size: 1in-3ft
Habitat: Tropical/sub-tropical, saltwater, brackish, freshwater

How it blows

As water enters the stomach, kilted pleats in the inner-lining allow it to flex and stretch under enormous pressure. As the stomach cavity fills, it balloons above and around the spine, continually pulling the inner-lining fibres so tight that they harden to form an almost perfect impenetrable sphere.

Mouth
To expand, the pufferfish enlarges its mouth; water enters and is prevented from leaving by an oral valve.

Stomach
Water flows from the mouth to the stomach by compressing the oral cavity. Its stomach bloats to 100 times its initial volume.

Organs
Despite its arching spine and absence of ribs, the internal organs are squeezed between the backbone and the stomach.

Pleated lining
A pleated lining allows for stretching.

Camouflage
Asides from spikes, patterning acts to camouflage the fish or ward as a deterrent.

Teeth
Pufferfish have four large teeth fused into an upper and lower plate.

Skin
It is pleats that allow this fibrous inner-layer to expand and are responsible when stretched for its rigid form.

Outer skin
This elastic layer provides a smooth hydrodynamic profile as cover to the inner pleated layer.

Spikes
Some species sport modified scales that lay flush to the skin. A tripod-shaped base causes them to snap up when the fish is puffed.

Fins
Pectoral, dorsal, caudal and anal fins optimise movement.

TTX
The most potent repellent lies in high concentrations of TTX found in the skin, gonads, liver and intestines.

Tetrodotoxin

Second only to the golden dart frog, pufferfish are said to rank as the most deadly vertebrate on Earth. The poison it carries, tetrodotoxin (TTX), is not of its own making; it is produced, in association, by relatively common marine bacteria and dinoflagellates.

In susceptible animals, TTX binds to the sodium channels of nerve cells, halting the influx of sodium and causing a cessation of nerve function; this leads to suffocation, paralysing the diaphragm and causing the death of its victim. There is no known cure.

Humans are most likely to taste its deadly effect from improperly prepared Japanese delicacy, fugu. The diner can expect a deadening of the mouth, dizziness, vomiting and difficulty breathing. This is followed by respiratory failure and coma or death within 24 hours if treatment is not forthcoming.

Each atom of the molecule is colour-coded: carbon (grey), hydrogen (turquoise), oxygen (red) and nitrogen (blue). It binds to sodium channels, blocking the transmission of nerve impulses and poisoning the nervous system.

Scorpions

The mascot of choice for international supervillains, these sinister stingers are also fearsome hunters

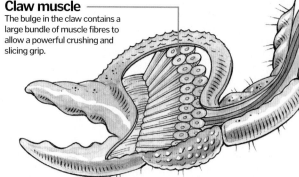

Arching its tail over its back, the scorpion delivers its deadly venom

© Guy Haimovitch

Scorpions are arachnids, like spiders. However, whereas spiders are mainly ambush predators, scorpions go looking for their lunch. Scorpions have between two and ten eyes, depending on the species, but their eyesight is poor and most scorpions are nocturnal anyway.

Instead they rely on vibration-sensitive legs, and hairs on their body that can detect the lightest touch or air current. A desert scorpion can feel the vibrations caused by the footsteps of a walking insect from a metre away. By comparing the time it takes the surface vibration to reach each leg, the scorpion can triangulate the position of its target. When it is close enough, the scorpion makes a brief dash to snatch its prey in powerful pincers. These claws, or chelae, are not true legs but are instead modified feelers. With the victim firmly grasped in its clutches, the scorpion arches its tail over its back to inject a powerful venom that incapacitates its meal within seconds.

Scorpions can't eat solid food directly, so they feed in a two-stage process. First they tear off small pieces with claw-like mouthparts, called chelicerae. These morsels are placed in a small cavity under the mouth and digestive juices are squirted up from the gut like ketchup. After the enzymes have liquidised the food, it can be slurped down into the stomach. Scorpions can eat several times their body weight at a single sitting and store this away for leaner times. They have very slow metabolisms and many species live for over ten years. If necessary they can manage with just one or two meals a year. ✿

ON THE MAP

Finding scorpions
Scorpions have a very wide distribution and are found on every continent apart from Antarctica. The dark zone on the map represents the greatest scorpion diversity but they can be found as far north as Kent in the UK and as far south as New Zealand.

Claw
The outer half of the claw is fixed and called the tarsus. The inner, movable, section is called the manus. Collectively, the pincer is called a chela.

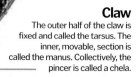

Cephalic ganglion
It's not complex enough to call it a brain but this bundle of nerves controls all the actions of the scorpion.

Claw muscle
The bulge in the claw contains a large bundle of muscle fibres to allow a powerful crushing and slicing grip.

Party animals

How do scorpions glow in ultraviolet?

All scorpions are fluorescent. This means that they glow when shone with ultraviolet light. This rather funky property is an accidental side effect of the way their armour plating is constructed. When scorpions first shed their skin, the new skin underneath is soft and vulnerable. To harden it up, the protein chains are cross-linked using other compounds. This process is called sclerotisation and is similar to the way that cowhide is turned into leather. In scorpions, the cross-linking compound is beta-carboline, which is strongly fluorescent. As a result scorpions glow more and more brightly under UV light with each successive moult.

A deadly and bright creature
© Fritz Geller-Grimm

Only 25 species have venom capable of killing a human
© Siga

Prosoma
This is also sometimes called the cephalothorax, as with spiders, and it is a fused head and body segment that holds the sensory organs and the legs.

Mesosoma
This corresponds roughly with the abdomen of an insect or spider. The digestive and reproductive organs are contained here.

Telson
The sting or telson is a hollow needle that injects the venom. The two poison glands can adjust the dose according to the size of prey.

Metasoma
The tail is made from the last six segments of the body. The anus opens at the end, just before the sting.

Intestine
Scorpions do most of their digestion externally and have quite a simple digestive tract.

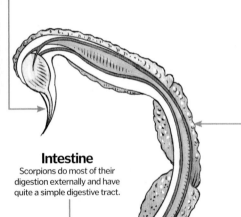

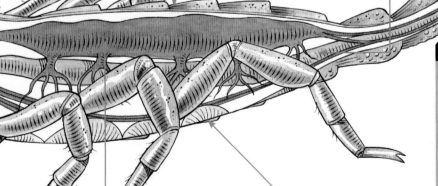
© DK Images

Dorsal blood vessel
This also functions as a primitive heart, sloshing blood between the lungs and the bodily extremities.

Book lung
Four simple folded structures on segments three to seven of the mesosoma supply oxygen to the blood.

The Statistics...

© Danny Steaven

Scorpions

Type:	Arachnid
Diet:	Carnivore
Average life span in the wild:	4-25 years
Weight:	4-60g
Size:	12mm-20cm

Hairs
These tiny hairs allow the scorpion to detect touch and air currents.

Telson
A hollow needle that injects venom into its prey.

Sting in the tail

Scorpions are fast, strong and armoured, but they aren't invulnerable and relying on sheer brute strength when you are tackling prey almost as large as you is always risky. To tilt the scales in their favour, all scorpions are equipped with fast-acting venom which is delivered through a hollow barb located on the end of their tail.

Scorpion venom is a cocktail of hundreds of different neurotoxins and enzyme inhibitors. This broad spectrum of chemicals allows the scorpion to target several different biological systems at once; some compounds paralyse muscles, others cause cell damage. Scorpions have also evolved different toxins to target different animals. For example, insect and mammal nervous systems work in quite different ways, and by combining all these chemicals into a single venom, scorpions have created a silver bullet that can take down almost anything. Despite this, our sheer size is our biggest defence and only 25 species of scorpion are deadly to humans.

The planet's smartest animals

Think your brain separates you from the beasts? The gap is not as wide as you might think...

Humans are intelligent animals. We aren't the strongest, nor the largest, nor the longest lived, but we flatter ourselves that we are the cleverest. In fact, it is so central to our sense of superiority, that we assume intelligence automatically improves the survival chances of any animal. But, in fact, there is no good evidence for this. A brain is a very expensive organ to grow and maintain – 20 per cent of the food we eat every day is used just to keep our brain alive – and complex brains take a long time to fill with data before they become useful. Bacteria, plants and fungi have shown vastly more diversity and reproductive success than us without any intelligence at all.

But high intelligence does offer one important advantage: flexibility. Animals with simple nervous systems may be extremely good at what they do, but their behavioural repertoire is hard-coded within an arrangement of neurons that is fixed at birth. New behaviours can only emerge as a result of the painfully slow processes of mutation and natural selection. An intelligent animal is an improviser. New strategies to deal with changing conditions or newly conquered territories can emerge as required and successful techniques can spread through a family group or tribe by observation and imitation over days or weeks, rather than waiting generations for new genes to spread.

Most mammals are born with brains that are already 90 per cent of their final adult weight. But to allow room for new behaviours, intelligent animals must begin life with brains that are still undeveloped. Newborn chimpanzees' brains are 54 per cent of their adult weight; with dolphins it's 42.5 per cent and elephants 35 per cent. So the elephant is the animal that learns most throughout life, after humans, who are born with just 28 per cent of their adult brain mass.

In the *Hitchhiker's Guide To The Galaxy*, Douglas Adams wrote that "Man had always assumed that he was more intelligent than dolphins because he had achieved so much – the wheel, New York, wars and so on – while all the dolphins had ever done was muck about in the water having

Monkey World rehabilitates mistreated apes from across the globe

To learn more about the rescue and rehabilitation work that goes on at Monkey World visit www.monkeyworld.org.

a good time. But conversely, the dolphins always believed that they were far more intelligent than man – for precisely the same reasons." This neatly illustrates the problem of studying animal intelligence; we tend to measure it by how closely an animal's behaviour resembles our own. We are gregarious, competitive builders, so relatively solitary, peaceful animals that don't make anything, like whales and giant pandas, get dismissed in favour of more showy animals like chimpanzees and dolphins, which can learn behaviour.

To counter this, there are several traits that researchers look for when assessing the cognitive ability of animals. At the simplest level there are planning and problem-solving tests, such as maze puzzles. Then there is evidence of tool use in the wild. At one time it was believed that humans were the only animals to use tools, but there are now more than a dozen different species that have been observed using sticks, stones and thorns in various ways to hunt for food, swat flies or defend themselves. Even dolphins, which don't have grasping hands or feet, are known to use conical sponges to protect their noses when foraging along the abrasive seabed.

Humans are not the only animals to lie, to cheat, to plan for the future, to appreciate beauty, to make toys or to show self-awareness. The more we learn about animal behaviour, the more intelligent they seem, as illustrated by our examples of some of the savviest and smartest species out there.

Category of intelligence:
Language, tool use, empathy, deception

Brain size:
420g

The chimps at Monkey World enjoy clicker training

Chimpanzees

These primates have an intelligent and self-assured personality

Chimpanzees are our closest living relatives, and so their intelligence is the easiest to understand and measure. In the wild chimpanzees use tools, hunt co-operatively, display signs of mourning, romantic love, appreciation of natural beauty and complex play. Chimpanzees lack the vocal apparatus to manage human speech, but in captivity they have been trained to use and understand American sign language. There is still some scientific debate over whether chimpanzees actually understand the language or are simply responding to cues, but in one study, a bonobo chimpanzee called Kanzi was asked a question he had never heard before: "Can you make the dog bite the snake?" Kanzi searched through his toys to find a dog and a snake, placed the snake in the dog's mouth and closed it shut using his finger and thumb.

Chimpanzees have a sense of humour and their own version of laughter (a sort of panting sound); they are ticklish and use tickling in their play. They also use simple dollies, grooming and cuddling sticks or stones as if they were babies.

Intelligence rating: ▪▪▪▪▪

Interview

Name: Dr Alison Cronin MBE

Bio: Director, Monkey World – Ape Rescue Centre. Monkey World was started in 1987 by my late-husband, who wanted to provide a home for chimps that had been smuggled from the wild to be used as beach photographer's props in Spain. In the past 25 years the park has assisted the governments of 21 countries to stop the smuggling or abuse of monkeys and apes.

Tell us about the chimps at Monkey World.

Dr Alison Cronin MBE: There are currently 59 chimpanzees at the park that have been rescued from the illegal pet trade, beach photographers, the entertainment industry and laboratories. Monkey World assists governments to stop the smuggling, abuse or neglect of primates. At the park, the refugees of these trades are rehabilitated into natural living family groups.

Can you give us some examples of times when your chimpanzees have displayed some degree of intelligence?

AC: By definition chimpanzees are intelligent and they also share the full range of emotions that humans experience – grief, fear, excitement, happiness, etc. Understanding the feeling and emotions of others in your community is an important part of life for a chimp, just as it is for a human.

Chimpanzees are very good tool users as they are clever, good at solving problems, have good hand/eye motor skills, and a pretty good precision grip with both their hands and feet. They make and use 'dipping sticks' from leafy branches we give them, to fish for insects inside of rotten logs in their enclosure or in the mock termite mound we have for them in their house. The Primate Care Staff give them many types of feeding puzzles to keep them busy and the chimps are also very keen on clicker training games, where we ask them to put their ear up for us to use an electronic thermometer.

The fact that apes are so clever has led to the abuse of chimps for the illegal tourist entertainment – what's being done to stop this?

AC: The CITES is an international treaty that protects endangered species. Monkey World assists governments to enforce the treaty by providing professional support to 'handle', move and re-home monkeys and apes that have been smuggled into their country. There was a big problem with beach photographers in Spain with baby chimps that had been poached from the wild. With Monkey World's assistance the trade in Spain has stopped and we have tracked the smugglers to Turkey, where we are now in discussions with the Turkish authorities. There is also a large black market trade in the Middle East, and Egypt in particular.

What other apes at the rescue centre display the most intelligence?

AC: By far the most intelligent of all are the orangutans. They are focused and thoughtful and always a challenge to keep busy and occupied.

151

Category of intelligence: Navigation

Brain size: 0.1g per bee, 3,000g for a hive

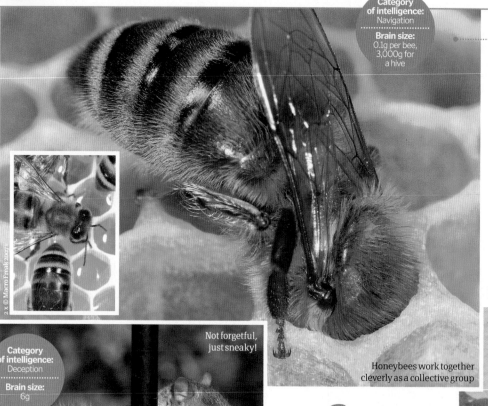

Honeybees
Show me the honey

Honeybees are highly social insects, with colonies of 30,000 or more. A single honeybee only has about 950,000 neurons in its brain, but if you consider the whole hive as a single diffuse entity, it has almost 3 billion to play with. The human brain only has 10 billion neurons. Honeybees returning to the hive use a special waggling dance to communicate their discoveries to other workers, and the colony uses a kind of democratic consensus to choose foraging locations and find a new site for the hive at swarming time. Studies show that this method consistently allocates workers in the most efficient way. Bees can also maintain a map of their surroundings in their head and will take the shortest route between multiple sites.

Intelligence rating: ▮▮▮▮▯▯

© Oxford University

Purposeful porpoises...

Honeybees work together cleverly as a collective group

Not forgetful, just sneaky!

Category of intelligence: Deception

Brain size: 6g

Grey squirrels
More than just nuts

Squirrels have a reputation for being rather dizzy – burying nuts and acorns at random and promptly forgetting where. It turns out that this is just a front. The biggest threat to a squirrel is from other squirrels stealing their caches, so they make a big show of pretending to bury non-existent nuts to fool would-be thieves. Studies have shown that the proportion of fake burials increases when the squirrel thinks it is being watched.

Intelligence rating: ▮▮▯▯▯▯

Category of intelligence: Play

Brain size: 1,600g

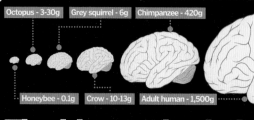

Octopus - 3-30g | Grey squirrel - 6g | Chimpanzee - 420g | Bottlenose dolphin - 1,600g | Elephant - 4,700-6,000g

Honeybee - 0.1g | Crow - 10-13g | Adult human - 1,500g

The biggest brain isn't always the smartest

Brains are not same thing as intelligence. In any animal, most of the neurons in the brain are taken up with controlling the muscles and collecting sensory information from all the nerve endings in the body. So a larger body requires a larger brain, simply to co-ordinate its movement and operate the basic metabolism. Broadly speaking, the size of an animal's brain rises with the two-thirds power of body weight. So doubling the body weight increases the brain weight by 1.6 times.

Animals with brains larger than this formula would predict might be assumed to have brain tissue 'left over' that is available for more complex reasoning. This includes whales, dolphins, elephants and primates. But there are problems with this. The animal with the highest ratio of brain size to body size is the African tree shrew, and it may be that disproportionately large brains are used for other things besides intelligence, such as a highly developed sense of smell.

Brain image © Patrick J Lynch

Abel is a wild-caught crow. Here he makes and uses tools to help retrieve food from the bottom of a vertical tube.

Crows
Plenty to crow about

Crows are the most intelligent birds. The New Caledonian crow can fashion a variety of tools by plucking and bending grass stems and twigs and use them to extract grubs and insects from their nests. In the lab, they will bend wire to form a hook to extract a reward from a narrow jar. The hooded crow uses scavenged breadcrumbs as bait to catch fish. Crows in Japan will drop nuts onto busy streets so that passing cars will crack the shells and then patiently wait at the crossing for the lights to turn red, so they can retrieve them.

Intelligence rating: ▓▓░░░

Elephants make good use of tools

Category of intelligence: Empathy, tool use

Brain size: 4,700-6,000g

Bottlenose dolphins
So long, and thanks for all the fish...

Bottlenose dolphins have larger brains than us. They hunt co-operatively and will assist injured family members or even human swimmers by keeping them close to the surface. Dolphins also seem to devote much of their intelligence to inventing complex games. For example, they will swim rapidly in a circle and then blow air into the vortex created, so the bubble forms a doughnut shape. Sometimes they will admire their creation, other times they will chase it as it rises and bite it. Experiments using mirrors and playing video footage back to dolphins have shown some evidence that they may also be self-aware.

Intelligence rating: ▓▓▓▓░

Elephants
They never forget

The elephant is obviously a very large animal, so you would expect it to have a large brain. But the structure of an elephant's brain is more surprising. The neocortex is as complex and has as many neurons as the neocortex of the human brain. This part of the brain is believed to be associated with intelligence and problem solving. Elephants also have the largest hippocampus of any animal, including humans. The hippocampus is involved in the processing of memory and emotion. Elephants belong to very close-knit societies and have been observed burying their dead and standing over the grave, as if in mourning. They also make extensive use of tools to swat flies and will cover small watering holes with bark and sand to reduce evaporation.

Intelligence rating: ▓▓▓▓▓

Category of intelligence: Learning, tool use

Brain size: 3-30g

Octopuses
A brain in every arm

Octopuses only live a few years and have no contact with their parents, so they have to learn fast and teach themselves. They are the most intelligent invertebrate organisms, and studies have shown that they can solve mazes and be taught to unscrew jar lids. The nervous system of an octopus is quite decentralised: two-thirds of its neurons are in the tentacles, allowing them to behave semi-independently. The veined octopus will pick up coconut shells and use them to build a protective shelter. This makes it the only invertebrate to use tools. Octopuses also engage in play, catching and releasing objects caught in circular currents.

Intelligence rating: ▓░░░░

TEN MORE CLEVER CRITTERS

Some more that you did (and didn't) expect to be included in the brainy bunch...

DOG
Eager to please and easy to train to perform a wide range of different tasks.

CAT
Much more independent than dogs, but with a strong sense of play.

PIG
Can learn what a mirror's image represents and use it to obtain information.

RAT
Exhibits 'metacognition' – making decisions based on whether it thinks it will be able to solve a puzzle.

PARROT
Can mimic human speech and even associate some words with their meanings.

WHALE
Whale brains contain spindle cells, previously only discovered in the great apes, elephants and humans.

ORANGUTAN
Uses leaves to make loud squeaking sounds and tools to extract seeds from fruit.

PIGEON
Can remember hundreds of different images for several years at a time.

ANT
Experienced foragers act as mentors to newcomers, so the nest quickly learns about food sources.

COW
Forms friendship groups within the herd and holds grudges for months or years.

Kings of the

The polar bear may seem cute and cuddly, but these mammoth mammals of the Arctic are a hardened species, set out to survive in these subzero temperatures, plunging to as much as -45° Celsius.

The polar bear, or Ursus maritimus – which means sea bear – have been recorded to weigh as much as 2,209 pounds, and can grow to as big as ten feet tall, when standing on their hind legs. That's a massive body mass, which includes a thick layer of blubber nearly 4.5 inches thick. Wrap this up with

two additional layers of fur, which covers all of the bear's anatomy except their nose and foot pads, and Ursus maritimus stays as snug as a bug. Pure white to creamy yellow/light brown in colouration, depending upon season and angle of light, makes for a perfect combination for surprising prey.

Other essential parts of the anatomy, such as the paws and snout, help them thrive in these harsh conditions. Polar bears' paws are large compared to its body size. Measuring 12 inches, they include thick, curved, non-retractable claws, essential for

catching large prey, as well as for traction when running on ice.

Small bumps, known as papillae, are also present and these help them keep their grip when manoeuvring slippery ice. Up to half the length of the bear's toes is covered with a swimming membrane, which enables them to swim at a rate of six miles per hour, and they're known to be competent swimmers as far as 320km from shore.

The bear's sense of smell is extremely acute, and becomes the most important sensory for detecting

A family of polar bears receive a surprise visit from a Russian sub

Polar bears are animals without boundaries, padding across the ice from Russia to Alaska, from Canada to Greenland and onto Norway's Svalbard archipelago

© Ansgar Walk 1996

ON THE MAP

Where can you find the king of the arctic?

Found throughout the Arctic circle, polar bears can be found in five countries: Denmark (Greenland), USA (Alaska), Canada, Norway (Svalbard) and Russia. Estimates suggest that only 20,000-25,000 polar bears remain worldwide.

Arctic

How polar bears hunt and survive

land prey. Able to smell a seal from over one kilometre away, under three feet of snow, this is extremely important to this species' survival, as snowy weather conditions impair its eyesight, which is no better than that of a normal human being. These factors firmly put Ursus maritimus at the top of the Arctic food chain.

Unfortunately, despite their great prowess, the polar bear population is dropping quickly, mainly due to the damaging effects of global warming. As the Earth heats up, larger

quantities of ice are melting earlier in the year, removing the vital hunting platforms which polar bears use to hunt seals. This habitat loss is preventing polar bears from building up the requisite fat reserves to survive in the harsher and leaner parts of the year, with many succumbing to malnutrition. In addition, the loss of ice is forcing the bears to swim further and further between landmasses, draining energy that is vital for healthy reproduction, body conditioning and general survival. ❁

Every family has its fall-outs...

5 TOP FACTS
POLAR BEARS

1 Diving depths
The polar bear makes shallow dives to catch prey, but can stay submerged for up to two minutes, in depths of up to 15 feet.

2 Female of the species
A female polar bear can bare offspring as young as four or five years old. Cub litters are most commonly twins.

3 Boys are bigger
The male is the larger of the two sexes, growing up to ten feet tall and weighing in at over 1,400 pounds. The female is a little more slender, at seven feet tall and only 650 pounds.

4 Translucent fur
Ever wondered why a polar bear looks white? Well, each hair is a transparent and pigment-free hollow tube, reflecting the light around it. Perfect camouflage for hunting prey.

5 Bear on standby
The polar bear can slow down its own metabolism, which enables it to conserve energy at any time of the year.

Locating prey
To catch prey, polar bears wait in silence outside seal breathing holes in the ice, before dragging them out when they surface to breathe. They then crush the seal's skull to kill it.

Big diet
Polar bears' diet consists mainly of land-caught seals and their pups. During the summer months they also eat a plethora of sea creatures and fish.

Devouring prey
Polar bears tend to be selective in what parts of their prey they consume, focusing on the calorie-rich skin and blubber.

On the hunt
Land or sea, nothing stops the polar bear

🔽 Learn more
For more information about polar bears head over to **polarbearsinternational.org/** where you can learn more about these incredibly cute but ultimately deadly beasts, and even adopt your very own cub!

© DK Images

Giant pandas explained

The carnivore that thinks it's vegetarian

© Science Photo Library

There he sits, the giant panda. Solitary, peaceful, resting upright on his furry haunches like a black-and-white Buddha. A born carnivore, this perplexing member of the bear family passes on the meat course almost entirely, choosing to persist on nature's version of a celery diet: bamboo.

A highly endangered animal – less than 2,500 exist in the wild – the panda's monotonous (nearly monovorous) diet is part of its undoing. The nutritional value of bamboo is negligible, exacerbated by the fact that the panda is genetically incapable of digesting cellulose. The result is that much of the panda's extremely high-fibre diet passes right through it, providing only minimal calories to an animal that can grow up to 136kg (300lbs) in the wild.

So there the giant panda sits, for up to 16 hours every day, tearing and grinding away at piles of this nearly indigestible plant simply to eke out enough caloric energy to wake up the next day and do it all again. That peaceful, almost Zen-like demeanour has less to do with temperament than low blood sugar. The poor panda can hardly muster the energy to mate, and when he does successfully reproduce, the female will only raise one young at a time, even though the majority of births are twins. Such a slow reproductive rate makes the giant panda population highly susceptible to outside pressures, of which there are many.

Habitat loss is the panda's greatest threat, then poaching. Because of their singular devotion to bamboo, pandas must live where the plant is abundant. Today, the only suitable habitat is limited to 20 isolated sections of mountain forest in south-western China, all of which have thankfully been protected by the Chinese government with help from conservationist organisations like the World Wildlife Fund. ✿

A newborn panda is practically hairless
© The GIMP

Calories from food

The amount of energy an animal obtains from food is measured in calories. The following information reveals how many calories a panda must consume per day compared with other creatures.

ANIMAL	CALORIES CONSUMED PER DAY
Elephant	40,000
Giant panda	20,000
Adult humans	2,300-2,600
Mouse	20

Giant panda anatomy

Paws
A pseudo-thumb, an elongated wrist bone covered with a thick pad of skin, is used for grasping bamboo stalks.

Fur
Pandas have two types of fur: long bristly hairs and a thick wool-like undercoat. The reason for their black-and-white colouring is unknown.

Teeth
A set of knife-like front teeth rip the bamboo, then the panda uses its jaw to grind down the plant with four flat molars.

Front legs
The panda relies on its strong, flexible front legs to pull out bamboo shoots, break them into usable pieces and to even climb trees.

Hind legs
The panda's hind legs are spread widely apart, helping it to sit comfortably for hours on end, but making it difficult to run.

Skin
The skin under a panda's black fur is grey and the skin under its white fur is pink. Newborn pandas are entirely pink and nearly hairless.

Stomach
With the stomach of a carnivore, pandas rely on microbes to help break down the abundant cellulose in bamboo. A thick layer of mucus protects against splinters.

The Statistics...

Giant panda

Species: Ailuropoda melanoleuca

Type: Mammal

Diet: Omnivore

Average life span in the wild: 20 years

Weight: Up to 136kg (300lbs)

Size: Up to two metres (6ft) head to tail and one metre (3ft) at the shoulders

Without opposable thumbs, the panda had to adapt to grip bamboo

The grip of a panda...

Thumb
An evolved bone pseudo-thumb helps dexterity and grip strength.

Fingers
Five strong, bulbous fingers help strip bamboo for consumption.

Pads
Toughened skinned pads have developed to increase grip friction.

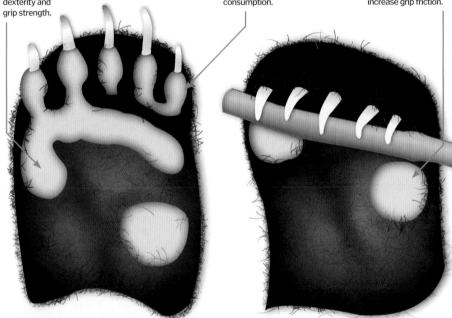

Adapting to bamboo

It's the diet they were designed for, so why do pandas shun meat?

Although giant pandas are technically carnivores, they have adapted to eating a diet of 99 per cent bamboo, which they can barely digest. Pandas are genetically unable to turn cellulose into energy, so they must eat up to 38kg (84lbs) of the fibrous plant every day to get enough calories to survive. The task requires 12-16 hours of foraging and eating.

The panda's gut has developed a thick layer of mucus to protect against bamboo splinters. So, aside from the rare rodent or bird, why don't pandas eat meat? Clues in the recently sequenced panda genome point to a genetic mutation that may render them unable to taste flesh. Fossil studies show that the giant panda's ancestors swapped meat for bamboo between 2 and 7 million years ago – perhaps due to a major environmental event wiping out their prey. Being forced to change their diet may have caused the gene responsible for tasting savoury to become obsolete, and without it they might not have wanted to eat meat even when it became plentiful.

A 'carnivorous' panda will opt for bamboo over meat, every time

ON THE MAP

Where the wild pandas are...
1 Minshan mountains: 45% of the wild panda population live in these biodiverse Chinese mountain forests.
2 Qinling mountains: 200-300 pandas live on the cool, wet southern slopes of this Chinese range.

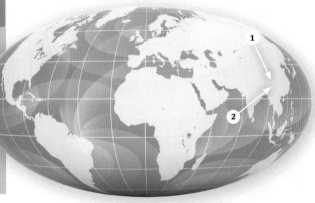

Hippo jaws

How do these creatures open their mouths so wide?

A hippo may open its mouth wide as a sign of aggression, similar to other animals such as lions and baboons. Opening their jaws shows others their fearsome set of weaponry: their teeth.

Although hippos eat vegetation, they do not use their teeth to do so. Their giant canines and incisors are used only for killing. Instead, they use their huge lips to rip grass from the ground for consumption. A hippo is able to spread its lips through a jaw-dropping 150 degrees and up to 1.2m (3.9ft) in width. The strength of a hippo's jaw muscles – a bite force of 1,800lb – is such that it can use its fearsome teeth to bite a crocodile, human, or even a small boat in half.

The skull of a hippopotamus contains tusk-like canines as long as your arm

Each of a hippo's two lips is about 0.6m (2ft) wide

Incisors
Razor-sharp incisors can rip through the skin of a hippo's latest meal.

Jaw-dropping
A hippo can spread its gums to an enormous 1.2m (3.9ft).

Yawn
The apparent 'yawn' of a hippo is actually a display of aggression and alerts others to its aggressive mood.

Canine
The tusk-like canines of a hippo are not only used as weapons, but also warn off potential predators when displayed.

© Raul654

A lie-in that we could only dream of...

Image © DK Images

Hibernation explained

Why can mammals go to sleep for months on end?

While birds and winged creatures can fly to warmer climes to escape cold and fruitless winters, many mammals enter a deep sleep to survive. This state is called hibernation and, depending on the animal, it can last between a few days, weeks, or even months.

In preparation for true hibernation, the animal must make a cosy burrow in which to sleep, and eat lots of food to store up as fat. Some animals can survive the whole winter on little or no food as the animal's heart rate and body temperature decrease, which means they use very little energy during hibernation.

Hibernating mammals also have two types of fat: regular white fat, which is used for storing energy and insulating the body, and a special brown fat that isn't burned for energy. This brown fat is most important to hibernation because it forms around the organs that need it most – the brain, heart and lungs – and generates heat to keep the animal alive. ✿

Wasp stings

The wasp holds a potent and reusable form of attack

A wasp stings by transferring venom from an internal venom sac through its egg-laying tube into its victim. The wasp's sting differs from the bee's sting due to the smooth surface of its egg-laying tube, allowing retention of it after an attack for reuse. The bee's jagged equivalent sting however, does not allow for such action, forcing it to literally wrench itself in two and leaving its rear-end and stinger stuck in its victim.

The wasp's sting holds another unique ability. While the venom of a wasp contains many active ingredients, it also carries a pheromone that alarms all other wasps in the area, calling for backup in its attack on its target. This talent is an evolutionary bonus card the bee does not share. Therefore, while bees are more likely to be seen flying in swarms there is greater probability that a sting by a solitary wasp will end up leading to a mass attack. ✿

Inside a wasp's abdomen

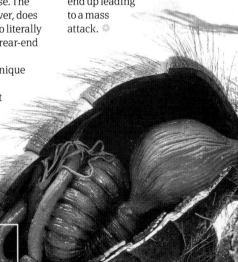

Venom sac
Housing the venom, before being passed through the egg-laying tube and into the victim.

Egg-laying tube
The smooth surface allows the wasp to retain the tube after stinging.

© DK Images

A massive flock can be a truly awesome sight

Followers
Each bird will benefit from the updraft created by the flapping of the bird in front's wings (which creates currents of circulating air), generating lift for the birds behind to take advantage of.

Resistance
If a bird falls out of formation it will notice the extra resistance and immediately get back in line.

Leader
Flying in a V formation is a good way to reduce fatigue in the members of the flock and a large or strong bird will take the lead.

Fatigue
If the leader becomes tired it will rotate back into formation and another bird will then take the lead.

Replacement
When the flock changes direction, a new leader will take the helm.

Sick birds
A sick or wounded bird will drop out of formation and one other bird will follow it until it recovers or dies.

Flying in a flock

How and why do birds flock together, and why don't they bump into each other?

Watching as a massive collection of birds float across the sky like an unpredictable wave, it's difficult to comprehend how birds can fly in formation without the aid of the high-tech location equipment used by aerobatic teams like the Red Arrows. Such patterns may look like the result of extrasensory communication, but they're in fact the product of emergent animal group behaviour known as flocking. Every change of direction comes not as a result of an individual member of the flock, but rather of the snap decisions made by those individuals in response to the movements of their neighbours.

To comprehend how it works, in 1986 American computer programmer Craig Reynolds applied simple rules to bird behaviour to simulate flocking in his computer program Boids. The three rules he outlines include the fact that each bird steers itself to avoid crowding or bumping its neighbours (separation), each bird tries to match the average heading of its neighbours (alignment), and that each bird steers towards the average position of its neighbours, maintaining flock structure (cohesion). ❁

© Science Photo Library

5 TOP FACTS
FLOCKING

1 When to watch
The best time of year to witness flocking is winter as migratory birds prepare to head for warmer climes, and those that stick around for winter will be foraging and roosting together.

2 Honk honk
Sometimes geese at the back of their flock will make honking sounds to encourage the birds ahead to maintain their speed.

3 Sort Sol
Twice a year in Denmark massive flocks of starlings block out the sun during an event called Sort Sol or 'Black Sun'.

4 Movie sims
Craig Reynolds' Boids program inspired the film *Batman Begins* to simulate a swarm of bats. It was also the simulation behind the stampede of wildebeest in *The Lion King* animation.

5 Big flocks
There are more sub-Saharan red-billed Queleas in the world than any other species and their flocks can comprise tens of thousands – the flock can take hours to pass by.

The benefit of the flock

There are several benefits to flying as a flock. It improves a bird's chance of survival against predators because a large group of birds is stronger and better protected and with many eyes the flock is far more likely to spot a would-be marauder. Also, the predator will find it harder to concentrate on a single victim, increasing the individual member of the flock's chance of survival.

Flocking also enables birds to fly further using less energy because when the strong leader bird flaps its wings it creates uplift for the birds behind – each bird (except the leader) is flying in the up-wash from the wing of the bird in front. This enables the flock to use less energy and reduces fatigue.

Don't park you car under here!

Woodpeckers explained

Woodpeckers whack their heads against wood up to 20 times a second, at 1,200 times the force of gravity, without suffering concussion, detached retinas or any other symptoms of head injury. But why?

Woodpeckers' tongues have longitudinal muscles for side-to-side movement when poking around for insects

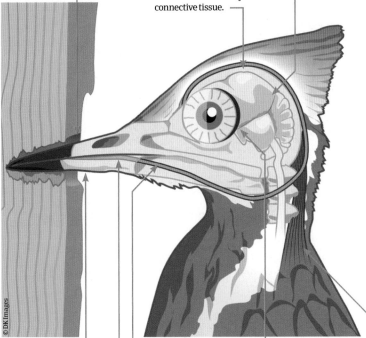

© DK Images

Holes
Woodpeckers excavate small rectangular holes on the sides of tree trunks, prying off wood to expose tasty beetle larvae and carpenter ants.

Skull
Woodpeckers have a thicker skull than most other birds. It's made of extremely strong yet spongy compressible bone, to help cushion the blow. The beak and skull are linked by elastic connective tissue.

Brain
Unlike human brains, which are floating about in a pool of cushioning cerebrospinal fluid, woodpecker brains are tightly enclosed in the skull with practically no cerebrospinal fluid.

Beak
The strong bones that comprise the woodpecker's straight bill are strengthened by a horn-covered beak, which hammers into the wood and bark of a tree at something like 12,000 impacts per day in search of bugs and ants.

Hyoid apparatus
Within the long tongue is a skeletal structure called the 'hyoid apparatus'. This is a collection of small bones supported by cartilage and muscles, which fold up like an accordion and enable the woodpecker to stick its tongue out further.

Third eyelid
Woodpeckers have a thick inner eyelid, which acts as a seatbelt to ensure the bird's eyeballs don't pop out and also prevents tearing the retina. The eye is filled with blood to support the retina.

Zygodactyl feet
For optimum insect foraging, woodpeckers' feet are zygodactyl, which helps them cling onto vertical tree trunks. Zygodactyl means they have two front-facing toes and two back-facing toes.

Stiff tail feathers
The woodpecker can prop itself up like a tripod, using its strong tail-feather muscles.

Barbed tongue
Because a woodpecker probes around inside tree trunks for insects, its barbed tongue needs to be longer than its beak – sometimes up to four times longer. In some species the tongue actually forks in the throat and disappears below the base of the jaw, wrapping up and over the head before rejoining behind the eye socket or nostril.

Neck muscles
A split second before every tap, the dense muscles in the bird's neck contract and distribute the force of the impact away from the skull down through the rest of the body, like shock absorbers.

How does pollen work?

Discover how this 'irritating' flower powder functions, enabling germination

Pollen is the fine powder produced by the male sex organs of a flower. It contains the male gametes (or sex cells). When a grain lands on the stigma of a flower of the same species, a special pollen tube grows from the grain of pollen down through the flower's style to link the sperm cells to the unfertilised eggs in the flower's ovaries. Here germination takes place, as the ovules are fertilised and a seed forms.

Heavier pollen is transferred to plants by insects going from flower to flower. However, the lighter airborne pollen that gets blown from one flower to another is the stuff that causes people with pollen allergies to experience hay fever. ❁

Sex cells
Inside a grain of pollen are the male sex cells, called 'gametes'.

Inner lining
The inner wall of a grain of pollen is the intine. It encloses the sex cells and other vegetative cells.

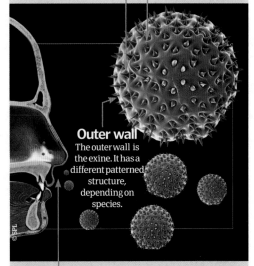

Outer wall
The outer wall is the exine. It has a different patterned structure, depending on species.

Hay fever
When someone with a pollen allergy breathes in pollen, chemicals and antibodies are produced and released to fight the infection.

Pollen count
The pollen count is a measure of the number of grains of pollen present in a cubic metre of air. The higher the pollen count, the worse the hay fever symptoms.

LOW	30
MODERATE	30-49
HIGH	50-149
VERY HIGH	149 AND OVER

A guide to bird respiration

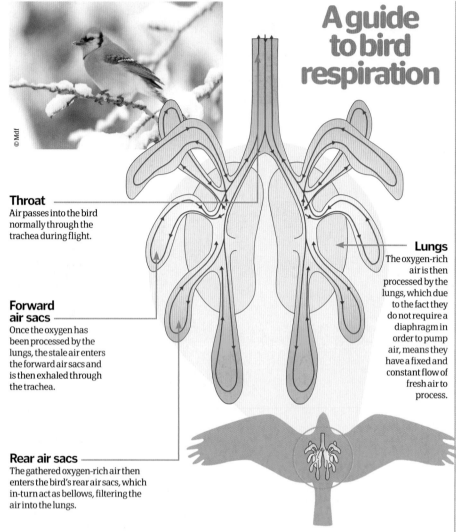

© Mdf

Throat
Air passes into the bird normally through the trachea during flight.

Forward air sacs
Once the oxygen has been processed by the lungs, the stale air enters the forward air sacs and is then exhaled through the trachea.

Rear air sacs
The gathered oxygen-rich air then enters the bird's rear air sacs, which in-turn act as bellows, filtering the air into the lungs.

Lungs
The oxygen-rich air is then processed by the lungs, which due to the fact they do not require a diaphragm in order to pump air, means they have a fixed and constant flow of fresh air to process.

How do birds breathe?

Forced to evolve due to an exceedingly high metabolic rate and oxygen demand, birds sport an efficient and refined respiratory system

Birds breathe by partnering a pair of lungs without a diaphragm with a system of internal air sacs that act as bellows. The reason for this is due to the bird's high metabolic rate and oxygen demand when flying, constantly needing a stream of oxygen-rich air to process in order to remain active.

This would not be possible with the bi-directional lungs of mammals as oxygen-rich air is mixed with oxygen-deficient stale air during the breathing process, reducing the amount of oxygen that can be processed in the lungs at any one time.

However, with the unidirectional flow that is made possible by separating the pump part of the breathing process (the sacs) with the absorption part (the lungs), a constant oxygen-rich stream can be maintained. Avian lungs do not process oxygen with alveoli as mammal lungs do, but absorb it through honeycombed-structured passages referred to as parabronchi into air vesicles, which themselves contain oxygen/carbon dioxide trading capillaries. ✿

Earthworms

Worms are well known to us, often spotted in back gardens across the country – but more importantly, can they actually survive if they are cut in two?

Earthworms need moisture to survive and consequently commonly live underground in damp soil. They are cylindrical in shape, and their body structure is surprisingly simple with a muscular outside body that lines their digestive tract and circulatory system.

This circulatory system is very simple, with only two blood vessels (the dorsal and the ventral) which run between the anterior and posterior of the creature, with blood being pumped by aoertic arches in the case of the ventral vessel, or moved back to the anterior by the dorsal vessel contracting. However, although simple, earthworms do display distinct segments, which are more specialised towards the anterior (head). Consequently, segments situated further back in the body can be regenerated in many cases, but it is dependant on the type of species and the actual extent of damage.

Earthworms are also hermaphrodites, holding both male and female sexual organs, however they commonly mate and then store the other individual's sperm for reproduction. ✿

Muscular body
This allows movement by stretching out, pushing the anterior segments forward, and then pulling the rest of the body after.

Digestive tract
This stretches throughout the individual, and is where food taken in through the mouth is processed.

Clitellum

Ventral nerve

Mouth

Dorsal vessel
This brings blood which has been pumped down the body back to the front to be oxygenated and then pumped back down the ventral vessel.

Ventral vessel
Blood gets pumped by the aoertic arches down the body to supply oxygen where needed.

Aoertic arches
These work like a human heart, pumping the blood around the earthworm's body. The number of these present varies between species.

Anatomy 101
Upon dissecting an earthworm it's easy to see the digestive tract wrapped in aoertic arches, transporting blood down the body.

Beaver dams

We explore how these aquatic mammals design and construct their habitats

Home sweet home
A beaver's lodge, often found in the middle of a pond, is accessible only by water. These dwellings are home to extended families.

Safe depths
Winter seasons are perilous for all aquatic creatures. To stop the hazard of ice blocking the dam entrance at this time of year, beavers will submerge its foundations three feet beneath surface level.

Standing tall
The average height of a beaver lodge reaches up to six feet tall, with an average depth of water behind the dam of four to six feet. This makes it a great place to look out for predators, and keeps it a safe distance from shore.

Made to last
The thickness of the dam can measure up to five feet or more. The length depends on the width of the habitable stream, averaging 15 feet. This makes for a very sturdy home in all weather conditions.

Rodent renovation
Renovation is the name of a beaver's game. Apart from building dams, they can gnaw at trees and felling, creating large log and branch obstructions that turn fields and forests into large ponds to build their habitat.

Food fuel
Beavers are among the largest rodents on Earth. They live on a herbivore diet, eating leaves, bark, twigs, roots and aquatic plants.

© DK Images

Beavers are aquatic mammals with a keen affection for engineering, demonstrated in the construction of their artificial dam habitat. This ingenuity is one of nature's greatest wonders, and has been happening for well over 10 million years. Fundamentally, the building of a dam suits the natural instinct of this species. The beaver is an adapted swimmer, that is fairly immobile upon land. This makes it susceptible to predators such as the bear.

Their strong aquatic skills make deep water habitats far more secure. Skilled teams of constructer beavers, usually working in pairs, can build a dam in a matter of days. The dam itself is constructed from an eclectic mix of natural materials, including rocks, wet grass, wood and mud to build the superstructure. A minimum level of three feet is required to keep the dam's underwater entrance from freezing over in winter. A beaver's dam will vary in construct and design, dependent on water speeds in the river. If the dam is straight, then the water current is slow. If it's curved, the water current is fast moving.

Bats' ultrasonic sonar system

We reveal how Chiroptera's supersonic hearing happens

Contrary to belief, bats (Chiroptera) do demonstrate an acute sense of vision, however this is accommodated during daylight conditions. When night falls, these small mammals are more inclined to use their heightened sense of hearing when hunting prey and manoeuvring around habitats, never being at a disadvantage. This is complemented by their incredible biological sonar navigation system.

But how does this work? Well, bats are inclined to emit ultrasonic sounds, with a frequency of between 50,000 and 200,000 vibrations per second, too high-pitched for human ears to comprehend.

These sound are emitted 20 to 30 times each second in all directions, with the bat listening between pulses, scanning for echoes with its head in perpetual motion. Bats separately perceive and process overlapping echo delays, arriving as little as two microseconds apart, that's an impressive two thousandths of a second. The bat's own nervous system supports this fined-tuned capability, allowing Chiroptera to identify echo-reflecting points on an object the width of a pen line on paper, or objects as close together as three-tenths of a millimetre.

Emitting sound
Bats emit ultrasonic sounds 20 to 30 times each second, listening between pulses for echoes.

Timing and direction
The bat then registers distance and location of prey through the timing and direction of returning sound waves.

Translating echo
The time between sending out a cry and then receiving a response is translated by the bat into distance, between itself and whatever object is in the vicinity.

Moving prey
The bat realises moving prey through delayed sound and a slightly lower or higher pitch, due to the Doppler effect.

Sourcing insects
Echoes from prey such as mosquitoes, moths and butterflies reveal fluctuations, which are caused by the flutter of their wings, easily recognised by the bat.

Stationary prey
Stationary objects are instantly recognisable, as these yield an echo that is a replica of the pulse sent out by the bat.

Ligers and tigons

When lions and tigers mate, new species are born

Size
Ligers can grow to twice the size of their parents.

Inherited
Ligers enjoy swimming like their mother, and can have spots like their father.

A male liger in Novosibirsk Zoo, Russia

Ligers and tigons are two resultant species that emanate when lions and tigers cross breed. If a male lion mates with a tigress then a liger is born, if a male tiger mates with a lioness then a tigon is born. Both hybrid species are extinct in the wild as their respective habitats lead to minimal interaction, however many examples of both species can be found in captivity across the world in zoos and wildlife parks.

Ligers are now the more prevalent of the two species due to the greater probability of them living past birth, although during the early 20th Century this was not the case. The liger, as with the tigon, shares characteristics from both parent species – ligers enjoy swimming for example, a trait which is associated with tigers, however they also have spots, a characteristic gene of the lion – and tend to be bigger due to imprinted genes. Indeed, the current largest liger in the world weighs over 400 kilograms and is twice the size of its parents. Interestingly, though, tigons tend to suffer from dwarfism rather than gigantism as they always inherit the growth-inhibitory genes from the lioness mother, often weighing only around 200 kilograms.

Unfortunately, due to the hybrid man-made nature of ligers and tigons, growth disorders and degenerative diseases are common, as well as shortened life spans.

Black widows

How do these deadly spiders kill their prey?

The black widow spider (genus Latrodectus) begins by using its silk glands (spinnerets) at the rear of its abdomen to create a sticky web. It waits at the edge of the trap until its prey either flies or walks into it.

When an insect is trapped in the web, the black widow can sense the vibrations caused by the struggling prey. From these vibrations it can tell how big and strong the prey is, and if it is too big, it will leave well alone.

If the prey is small enough, however, the black widow will use its spinnerets to cover it in stronger webbing. It then firmly holds the prey with its chelicerae, which is a pair of hollow appendages above its mouth that send poison into the victim.

The spider's latrotoxin, neurotoxic poison causes the prey to suffer spasms, paralysis and death within ten minutes. After this, enzymes inside the victim liquefy its body allowing the spider to feed on it.

DID YOU KNOW?

The poison of the black widow spider is 15 times stronger than a rattlesnake's venom. It rarely bites humans and although painful, less than one per cent of them cause human death.

Cat paws

A cat's paws are vital to keep the feline alive and kicking. They can help perform many functions from shock absorbing and self-defence to cleaning, killing and climbing

Unlike other creatures, such as humans who walk on the soles of their feet, cats are digitigrades and walk on their tiptoes. This makes them very agile, quick, and quiet too – hence the phrase 'cat burglar'.

Both front paws have five digits (toes) while the rear two have just four. The back paws are stronger than the front and can better tolerate impacts when running and jumping. For every digit there is a digital pad, which cushions the foot. An additional large pad in the middle of each paw consists of three fleshy lobes to help absorb shocks and support the main leg bone. This is called the metatarsal pad on the hind paws and the metacarpal pad on the fore paws.

As well as the pads, each digit also features a sharp claw. Like human fingernails, the claws grow constantly and are made of keratin protein encased in hard, dead keratin cells. The front claws are usually sharper than the rear ones and to keep them sharp, when not in use the claws are protected by the skin and fur around the paw. Meanwhile, to prevent them growing too long and potentially resulting in painful ingrown claws, cats can keep their claws short by using them for climbing, fighting and self-defence. They can also be trimmed by a vet and the use of a scratching pole will help file them down a bit too. ⚙

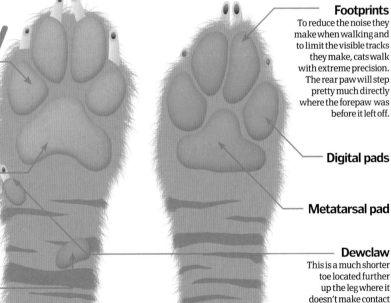

Protractile claws

When a cat's paw muscles are relaxed you won't see much of the claws because they are concealed, or retracted, behind the skin and fur of the paw when walking around or lazing in the sun. However, cats are capable of extending, or protracting, their claws for fighting, climbing and scratching if required. When an adult cat decides to tighten its digital flexor tendon – ready for, say, a catfight – the claw extends and becomes much more visible outside the digital pad. Once the cat relaxes its muscles again, the claw will retract back to its normal resting position. Kittens are less aware of taking control of their paw muscles and some young cats cannot retract their claws until they are older.

Claw retracted

Keratin cuticle
The outer cuticle is made of a tough protein called keratin.

Quick
The soft pink dermis tissue within the claw is the quick. It receives the blood supply and is sensitive to pain.

Relaxed elastic ligament

Middle phalanx

Relaxed digital flexor tendon
When relaxed, the claw is pulled up inside the skin and fur, protecting the claw and keeping it sharp.

Distal phalanx
A claw grows outwards from the tip of the last bone on the toe, the distal phalanx.

Claw protracted

Extensor process
The claw extends outwards revealing a sharp talon.

Pivot point

Taut digital flexor tendon
By contracting the flexor muscles in the cat's legs, the tendon beneath the paw – which anchors the claw – is pulled taut. A pivot action causes the distal phalanx to move forward and out, revealing the claw.

Taut elastic ligament
When the cat relaxes its muscles again, the taut elastic ligament will also relax allowing the claw to return to its resting retracted position.

Paw anatomy

Digital pads
For every toe, or digit, the cat has a hairless digital pad. There are usually five digits on the front foot, which includes the dewclaw, and four digits on the back paw.

Metacarpal pad
These are the large fatty pads located in the middle of the paws. They consist of three lobes and protect the main weight-bearing leg bones.

Carpal pad
These smaller pads, also known as the pisiform pads, are situated on the inside of the wrists further back up the front legs. Pisiform means pea-shaped and relates to the shape of the wrist bone.

Footprints
To reduce the noise they make when walking and to limit the visible tracks they make, cats walk with extreme precision. The rear paw will step pretty much directly where the forepaw was before it left off.

Digital pads

Metatarsal pad

Dewclaw
This is a much shorter toe located further up the leg where it doesn't make contact with the floor. It's like a redundant thumb and has no major function other than possibly to offer stability when running.

Forelimb

Hindlimb

Dogs
What makes man's best friend tick?

 Dogs evolved around 15,000 years ago in China and are descended from the Asian wolf. DNA studies have shown that 95 per cent of the dogs in the world are descended from the same three females. This is probably because those ancestral dogs showed a special trait that made them much more useful to humans. Dogs are better than any other animal at correctly recognising and interpreting human social cues; better even than our closest relative the chimpanzee, and far better than a wolf. This is true even with puppies as young as nine weeks, which shows this is an innate ability,

rather than something they learn from close association with us.

Originally dogs were kept exclusively for their hunting and defensive value but about 12,000 years ago, a mutation emerged that resulted in miniature dog breeds. Later, breeders began selecting for 'cute' features to create dogs that keep puppy characteristics into adulthood, such as floppy ears and rounder faces. At the same time, much of the pack instinct of many dog breeds was lost. Dogs became pets, rather than just weapons.

Dogs show more physical variation between breeds than any other domesticated animal.

Genetically, the Tibetan Lhasa Apso and the Chinese Shih Tzu are closest to the ancestral dog but the earliest dogs would have been sight hounds, like the wolf. These are dogs that track their prey visually and rely on short bursts of speed to bring them down. They have long thin heads and long legs. Later, scent hounds emerged with shorter faces and short legs to keep their nose close to the ground. These dogs hunt game over much larger distances by following a scent trail and they use their superior endurance to exhaust an animal. ✺

The bulldog has come to epitomise British spirit

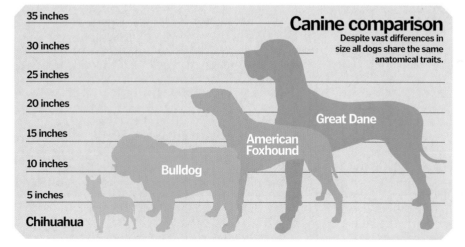

Canine comparison
Despite vast differences in size all dogs share the same anatomical traits.

35 inches
30 inches
25 inches
20 inches
15 inches
10 inches
5 inches

Great Dane
American Foxhound
Bulldog
Chihuahua

Dogs can come in a range of different shapes and sizes

Dog anatomy

Regardless of breed, shape or size, all dogs share the same basic anatomy

Clever dog!

Just how bright are our four-legged friends?

The average domestic dog can exhibit social intelligence that's seldom found in the animal world, even in our closest relative the chimp. Dogs can learn, and therefore be trained, in a number of ways by reinforcement (punishment and reward) and by observation. For instance, puppies will learn behaviour more quickly if they follow the examples set by older dogs and will even learn from watching humans perform tasks.

Dogs can demonstrate a sophisticated social cognition by associating behavioural cues with an abstract meaning, in tests dogs have successfully located a treat hidden under one of two buckets from a wide range of signals including taps, nods and even looks. In fact they out-performed chimpanzees, wolves and human infants at the task.

Dogs can perform a number of tasks to aid humans

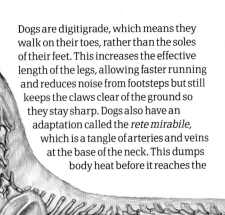

Dogs are digitigrade, which means they walk on their toes, rather than the soles of their feet. This increases the effective length of the legs, allowing faster running and reduces noise from footsteps but still keeps the claws clear of the ground so they stay sharp. Dogs also have an adaptation called the *rete mirabile*, which is a tangle of arteries and veins at the base of the neck. This dumps body heat before it reaches the brain and allows dogs to run for long periods without overheating.

Dogs have limited colour vision but they are classed as *dichromats* because they can't distinguish red and green colours. Long-nosed dogs have a highly sensitive stripe running across their retina, called a visual streak, which gives them a very wide field of view. In the short-nosed breeds, this sensitive area is more circular and allows more detailed frontal vision.

Nose
220 million scent receptors cover a small area of skin.

Tapetum lucidum
This reflective lining behind the retina bounces light back to improve night vision.

Disconnected shoulder
Dogs don't have a collarbone. This allows longer strides when running.

Fused wrists
The wrist bones have become fused together to make them stronger.

Deep chest
Sight hound breeds have a deep chest cavity to support a large heart and powerful lungs.

Dewclaw
This vestigial claw roughly corresponds to the thumb.

Paw
Dog paws are only half the size of the paws of wolves, relative to body size.

Tail
Many dog breeds have tails that curve upwards. Wolf tails don't do this.

© Science photo library

Internal organs

Unlike the cat family, dogs are not compulsory carnivores. Their intestine is long enough to digest a wide range of vegetables and grains and plant proteins can make up a large part of a healthy diet. Some human foods are quite toxic to dogs though, including chocolate and grapes.

Muscular system

Dogs have 18 separate muscles that are used to raise, tilt and rotate the ears. As well as being used to communicate with humans and other dogs, steerable ears allow a dog to accurately identify where a sound is coming from quicker and hear sounds four times further away than we can.

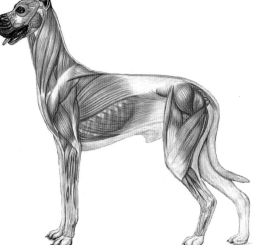

A yellow-winged darter dragonfly, commonly found in northern China

Abdomen
This streamlined part of the body helps to increase power and speed.

Wings
Intricately veined membrane wings need to be warmed up before flight.

Legs
Six bristle-covered legs help the dragonfly to catch its prey.

Eyes
Large, bulging compound eyes can view up to 360 degrees.

© Andre Karwath

Dragonflies

One of the world's largest and most exotic insects, dragonflies are valuable, carnivorous predators

Similar to but typically much larger than damselflies, dragonflies are large, agile insects that undertake a valuable role in the Earth's ecosystems, eating mosquitoes and other smaller insects. Their powerful flight abilities stem from their streamlined abdomen and dual sets of intricately veined, membrane wings, which allow them to fly at speeds up to 60mph. Dragonfly wingspans range from one-inch up to six inches. Their agility also stems from large bulging compound eyes, which on some of the larger species grant them almost 360-degree vision.

Unfortunately, this high performance comes at a cost – dragonfly muscles need to be warm in order to function properly. Therefore, for dragonfly wings to function optimally, the insect has to engage in a series of stationary wing-whirring exercises and elongated periods of basking in the Sun to generate requisite heat before taking off. However, when in flight, the large, warm and toned muscles deliver the dragonfly complete six-way propulsion, moving from a stationary/hovering position directly upwards, downwards, forwards, backwards and left to right.

Young dragonflies are called larvae and are aquatic rather than aerial predators. At this stage of their lifespan, they don't possess any wings but sport a formidable anatomical structure not present in adults called the 'mask'. The mask is a disproportionately large structure, to which a set of larger fangs is attached. When not in use, the mask is concealed under the larvae's thorax, extended to capture prey such as tadpoles and aquatic worms. Larvae transform into full-grown dragonflies through a series of moultings, the final one leaving a distinctive exuvia (cast skin) behind.

Metamorphosis

We explore how Lepidoptera metamorphosis takes shape

Belonging to the Lepidoptera family, butterflies are insects that achieve four life stages before turning into all manner of beautiful specimens, including the Hesperiidae, Papilionidae and Nymphalidae. This amazing journey sees Lepidoptera begin life as a plain egg that hatches into a larva, or caterpillar, after a period of six days.

The caterpillar is an eating machine, consuming for up to four weeks constantly until pupation takes place. The caterpillar's anatomy makes it adept at consuming all types of plant matter. Using its three pairs of true legs and five further pairs of 'prolegs' – sucker-like structures with clever little hooks on the end – it grips to leaves and plant stems, munching away with powerful mandibles. The caterpillar has an astonishing 4,000 muscles to compliment these feeding habits and a long gut track to quickly digest foodstuff.

As these creatures feast this fuels their growth and a caterpillar will shed its husk several times, becoming stronger and larger with each turn. At this stage larvae begin to secrete signature hormones, which instinctively kick in its need to produce a protective silk cocoon – known as pupa or chrysalides – and initiate the metamorphic stage. They achieve this by using their modified set of salivary glands, known as spinnerets. This cocoon may take the form of a small hollow in the earth lined with silk, or a roll of leaves, camouflaged to deter predators.

What really goes on inside this cocoon is fascinating. Larva anatomy and organs are rapidly dissolving and re-forming into new tissue, limbs and wings of the adult butterfly. This process varies from species to species, some taking no more than two weeks, others over winter, but eventually emerging as a butterfly. Blood is pumped into the insect wings, making them expandable and ready to fly.

Beautiful butterfly
Emerging butterflies range in size, from 1/8 of an inch up to 12 inches, and can fly at speeds up to 12 miles per hour. There are 24,000 catalogued species of butterfly.

Baby butterfly
Butterfly and moth eggs are very small and cylindrical in shape. Females lay their eggs on or near the plants that will later become larva food supply.

Hungry caterpillar
The caterpillar, or larva, consumes copious amounts of plant matter with powerful mandibles, before secreting signal hormones, setting the metamorphic stage in motion.

Chrysalides
Inside the chrysalides, larvae go through dramatic biological changes. Just before the adult butterfly hatches, the pupa skin becomes transparent and the wing pattern is visible inside.

© Science Photo Library

Ladybirds explained

The red-caped heroes of the insect world, ladybirds save the day for gardeners and farmers everywhere

Aphids are popular ladybird fodder

Coccinellids, more commonly known as ladybirds, or ladybugs in North America, are members of the beetle family. There are more than four and a half thousand different species of ladybirds throughout the world living in warm and temperate regions. Though they vary widely in size and colouration, most of us know them as small red beetles with distinctive black spots, a friend of farmers and gardeners.

Like all beetles, ladybirds go through a huge metamorphosis on their way to adulthood. Ladybird eggs hatch into larvae, which oddly look a bit like tiny black-and-yellow alligators. These larvae grow and moult, going through several instars, or developmental phases, over a period of two to three weeks, before pupating into adults.

Ladybirds feature aposematic or 'warning' colouration that gives potential predators advanced warning of their bad taste, and when threatened, they can exude a toxic and foul-smelling alkaloid liquid from their joints. In spite of their excellent defence system, ladybirds are not without enemies; parasitic wasps and flies occasionally attack them and some ladybirds fall victim to intrepid spiders and toads too.

Many native ladybird species are under threat from another ladybird species – the Asian or harlequin ladybird (harmonia axyridis). These invaders are generalist feeders and can out-compete resident ladybirds in their native range. They're also somewhat infamous for attempting to hibernate inside human dwellings where they may swarm, stain fabric and even cause allergic reactions.

Currently one-fifth of indigenous British ladybird species are on the decline. In addition to competition with the aforementioned Asian ladybird, climate change and altered land use patterns are likely contributors.

Not all the news is bleak however – a few native ladybirds are expanding their range, and one species – the 13-spot ladybird – previously thought to be extinct has recently been found in Cornwall and Devon.

What do ladybirds feed on?

Carnivores and cannibals, ladybirds are justifiably famous (and appreciated) for their habit of eating crop pests. Most ladybird species are carnivorous, consuming soft-bodied insects including aphids, mites, scale insects and white flies. Foraging ladybirds use visual and olfactory clues to home in on food-rich hunting and laying grounds. Newly hatched ladybird larvae have voracious appetites and, if there's insufficient prey available, they may even eat one another! Ladybird mothers also sometimes lay infertile eggs as an additional food source for their young during hard times.

A single ladybird may devour as many as 65 aphids per day. Females consume more than males and both genders eat more when the temperature is warmer, such as in a greenhouse. However, in spite of their reputation, not all ladybird species eat other insects and even the carnivorous species aren't carnivores all the time. Predatory ladybirds rely on pollen, nectar and other plant foods during periods of prey scarcity, and there is a small number of species who spend their lives dining on such delicacies as mildew and fungus.

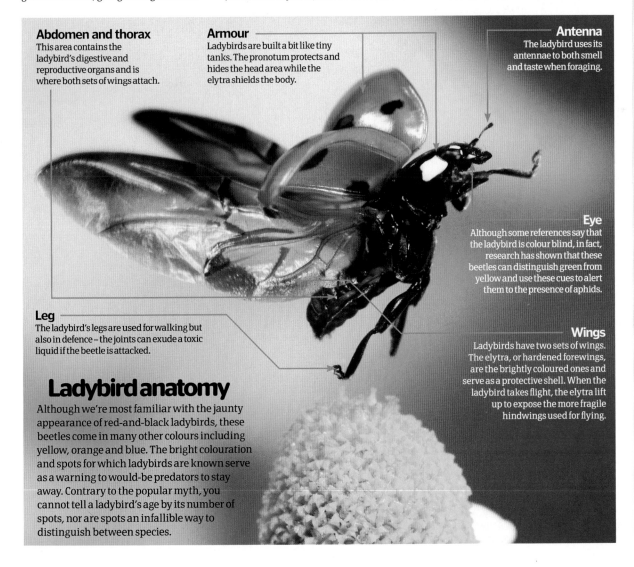

Abdomen and thorax This area contains the ladybird's digestive and reproductive organs and is where both sets of wings attach.

Armour Ladybirds are built a bit like tiny tanks. The pronotum protects and hides the head area while the elytra shields the body.

Antenna The ladybird uses its antennae to both smell and taste when foraging.

Eye Although some references say that the ladybird is colour blind, in fact, research has shown that these beetles can distinguish green from yellow and use these cues to alert them to the presence of aphids.

Leg The ladybird's legs are used for walking but also in defence – the joints can exude a toxic liquid if the beetle is attacked.

Wings Ladybirds have two sets of wings. The elytra, or hardened forewings, are the brightly coloured ones and serve as a protective shell. When the ladybird takes flight, the elytra lift up to expose the more fragile hindwings used for flying.

Ladybird anatomy

Although we're most familiar with the jaunty appearance of red-and-black ladybirds, these beetles come in many other colours including yellow, orange and blue. The bright colouration and spots for which ladybirds are known serve as a warning to would-be predators to stay away. Contrary to the popular myth, you cannot tell a ladybird's age by its number of spots, nor are spots an infallible way to distinguish between species.

Tardigrades

They may be small but are these minibeasts really the toughest creatures on the planet?

Tardigrades are tiny aquatic invertebrates, sometimes called water bears because of the loping way that they move. The largest species are 1.5 millimetres long, the smallest are under 0.1mm. Despite their squishy and vulnerable appearance, they are virtually indestructible. Experiments in laboratories have shown that they can survive pressures of 6,000 atmospheres, temperatures as low as -272°C or as high as 151°C and radiation doses that would most certainly kill us a thousand times over.

They achieve this by dehydrating their own bodies using a special sugar called trehalose, which acts as scaffolding to protect the cell contents. Their water content drops to one per cent of normal in this state and their metabolism slows by 99.99 per cent. Ice can't form in a body this dry and all the chemical reactions that might harm them simply happen too slowly to be dangerous. ⚙

Legs
All tardigrades have eight legs. Their name means 'slow walker'.

Cell count
Tardigrades are eutelic, which means that individuals of the same species all have the same number of cells.

Mouthparts
Tardigrades have a circular mouth that pierces and sucks. Most feed on plants.

Moulting
Some species only defecate when they shed their skin, leaving the faeces behind inside the old skin.

Senses
Some species have very simple, non-image-forming eyes, as well as sensory bristles.

© Science Photo Library

Slugs and snails

The gardener's least favourite visitors, slugs and snails are quite incredible little slime balls

Shell
Made of calcium carbonate, a snail's strong shell will remain so if the animal's diet contains enough calcium.

Stomach
This section of the digestive tract receives food to be digested.

Kidney
During digestion, harmful side-products can accumulate and poison the snail. The kidney can expel this poison.

Mantle
Covering the body is a layer called the mantle, which can secrete a shell in snails but not in slugs.

Foot
This consists mainly of muscle tissue that contracts and expands enabling the snail to move.

Heart

Oviduct

Lung
Not all snails have lungs but those that do have a single cavity containing a network of blood vessels that functions like a lung.

Liver

Anus
The intestine opens outside near the anus. As the snail crawls away it leaves behind a dark trail of faeces.

Crop
The crop is a sack where food pulp is stored before heading to the stomach. Digestive fluids are produced by the main gland or hepatopancreas.

Salivary gland
Found in the buccal cavity, the salivary gland secretes saliva to aid digestion.

Respiratory pore
Also called a pneumostome, this breathing pore is an opening through which air is breathed into the lung.

Tentacle
Snails have one or two sets of retractable tentacles projecting from the top of the head depending on the species.

Eye
If there are two tentacles, the shorter front set will be sensitive to touch and the longer set behind will bear eyes.

Cerebral ganglia

Salivary duct

Mucous gland
The mucous gland in the foot secretes thick, sticky slime to help the snail traverse tricky ground without injury.

Dart sac
Some land snails shoot a mucus-covered 'dart' into mates, delivering a substance that improves sperm survival.

Vagina
Female reproductive organ located on the ventral surface of the foot.

Penis
Male reproductive organ is located internally when not in use and is found on the ventral face of the foot.

Genital pore
Found at the side of the head, this opening allows copulation and exchange of sperm.

Mouth
The mouth features a jaw and a rough ribbon-like tongue called the radula for grazing on plants.

Although they look very different, slugs, snails, octopuses, oysters and cuttlefish are all molluscs – Latin for 'thin shelled' – and either have a calcium-carbonate external shell, a small shell under the surface, or no shell at all. Slugs are shell-less while adult snails have coiled shells big enough to withdraw into.

Slugs and snails belong to the large group of molluscs called gastropods and make their home in a variety of locations from back gardens to oceans and everywhere in-between. They are the only molluscs that can live on dry land, and breathe using either lungs, gills or both.

Gastropods are hermaphroditic, which means they have both male and female reproductive organs, and can mate with themselves if no partner is available. During an elaborate mating ritual slugs entwine and stimulate each other until sperm is exchanged via their disproportionately large genitals. Another peculiar trait is apophallation, whereby one slug chews off the other's penis after mating. The apophallated slug may now only reproduce using its female genitalia. ⚙

Termite mounds

How does the wood-loving termite construct its home?

Termites are cellulose-eating insects that share many similarities with ants and bees, although, perhaps surprisingly, their closest relative is believed to be the cockroach. There are about 2,750 species of termite around the world, living in habitats as varied as tropical forests and the African savannah, through to the Pacific coast.

The eating habits of termites make them very important insects in an ecosystem. By consuming wooden structures and plant life they help convert dead trees into organic matter to trigger new life. However, this can cause problems, as they can eat through structural supports in buildings, eventually leading to their collapse.

Termites have evolved to eat wood largely because few other animals can; they carry a special bacteria that enables them to digest the tough cellulose fibres. This innate survival mechanism means termite colonies can be around for a very long time – indeed, some last up to 100 years. A termite mound (or termitarium) will reach its maximum size after four to five years, when it can be home to as many as 200,000 inhabitants. ✿

Here you can see why the termite's closest relative is thought to be the cockroach

Building material
Termite mounds like this one are made from a mix of fine soil and faecal pellets that dry super-hard.

Location
Termites can build their home underground, in tree trunks or in tall earthen mounds; all are known as termitaria.

Structure
Inside a termite colony is an array of chambers and passages constructed by the little insects that allow air, and with it heat, to circulate throughout the mound and out the top.

Some termite mounds can reach as tall as 9m (30ft)

Garden
At the base of the mound is a fungus garden, where termites convert wood and plant matter into edible fungus.

Royalty
At the heart of the fungus garden is the royal chamber where the king and queen reside.

© Science Photo Library

171

Build
The average weight of a cheetah is 57kg (125lb) and its build is slender. It has a small head, flattened rib cage and long, thin legs that all minimise air resistance.

Tail
The cheetah's long tail acts as a counterweight, maintaining balance during sharp turns at high speed.

Heart
The heart is enlarged compared to other animals of its size, pumping a colossal amount of blood around the cheetah's body, especially during a chase.

Lungs
Engorged lungs – and nostrils for that matter – allow for a fast and deep air intake. Maintaining a high level of oxygen is critical when the cheetah is on a chase as its breath-rate increases three-fold.

Paws
The paws are blunt and sport exposed claws that provide superior grip, increasing the forward thrust of each stride.

World's fastest animals

The arms race of hunter and hunted is a ferocious battleground, with different species furiously evolving to remain, literally, one step ahead of the competition. We pit these speed demons against each other in the ultimate animal shootout

Cheetah

Accelerating to speeds of 70mph, the cheetah is the quickest on four legs!

Cheetahs are one of the fastest animals on Earth and have a terrifyingly quick 0-60 time of a mere three seconds. Cheetahs are unique in the fact they have evolved to such a degree in order to maximise their speed, that they regularly risk brain damage and starvation due to the great physical demands it places on their anatomy. The cheetah is fast, the fastest land animal on Earth, but that speed comes at a great price.

For example, lungs, nostrils and heart are all enlarged within the cheetah to ensure it can process enough oxygen and blood to maintain its explosive speed. However, it can only process this for short periods of time and at the close of a lengthy chase not only does it skirt dangerously close to oxygen deprivation but it must rest post-kill before it eats, leaving plenty of time for scavengers to surround it. In addition, while its muscle fibre is honed and holds superb elasticity, its physique is slender and lightweight, leaving it vulnerable to broken limbs and completely defenceless against a larger and heavier rival such as a lion or tiger.

Due to these facts – as well as through human-caused habitat loss and predation – cheetah numbers are now dwindling and the animal is an endangered species in many African countries.

Black mamba
12mph

The Statistics

Cheetah

Family: Felidae
Genus: Acinonyx
Weight: 36-65kg
Height: 67-94cm
Length: 200-220cm
0-60mph: 3 seconds
Top speed: 70mph

0-40mph in three strides

Check out the three stages a cheetah undertakes to reach 40mph in just three strides

© DK images

1. Brace
The cheetah employs its hard, ridged footpads and blunt, non-retractable claws to maximise traction with the ground. Its spine curves, coil-like, and head drops a fraction.

2. Snap
The spine uncoils and snaps straight, driving the hind legs into the earth and pushing the cheetah forward. The honed, slender muscles expand in conjunction, adding greater elasticity and drive to the forward thrust.

3. Kick
The combined spine and leg muscles give the cheetah an incredibly broad swing range and propel it 7.6 metres (25 feet) through the air in a colossal bound. At the culmination of the bound one foot is replanted onto the earth and the process is repeated. The cheetah completes three strides a second.

Cheetah anatomy

Just what makes it the fastest thing on four legs?

Eyes
The cheetah's eyes are long to provide a wide-angle view of its surroundings. This provides them with excellent vision when stalking and chasing prey in the native habitat of open plains.

Spine
The spine is incredibly flexible and has evolved so it curves with each stride, acting akin to a spring for the cheetah's hind legs.

© James Temple

The sailfish can rapidly turn its body light blue with stripes when excited, confusing its prey and making capture easier

Long nose
The sailfish's elongated bill is similar to a swordfish's and marlin's, placing it in the category of billfish.

Sailfish

Capable of swimming for long periods of time at over 40mph, and with a recorded top speed of over 70mph, the sailfish is the ocean's fastest animal

With a top speed on par with that of a cheetah, the sailfish is lightning fast and one of the most difficult-to-catch fish in the world. With its stiffened, tapered body and scissor-shaped caudal fin, the sailfish is built for speed – a speed that comes courtesy of a rapid and ferocious flicking of its tail. Indeed, during a chase to consume fish, crustaceans or cephalopods, the sailfish will flick its tail back and forth hundreds of times, utilising the powerful muscles which run down its compressed body.

As with the peregrine falcon, the sailfish's speed is also aided by its ability to retract parts of its body, in this instance its various fins (notably the large dorsal fin that adds over a foot on to its overall height). This feature helps it reduce the effects of drag and minimise resistance to its movements.

Its spine is also very flexible and as with the cheetah allows it to generate increased thrust through the rapid curves it bends its torso into while swimming.

The Statistics
Sailfish

Family: Istiophoridae
Genus: Istiophorus
Weight: 90kg
Height: 70cm
Length: 1.2-1.5m
0-60mph: Not recorded
Top speed: 70mph

Streamlined
Sailfish have an incredibly sleek and streamlined body.

© anon 09

Tiger beetle 5.6mph

Swift 106 mph

The fastest animals on Earth are...

Here's a the list of the most super-fast critters on the planet

FASTEST FISH	
Sailfish	68mph (110kph)
Marlin	50mph (80kph)
Wahoo	48mph (78kph)
Tunny	46mph (74kph)
Bluefish tuna	44mph (70kph)

FASTEST LAND INSECTS	
Tiger beetle	5.6mph (8.4kph)
Cockroach	3.4mph (5.4kph)

FASTEST BIRDS	
Peregrine falcon	200mph (322kph)
Spine-tailed swift	106mph (171kph)
Frigatebird	95mph (153kph)
Spur-winged goose	88mph (142kph)
Red-breasted merganser	80mph (129kph)

FASTEST MAMMALS	
Cheetah	71mph (114kph)
Pronghorn antelope	57mph (95kph)
Springbok	50mph (80kph)
Blue wildebeest	50mph (80kph)
Lion	45mph (72kph)

FASTEST REPTILES	
Spiny-tailed iguana	21mph (34kph)
Black mamba	12mph (20kph)

Sources: American Journal of Zoology, University of Michigan, Seattle Zoo, American Journal of Physiology, National Geographic, US Fish and Wildlife Service, Forest Preserve of Illinois

© Keven Law 08

Peregrine falcon

When in free fall, the peregrine falcon is just epically quick

1. Sight
Prey is spotted while soaring and then the peregrine begins to draw its wings into its body. It also retracts its tail and tucks its feet into its body.

2. Streamline
The wings are brought right into the falcon's sternum and – thanks to their pointed, slim, stiff and unslotted feathers – begins to rapidly reduce its air resistance.

3. Velocity
Speed is increased as the falcon bombs down with little-to-zero drag, soon reaching speeds up to 200mph. Its strong keel helps maintain structural solidity during the dive and its eyes are kept clear by nictitating membranes, which act like a third eyelid.

Diving to victory

The four stages a peregrine falcon undertakes to reach 200mph when diving in for a kill

If you thought the cheetah was fast, then think again. The peregrine falcon blows its top speed out of the water by over 130mph. Capable of hitting a monumental 200mph during a stoop (dive), the falcon has the highest top speed of any animal on Earth.

The peregrine's speed is caused by a combination of factors. Firstly it makes use of gravity, diving upon its prey from great height, even when they themselves are airborne. Secondly, its anatomy – as with the cheetah's – has been finely honed to maximise speed, evolving over millions of years into the swift and efficient killer it is today. For example, the peregrine's keel – which is located at its breastbone – is significantly larger than average birds', allowing for bigger muscles and a greater number to attach its wings to its body. This allows it to generate far more power per thrust when building speed. Further, the peregrine's wings have evolved to be incredibly pointed, with slim, stiff and unslotted feathers, which helps streamlining and reducing air resistance significantly.

Unlike the cheetah, however, arguably the peregrine handles its awesome speed much better. Firstly, while having the same enlarged heart and lungs, the peregrine does

Usain Bolt 28mph 100m in 9.58 seconds

Sailfish 68mph Finishing time in 3.28 seconds

Cheetah 71mph Finishing time in 3.15 seconds

Peregrine falcon 200mph Finishing time in 1.12 seconds

Tiger beetle 720mph Finishing time in 0.31 seconds

The Statistics
Peregrine falcon

Family: Falconidae
Genus: Falco
Weight: 910-1,500 grams
Height: 60cm
Length: 34-58cm
0-60mph: Not recorded
Top speed: 200mph

4. Contact
Prey is both struck and captured in mid-air. The peregrine strikes its prey with a clenched foot, which due to the immense speed either stuns or kills it, before then swooping round to catch it with its large claws. Prey is always consumed on the ground.

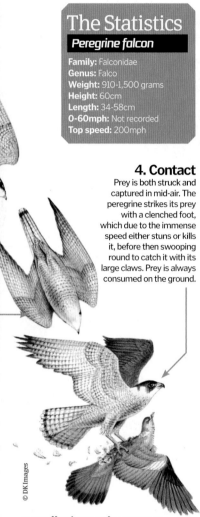

© DK Images

not suffer damage from oxygen deprivation at the close of its stoop. This is partly due to gravity's beneficial aid in generating its killer speed but also due to the peregrine's ability to absorb oxygen through its red muscle fibres, of which it has many. This allows it to keep a steady oxygen flow at all times and means that, consequentially, it does not need to rest post-kill, reducing its vulnerability to scavengers.

How muscles work – the contraction cycle
Muscle power is common to all these creatures so here's an explanation of how muscles provide the power that in turn provide the speed

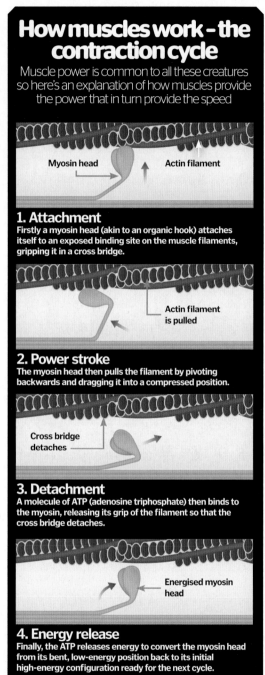

Myosin head   Actin filament

1. Attachment
Firstly a myosin head (akin to an organic hook) attaches itself to an exposed binding site on the muscle filaments, gripping it in a cross bridge.

Actin filament is pulled

2. Power stroke
The myosin head then pulls the filament by pivoting backwards and dragging it into a compressed position.

Cross bridge detaches

3. Detachment
A molecule of ATP (adenosine triphosphate) then binds to the myosin, releasing its grip of the filament so that the cross bridge detaches.

Energised myosin head

4. Energy release
Finally, the ATP releases energy to convert the myosin head from its bent, low-energy position back to its initial high-energy configuration ready for the next cycle.

Physique
Tall height, balanced weight and powerful muscles.

Metabolism
Converting 'fuels' like glucose into power, producing adenosine triphosphate.

The Statistics
Usain Bolt

Family: Hominidae
Genus: Homo
Weight: 93.9kg
Height: 1.95m
Length: 30cm
0-60mph: Not recorded
Top speed: 28mph

Usain Bolt
The fastest human alive, Usain Bolt broke the world 100-metre record with a staggeringly quick time of 9.58 seconds

One of the most successful species of animal on the planet, Homo sapiens have evolved over the last 120,000 years into creatures with formidable physical abilities. Currently, the fastest human is Usain Bolt, a Jamaican-born sprinter who has won the world 100 and 200-metre gold medals.

Bolt epitomises the ideal human anatomy needed to produce such high speeds: a tall height (1.95m), balanced weight (93.9kg) and long, powerful muscles with an excellent metabolism – muscles cannot utilise energy-rich "fuels" such as glucose, instead they must convert it into ATP (adenosine triphosphate) with the amount of ATP a muscle produces directly correlating to the amount of power it can generate.

How It Works
100m final
So who would win in a 100-metre race?

NB: For the purposes of this illustration the peregrine falcon's speed is taken from a stoop and all animals begin the race at their top speed.

This is the speed a tiger beetle could get to if it were the same size as an average six-foot man!

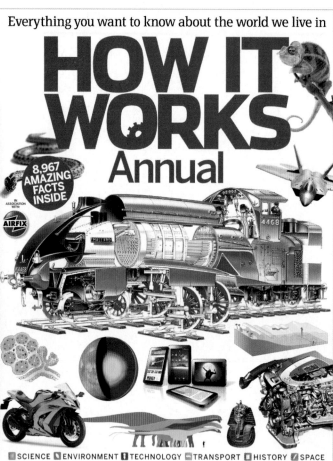